Biotechnology
Science for the New Millennium

Laboratory Manual

Ellyn Daugherty, MST

San Mateo Biotechnology Career Pathway

Paradigm
PUBLISHING

Senior Developmental Editor	Sonja M. Brown
Art Editor	Courtney Kost
Cover and Text Designer	Leslie Anderson
Illustrator	Precision Graphics
Compositor	Precision Graphics
Editorial Assistant	Susan Capecchi
Copyeditor	Colleen Duffy
Proofreader	Joy McComb

Reviewers: The author, editor , and publisher wish to thank the following individuals for their insightful feedback during the development of this lab manual:

- Dr. Jim DeKloe, Co-Director, Biotechnician Program, Solano Community College
- Dr. Toby Horn, Co-Director, Carnegie Academy for Science Education, Carnegie Institute of Washington
- Brian Robinson, Biochemistry Research Associate, Genentech, Inc.

Care has been taken to verify the accuracy of information presented in this book. However, the author, editor, and publisher cannot accept any responsibility for Web, e-mail, newsgroup, or chat room subject matter or content, or for consequences from application of the information in this book, and make no warranty, expressed or implied, with respect to its content.

Trademarks: Some of the product names and company names included in this book have been used for identification purposes only and may be trademarks or registered trademarks of their respective manufacturers and sellers. The author, editor, and publisher disclaim any affiliation, association, or connection with, or sponsorship or endorsement by, such owners.

© 2007 by Paradigm Publishing Inc.
    Published by EMC Corporation
    875 Montreal Way
    Saint Paul, MN 55102
    (800) 535-6865
    E-mail: educate@emcp.com
    Web Site: www.emcp.com

Printed in the United States of America
10 9 8 7 6 5 4 3 2 1

Contents

Be a Part of the Biotechnology Revolution

To the Student

Be a Part of the Biotechnology Revolution

Imagine a world where babies are born without defects, perpetrators of crimes are identified within minutes, diseases are diagnosed and treated right in your own home, and there is enough food to feed everyone. This scenario may sound like the makings of a science fiction novel, but this "fiction" is fast becoming reality. Every day, new advances in the field of biotechnology move us closer to the goals of curing disease, wiping out hunger, and improving the quality of life for all people. Because discoveries and new products are transforming the way we live, some observers say we are undergoing a biotechnology revolution.

As evidence of this revolution, just note the progress in the research and development of biotechnology products over the past 10 years. In the mid 1990s, hundreds of researchers and technicians at one of the largest biotechnology companies, Genentech, Inc, collaborated in producing human tissue plasminogen activator (t-PA), a protein that dissolves blood clots. When given within hours of a heart attack, t-PA clears blockages in blood vessels so that blood can flow more freely. This protein is credited with reducing damage to the heart that is caused by a heart attack. Soon after its release for use in heart attack cases, t-PA was marketed and used to treat stroke patients. More than 500,000 Americans die per year from heart attacks, and some 160,000 deaths per year are due to strokes. Imagine the number of lives potentially saved and prolonged by t-PA treatment, which is just one example of the products of biotechnology research and development.

Now, imagine being a part of this revolution. Imagine working on a team that constructs a vaccine for human immunodeficiency virus (HIV), the virus that causes acquired immunodeficiency syndrome (AIDS). Picture working for a company that produces a high-protein peanut that can be grown in drought conditions in third-world countries. Envision yourself in the laboratory developing a strain of bacterium that digests petroleum from oil spills.

Imagine the sense of accomplishment and gratification you would feel as a contributor to these breakthroughs. Think of how this type of work could help improve the quality of life for your friends and family.

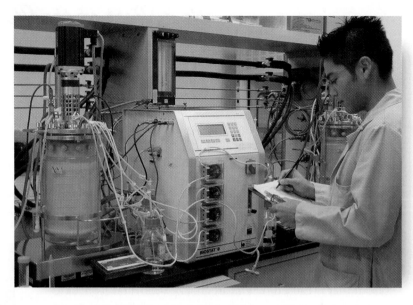

You could be part of the Biotechnology Revolution. Thousands of employees are needed to staff the hundreds of new biotechnology companies starting up every year. These fledgling companies need scientists and lab technicians to complete research and development on potential products. They also need workers to manufacture and package the products. Since testing has to be done on all products, employees are needed to design, run, and document these tests. Companies also require nonscientific support staff, including those in marketing, finance, and law. Human resource (HR) specialists are needed to choose the best employees. People who work in public relations and corporate communications keep the public informed about product development and keep employees aware of recent news on related items.

Whether you aspire to work in a lab, on research and development, in manufacturing, or in the financial or business end of the biotechnology industry, there is a surplus of jobs to entice people of all interests. No matter what your position, be it entry level or upper management, when a product is released that you have had some part in developing, you can expect to experience great satisfaction.

The purpose of this lab manual is to introduce the many concepts and laboratory skills you need to master to work in the field of biotechnology. No matter where your interest lies, or which position you may have (science or business), understanding the tools and techniques of basic biotechnology research will help you work effectively on a team charged with bringing a profit-making product to market.

Best wishes for your success!

Ellyn Daugherty
Redwood City, California

Photo by Kainaz Amaria

About the Author

A 25-year veteran biology teacher, Ellyn Daugherty has taught biotechnology since 1988. She is the author, lead teacher, and program administrator for the San Mateo Biotechnology Career Pathway (*www.SMBiotech.com*). Her model curriculum attracts adults and teenagers into an intensive, multiple-year program in biotechnology that leads students to higher education and into the biotechnology workplace.

Ellyn has received several awards for her innovative teaching and curriculum development, including:

- The National Biotechnology Teacher-Leader Award, Biotechnology Institute and Genzyme, 2004

- Presidential Award in Science Education, California State Finalist, 2000

- Intel Innovations in Teaching Award, California State Runner-Up, 2000

- Tandy Technology Prize, Outstanding Teacher Award, 1997

- LaBoskey Award, Stanford University, Master Teacher Award, 1995

- Access Excellence Award, NABT and Genentech, Inc., 1994

- National Distinguished Teacher, Commission on Presidential Scholars, 1992

Ellyn believes strongly in teacher professional development and conducts several workshops a year in her lab and at national conferences. Her Web site (*www.BiotechEd.com*) contains a collection of teacher support materials and information about upcoming workshops.

An avid San Francisco Giants fan, Ellyn spends her time outside of the lab at baseball games, on her boat, in the garden, or hiking with her husband, Paul, and their chihuahua, Rocky Balboa.

Acknowledgments

I have many people to thank for helping me learn the science I am now sharing.

I might never have started teaching biotech if Jack Chiridian, PhD and Dr. Carol Chihara hadn't let me into their *Recombinant DNA* workshop in 1998. When Jack gave participants 10 Edvotek, Inc lab kits, a gel box, and a power supply to take back to their classrooms, those 10 labs snowballed over 16 years into my 4-year curriculum.

I gratefully thank Pat Seawell of Gene Connection and Frank Stephenson, PhD of Applied Biosystems, Inc for the hundreds of mini-courses over the phone, online, and in the lab to help me get my science "right" and for providing support and reagents when I was testing new curricula. Frank was also the first person to brave examining the first draft of my manuscript.

Maureen Munn, PhD, Project Director of the Human Genome Program, University of Washington Genome Center, and Lane Conn, former Director of the Teacher Education in Biology program at San Francisco State University, spent many hours helping me bring DNA synthesis and DNA sequencing activities to my students. Maureen also read and gave feedback on some sections of my manuscript. Brock Siegel of Applied Biosystems, Inc has also been a champion of biotechnology education and my program.

I am indebted to Diane Sweeney, formerly of Genencor International and now at Crystal Springs-Uplands School, for the extensive teacher training and in-service she has conducted. Two of her Amylase Project labs, which she shared with me in a workshop in 1989, became the cornerstone for a few dozen amylase activities in my curriculum.

Several teachers used the early drafts of the text and lab manual and gave me valuable input. I want to thank Leslie Allen, Jimmy Ikeda, Karen Watts, Josephine Yu, PhD, Tina Doss, and Dan Raffa for their constant and considerable contributions and corrections. Dan and Tina also provided technical advice regarding instructional materials and spent the better part of a summer creating the lab skills tutorials for the Encore CD that is packaged with the text and lab manual. Regarding technical assistance, the creation of the manuscript would not have been possible without the untiring efforts of my computer technician and exceptional Webmaster, Skip Wagner.

I am immensely grateful to the science content editors of this first edition:
- Dr. Jim DeKloe, Co-Director, Biotechnician Program, Solano Community College
- Dr. Toby Horn, Co-Director, Carnegie Academy for Science Education, Carnegie Institute of Washington
- Brian Robinson, Biochemistry Research Associate, Genentech, Inc, and currently a medical student at Emory University Medical School.

In addition, a huge hug and lots of love to my mom, Lorna Kopel, who read every word of the text, lab manual, and instructor's guide and made grammatical corrections.

Many scientists, teachers, students, and colleagues have worked on curriculum development with me, or have provided feedback or scientific advice and support on one or more topics or techniques. I would like to thank Katy Korsmeyer, PhD, Maria Abilock, Shalini Prasad, Joey Mailman, Aylene Bao, Natasha Chen, Daniel Segal, and Luhua Zhang for their efforts in helping me complete the first draft of the manuscript. Aylene Bao was the original illustrator of the manuscript, and her extensive collection of drawings served as excellent models for the illustrators at Precision Graphics who created the beautiful drawings in the text and lab manual. Maria Abilock wrote the test bank questions and suggested several changes as she read through the manuscript. In addition, thank you to Dr. Timothy Gregory of Genentech, Inc for letting me be the first teacher intern at Genentech, Inc and allowing me to gain real science skills for two summers with Lavon, Allison, Millie, and Dave in the Protein Process Development Department.

The activities in the lab manual are significantly challenging because of the extensive amount of reagents and equipment, and assembling a good working version of the laboratory materials list was one of the biggest challenges in this project. Several years ago, I was fortunate to bring in VWR/Sargent-Welch as the premier vendor of my laboratory program materials. Many individuals have worked hundreds of hours over several years helping me determine the materials that would provide the best performance and value to my teacher users. I appreciate the hard work of the following current and former VWR employees: Becky Turner, Matt Witzky, Mark Barber, Mike Ryan, and especially, Joshua Burchacki and Regina Lynch.

I was extremely fortunate to find, early on, the right publisher. I thank Dr. Elaine Johnson of Bio-Link and Kristin Hershbell Charles of City College of San Francisco for all their efforts to support and promote my program, and especially for connecting me with EMC Corporation. I would also like to thank John Simpson for his extensive and valuable advice about getting my work published.

I am so grateful to George Provol who brought me in as an EMC author. He assembled a wonderful publishing team: Janice Johnson, Sonja Brown, and Courtney Kost, who agree with me philosophically about the goals of this project. I appreciate all of their efforts.

Chapter

1 Introduction to Biotechnology Methodologies

A quality control lab technician prepares samples to be tested on a DNA synthesizer. She will report the degree to which the samples meet the required quality standards. Attention to detail is critical in preparing and testing samples.
Photo by author.

From the very first day as a lab technician, you are expected to follow standard laboratory operating procedures (SLOPs). These SLOPs include the intuitive notions of following written and oral instructions, working in a safe manner, keeping detailed records of all work, and using all equipment and instruments accurately and as directed. Also included are the skills of setting up and running sophisticated instruments, such as spectrophotometers and bioreactors.

In the following laboratory activities, you will begin to learn some of the most basic SLOPs used by lab technicians, research associates, and scientists throughout biotechnology research and manufacturing facilities. These include the following:

- Setting up and maintaining a legal scientific notebook. All the work you do as a lab technician in this biotechnology course is recorded into your legal scientific notebook.
- Understanding safety concerns, precautions, equipment, and rules for the typical biotechnology facility.
- Setting up experiments, documenting conditions, analyzing data, and reporting results.

In each of the subsequent chapters, you will use these skills and learn additional ones in the areas of measurement, solution and media preparation, sterile technique, cell culture, and electrophoresis.

It is critical to learn to follow testing procedures exactly, and to document the conditions and results of each experiment, test, or reaction. Laboratory instruments and equipment are delicate and expensive. The chemical reagents and biological samples can be dangerous if you do not use them correctly, following specific safety protocols. On the positive side, the results of experiments could lead to discoveries or products that improve human life. You will be able to perform these tasks with confidence because you will have been trained and will have mastered the SLOPs that apply in any biotechnology facility.

Laboratory 1a   How to Set Up a Legal Scientific Notebook

Background

Everyone at a biotechnology company who is involved in research or product design and development must document all work. A laboratory employee documents experiments and other activities in a legal scientific notebook (see Figure 1.1). A legal scientific notebook becomes the historical record of all work done by the biotechnology employee.

A scientific notebook may be required in court cases. Examples of situations in which a scientific notebook may be used in court include the following:

1. To settle patent disputes, such as when someone argues that he/she made a discovery first and says a discovery or process belongs to him/her.
2. To report a specialist's findings from testing, such as in paternity suits or criminal cases.

If the scientific notebook is not maintained in an acceptable fashion, it will be inadmissible as evidence and will not be used. The following protocol will help you set up and maintain a legal scientific notebook.

Figure 1.1. **A lab employee receives an official legal scientific notebook from a company. Most companies number notebooks and keep a record of their location.**
Photo by author.

Setting Up a Legal Scientific Notebook

1. You may be using the *Laboratory Notebook* that is available with this text. If not, obtain a bound notebook with sewn pages. A composition-style notebook works well.
2. Use *only* black pen to make *all* entries into the notebook. Be careful when making entries. Incorrect entries may be lined out with a *single line only* and must be labeled with initials and the date.
3. Graphs and other small sheets of paper may be pasted into your notebook when necessary. When pasting, use a glue stick. There should be no loose papers in the notebook.

4. Number every page of the notebook, at the top outside corner, starting with the front side of the first page as number 1 and the back of the first page as number 2. Continue numbering the front and back of *every* page of the notebook (see Figure 1.2).

Figure 1.2. **Numbering and Title Page**

5. Make page 1 the title page. In the middle of the page, in bold print, write:

[name of course] NOTEBOOK
course section or class period
name of institution
your name
today's date

Also write this information on the front cover of your notebook

6. Make pages 2 through 5 the Table of Contents. Write "Table of Contents" at the top of each of these pages. Record the page and title of each new activity in the Table of Contents (see Figure 1.3).

(Continues)

7. Glue your "Employment Contract" (if your instructor uses one) onto the inside front cover of the notebook. Read the contract carefully before signing it.

8. Glue the "Laboratory Notebook Policy" sheet onto the inside back cover of the notebook. (If you are using the *Laboratory Notebook* that is available with this text, the policy is already printed on the inside back cover.) Read the policy carefully before recording information into your notebook. Glue the "Employee Participation Rubric" (if your instructor uses one) onto the last page of your notebook.

9. The record of work begins on page 6.

10. Sign and date the bottom of every page. Also, write, "go to page [number]" on the bottom right-hand side of the page to tell the reader where the rest of the information for this topic is located in the notebook. On the page you "go to," write, "from page [number]" on the top left-hand side of the page showing the page you came from. If you set your notebook up this way, it should be relatively easy for you or anyone familiar with the work you are doing to find the data, observations, and conclusions about a specific topic.

Figure 1.3.   Table of Contents

A record of all work performed and data collected is logged into the notebook.
Photo by author.

Laboratory Notebook Policy

Based on the Laboratory Notebook Policy used at Applied Biosystems, Inc., Foster City, CA.

Why is proper record keeping in a bound notebook important?
In the United States, the first person to conceive and show diligence to develop an invention, product, or process is awarded the patent for that product or process. Notebooks that are properly prepared, maintained, and witnessed are legal evidence of conception and diligence to practice an invention.

Record-Keeping Procedures
1. Use only your official biotechnology notebook to record your work. All work must be recorded in the notebook and in no other document.
2. Date and sign *every* page. Sign and date at the end of an experiment.
3. Maintain a Table of Contents as you make entries in the notebook. The first page of every lab investigation should be listed in the Table of Contents.
4. Make all entries legibly *only* in *black permanent ink*. No pencil entries are permitted. The use of colored pens or pencils is acceptable in some cases, as approved by the supervisor.
5. *Do not erase, ink over, or white out any errors*. Draw a single line through errors so they can still be read. Place your initials and the date next to the correction.
6. Briefly state the objective or purpose of each experiment, and reference previous work or projects.
7. Use "from. . ." or "go to. . ." statements to tie together sections of a lab report or continuous work.
8. Record all directions, materials, and quantities used, plus reactions or operating conditions, in sufficient detail and clarity so that someone of equal skill could understand or repeat the procedure if necessary.

(Continues)

9. Avoid abbreviations and codes when possible. Only the standard abbreviations for metric measurements may be used universally. Any coding or special labeling on samples or in procedural notes should be fully recorded and explained in the notebook.
10. List all persons from whom samples or data were obtained, shared, or transferred.
11. Attach as much original data as is practical in the notebook. Where it is not practical to attach original data, attach examples and make clear reference to where the original data are stored.
12. When procedures, data, or conclusions, etc, are continued from previous pages, each page must have a "from page ___" listed. When continuing to another page, there should be a "go to" statement directing the reader to the next page of that work.
13. For important entries, such as key conclusions or new ideas, have a coworker sign and date the entry. Be sure the coworker is not a coinventor, but someone who is capable of understanding the meaning of the notebook entry.
14. Write/print clearly so there is no ambiguity about the information recorded. Skip lines between data tables, graphs, and important conclusions to make it easier to find and read recorded information.

Laboratory 1b Laboratory Safety: Protecting Yourself and Your Coworkers

Background

A biotechnology laboratory may have several safety hazards. These can put an employee in danger as well as place the safety of others at risk. It is the responsibility of each employee to know and follow the basic laboratory safety rules, to recognize and understand the hazardous materials, equipment, and conditions in a facility, and to work to reduce potential risks.

In the event of an accident, an employee must know what to do to minimize the damage that might occur. Knowing the location of emergency equipment and how to use it is essential for each employee.

Basic Laboratory Safety Rules

1. No eating or drinking in the laboratory. No gum chewing. No makeup application.
2. Wear safety apparel, such as safety goggles, gloves, lab coats, and other protective clothing as necessary. Tie hair back if using Bunsen burners.
3. Know the location of fire exits, fire extinguishers, and safety showers (see Figure 1.4).
4. Wash hands regularly, especially after working with microorganisms or chemicals.
5. Be aware of potential dangers. Before using products or equipment, carefully read labels, experimental protocols, and equipment instructions and literature. Know the location of and how to read Material Safety Data Sheets (MSDS).
6. Contaminated samples (chemical, biological, glass, and radioactive wastes) must be disposed of in appropriate containers. Do not pick up broken glass with your hands. Learn the specific methods from your lab supervisor.

Figure 1.4. A safety shower and eyewash. Do not hesitate to use either one if your clothes are burning or any body parts are exposed to flame or hazardous chemicals. Photo by author.

(Continues)

7. Label all samples and reagents clearly with the name of the item, the name of the person who prepared the sample, and the date of preparation.
8. Know emergency phone numbers and the best way to contact the facility safety officer.
9. Report spills and accidents to your lab supervisor or safety officer immediately.
10. If you are taking antibiotics, or you are pregnant or ill, report your condition to your supervisor.

In summary, a technician who demonstrates good laboratory practices (GLPs) will:

- Know the location and use of all the personal protective equipment, such as goggles, gloves, and hoods, etc.
- Know the location and proper use of all the emergency equipment, such as Material Safety Data Sheets (MSDS), chemical showers, safety eyewash, and fire extinguishers, etc.
- Maintain a clean (and sterile, when appropriate) workspace free from clutter.
- Recognize chemical and biological hazards. Know how to handle and dispose of each hazard properly.
- Know who to contact and how to contact emergency services in the case of a fire, chemical, or biological emergency. Know how to contact the Environmental Health and Safety Officer at the worksite (see Figure 1.5).

Figure 1.5. **An Environmental Health & Safety Manager, like Fredric Rosqvist at Sunesis in South San Francisco, California, is responsible for ensuring that employees have the safest working environment possible. In doing so, Fredric must make certain that Sunesis adheres to highly regulated environmental, human health, and safety standards. These include chemical waste disposal, injury and illness prevention, and emergency response as in after earthquakes or other natural disasters, and also the occasional chemical spill or fire. Several regulatory agencies visit Sunesis periodically to inspect the facility. Inspectors can shut down the facility if the company is not in compliance with regulations, such as how chemicals and wastes are labeled. Fredric also trains employees on the proper use of personal protective equipment (PPE). He has a BS in biochemistry and a BS in general science, as well as multiple professional certifications.** Photo by author.

Purpose

To conduct a safety inventory of the biotechnology laboratory facility.

Procedure

1. The instructor will give everyone a quick tour of the lab facility, pointing out some of the most obvious safety hazards, risk-prevention equipment, and emergency equipment. After the tour, spend an additional 15 minutes with your lab group to completely explore the facility, looking for other safety hazards, risk-prevention equipment, and emergency equipment. In your notebook, record all of these and their uses on a chart similar to Table 1.1.
2. On a piece of graph paper, make a full-page, to-scale diagram that maps out the locations of these hazards and equipment. Glue this onto the last page in your notebook.
3. Record the name and phone numbers of the person, department, or agency to call in case any of the following occurs:
   a. fire
   b. chemical spill
   c. severe cut or laceration

*Environmental Health and Safety Officer

*In this manual, the Biotech Ed EHS Officer icon indicates a known safety hazard.

Table 1.1. Safety Hazards and Safety Equipment Chart

Potential Safety Hazards	Potential Harm	Risk Prevention and Safety Equipment Available	Emergency Equipment Available
Bunsen burner	burns to person or property	goggles and rubber bands for tying back long hair	fire extinguisher, fire blanket, and safety shower

Laboratory 1c   Cheese Production: The Evolution of Cheese-Making Technology

This activity was inspired by labs developed by Louann Carlmagno, formerly of Genencor International, Inc.

Background

The cheese-making industry is huge and has a great number and variety of products (see Figure 1.6). Cheese-making is a good example of how biotechnology has improved an industrial process.

Figure 1.6.   Consumers have many varieties of cheese to choose from. Recently, biotechnology products that make cheese faster than older methods have improved the cheese-making process.

Photo by author.

In the past, people made cheese simply by letting the naturally occurring bacteria in milk turn the milk sour. In that process, the bacteria use milk sugar (lactose) as an energy source and produce lactic acid, a waste product. Lactic acid also causes the mixture to have a mild to slightly bitter taste. Along with other flavorful compounds, the lactic acid gives the cheese a characteristic flavor.

The milk bacteria produce special enzymes (proteins that speed reactions) that convert the lactose to lactic acid. Lactic acid has a low pH (the hydrogen ion concentration, or a measure of the acidity) and causes the milk protein, casein, to denature (unwind) and fall out of solution. Other enzymes, called proteases, may also act on casein. Proteases cleave proteins, such as casein, into smaller fragments that will also fall out of solution. The lumps of denatured casein are called curds. Curds are pressed together to form cheese. The liquid remaining after curdling is called whey.

Using early methods, cheese makers started new batches with a small amount of cheese (containing the enzyme-producing bacteria) they had saved from a batch of curdled milk that produced a good cheese. Although some cheese is still produced in this fashion, today, most commercially made cheese is produced in one of the four ways listed below. In each method, sterilized milk is used as a starting reagent.

1. The milk may simply be left to age, exposed to air and naturally occurring bacteria (see Figure 1.7).
2. New batches of cheese are started with specific cultures of selected bacteria. These "known" bacteria also make the enzymes that curdle milk. Buttermilk has a good culture of *Lactobacillus* bacteria and can be used as a "starter" (see Figure 1.8).
3. New cultures may be started by the addition of purified enzymes, such as rennin, which is retrieved from the cells lining the stomachs of calves (see Figure 1.9). Rennin is a type of protease, and like other proteases, it cleaves the casein into small fragments that settle out

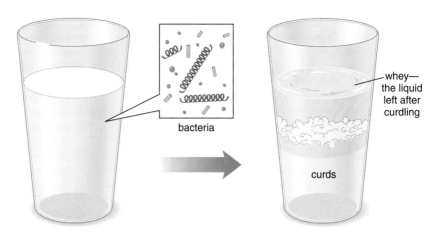

Even "fresh" milk has bacteria in it.
The bacteria use the milk protein,
casein, as food.

As the bacteria grow, they produce
products that make the protein fall out of
solution in lumps. The lumps are called "curds."

Figure 1.7. **Milk Curdling**   Milk left exposed to air curdles because of bacterial enzyme activity.

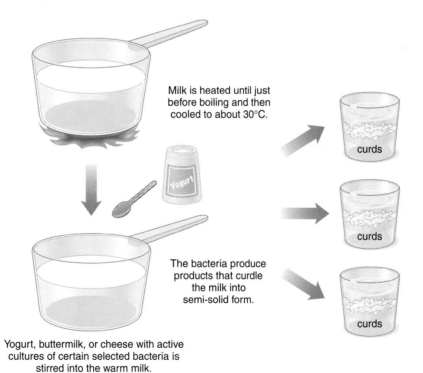

Milk is heated until just
before boiling and then
cooled to about 30°C.

The bacteria produce
products that curdle
the milk into
semi-solid form.

curds

curds

curds

Yogurt, buttermilk, or cheese with active
cultures of certain selected bacteria is
stirred into the warm milk.

Figure 1.8. **Milk Curdling with Starter**   Adding an existing culture of milk-curdling bacteria will speed curdling in a milk sample.

as curds. When calves nurse, their stomach cells produce rennin to digest the milk protein. To retrieve the calves' enzymes for commercial use, companies grind up the calf stomachs and purify the rennin enzyme from all of the other compounds made by the cells. For this reason, some vegetarians do not eat rennin cheeses. There are many rennin cheeses, including Asiago, most bries, most cheddars, and Roquefort.

4. New cultures may be started by adding purified enzymes produced by genetic engineering (see Figure 1.10). Scientists found the DNA code for the cheese-making enzymes produced by calves in regular cow cells. They cut out the cow's rennin cheese-making code (gene) and inserted it into fungus cells. Fungus cells then read the cow DNA and synthesized the

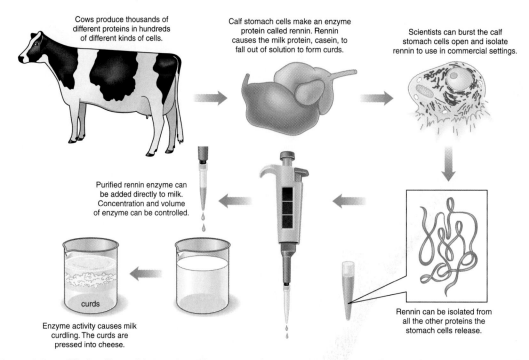

Figure 1.9. Milk Curdling with Rennin The enzyme rennin is extracted from calf stomachs. Rennin curdles milk by breaking bonds that hold the casein protein together.

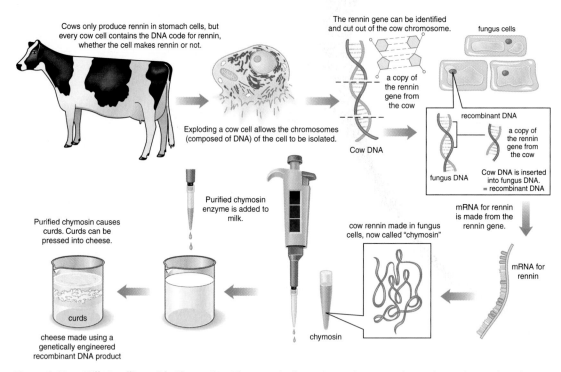

Figure 1.10. Milk Curdling with Chymosin The genetically engineered enzyme chymosin can be produced in fungi faster and more economically than in calves. Chymosin is a form of cow rennin produced in fungi.

rennin enzyme, which scientists called "chymosin." Then, cheese makers used the genetically engineered enzymes to speed curdling. Now, fungal cultures produce the curdling enzymes in a faster, cheaper manner, and in larger amounts than can be produced inside big, multicellular organisms, such as cows. Chymosin cheeses include Jack, mozzarella, and most Swiss cheeses, plus many others.

Scientists work to create new and improved versions of cheese-curdling enzymes, as well as to improve the yields and qualities of cheeses. Modern-day cheese makers want to produce large amounts of high-quality cheese in the most economical way.

Purpose

Determine which curdling agent produces cheese the fastest.
Determine which curdling agent produces the most cheese.
Examine numerical data to support predictions.
Examine variables that can lead to invalid experiments.

Hypothesis

Since chymosin is a product of scientific manipulation, it might be expected to produce the largest volume of cheese in the shortest amount of time.

Materials

Tubes, 15 mL, sterile	Pipet, 1 mL	Graduated cylinder, 25 mL
Pipet, 10 mL	Pipet pump, blue	Plastic funnels, short-stemmed
Pipet pump, green	Buttermilk	Filter paper, 12.5 cm
Whole milk	Rennin, bovine	Water bath, 37°C
Micropipet, P-1000	Chymosin, recombinant renin	Permanent lab marker pens
Micropipet tips for P-1000	Test tube racks for 15 mL tubes	

Procedure

37°C

1. Using a 10-mL pipet and pipet pump, transfer *exactly* 7 mL of whole milk into a labeled, 15-mL conical tube.
2. Using a preset P-1000 micropipet or a 1-mL pipet and pump, add 0.25 mL (250 µL) of one of the four curdling agents to the 7 mL of milk. Use buttermilk, rennin, chymosin, or more whole milk (negative control) as assigned by your supervisor.
3. Cap the tube and mix by gently inverting three times. Record this "initial time."
4. Place the milk-containing portion of the tube deep in your armpit, like a thermometer, and incubate it there for at least 15 minutes.
5. Check for curdling every 5 minutes, recording the time to curdle in minutes. To check for curdling, gently tilt the tube, being careful to not break up any curds. Curds are large lumps of solidified milk. After 15 minutes, place the tube upright at room temperature and check for curdling every 15 minutes for 2 hours. If curdling has not occurred within 2 hours, continue checking once every 4 hours. With the greatest accuracy possible, record the time, in minutes, until the milk curdles to the greatest extent.
6. If curdling has not occurred by the end of the laboratory period, bring the tube home (keep at room temperature) and back to class in 24 hours. Keep the tube upright so any curds fall to the bottom of the tube.
7. On your return to the lab, measure the volume of curds (solids) and whey (liquid) in the tube. You may be able to read the volume of each directly from the tube, although it may be difficult. Better yet, filter the curds as described below, using a "whey-o-meter" (see Figure 1.11).
8. On your return to the lab, pour the whey and curds mixture through a filter paper funnel into a 10-mL graduated cylinder (a "whey-o-meter"). Determine the volume of whey collected in the graduated cylinder, using a pipet, if necessary, to measure small amounts. By subtraction, determine the volume of curds. Can you suggest another method to determine the amount of curds produced in each treatment?

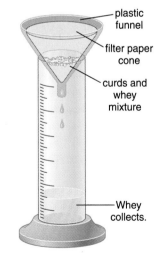

plastic funnel

filter paper cone

curds and whey mixture

Whey collects.

Figure 1.11. Whey-o-meter
A whey-o-meter measures the amount of whey in a curdled milk sample. By subtracting the whey volume from the total volume of reagents used, you can estimate the volume of curds.

Table 1.2. The Effects of Cheese-Curdling Agents on Curdling Time and Volume

Curdling Agent	Time to Curdling (min)	Volume of Whey (mL)	Volume of Curds (mL)	Technician/ Comments
buttermilk				
rennin				
chymosin				
milk (control)				

9. In your notebook, in a data table similar to Table 1.2, record the data for your sample plus one each of the other variable groups. This will give you data for one experimental trial of each curdling agent. Record the name of the person from whom you obtained data.

How well do these single trials of the experiment support the original hypothesis? Explain.

Using Microsoft® Excel®, the lab supervisor or a student colleague will enter each individual's data into a class data table showing multiple replications of the experiment. Averages for each variable group should also be recorded in this data table. Averaged data are the best answer to an experimental question. Can you explain why?

Data Analysis

Using Microsoft® Excel® or a piece of graph paper, produce two graphs: one showing the average time to curdling for each enzyme treatment and one showing the average volume of curds produced by each enzyme treatment. Use the Microsoft® Excel® tutorial, "How to create a chart," if necessary.

Conclusion

Imagine you are an employee at a cheese company and you must summarize the results of your experiments and give your supervisor the "best" answers to the scientific questions asked. Write a conclusion that thoroughly reports and analyzes the experimental data. Following the "REE, PE, PA" method of writing the conclusion ensures a thorough discussion of the experimental results. REE stands for "results" with "evidence" and "explanation," PE stands for "possible errors," and PA represents "practical applications."

In the first paragraph of your conclusion, describe the results of the experiment (answer to the purpose question), including evidence and explanations for your findings. Discuss how well the results support the hypothesis. (This is "REE.")

In the second paragraph, identify sources of errors in the procedure that may lead to variations in results or invalid data. Identify the error and explain what might happen as a result of the error. (This is "PE.")

In the third paragraph, make a recommendation to the company supervisor. Identify which curdling agent should be used for production or the target of continued testing. Include a discussion of any adjustments in the procedures that you think may improve cheese production. Include a proposal for the next set of experiments. (This is "PA.")

Witnessing

In the biotechnology industry, the work of others is reviewed and "OK'd" by peers. This is called "witnessing." When you witness data and review a concluding statement, check for the following:

- accuracy of statements (and that they make sense)
- completeness (REE, PE, PA)
- evidence (numerical data with units of measurement)
- grammar and spelling errors

Make corrections and suggestions right on the page in ink.

- For corrections, draw a single line through the error, correct it, and initial it.
- Write your suggestion for the correction in the margin and draw an arrow to where it should be placed. Then initial and date your entry.

Witness a colleague's conclusion. When you complete the witnessing, write, "Witnessed by" at the end of the conclusion, and then write your full name and the date.

Thinking Like a Biotechnician

The curdling agent experiment has so many factors or variables that can impact the results. To have confidence in the results, you will need a thorough examination of all factors to be controlled.

1. In your notebook, make a chart similar to Table 1.3 that has at least eight rows and four columns. You will use the table to analyze the variables in this experiment that need to be controlled if a technician were to have confidence in the results.
2. In this experiment, each curdling agent is tested multiple times and an average result is determined. Look at the class data. Does it appear that the number of replications for each curdling agent experiment was sufficient? Yes or no? Explain your answer.
3. Do you think that the whey-o-meter instrument was adequate for an accurate determination of whey volume and, indirectly, the curd volume? Why or why not? If yes, explain why. If no, propose a better system to determine the volume of curds or the volume of whey.

Table 1.3. Analysis of Variable(s) in Curdling Experiment

Variable or Factor That Could Affect Results	Why Control Is Needed	Suggested Ways to Control the Variable or Factor	Relative Importance 1 = very important 10 = not very important
temperature	Hands have different temperatures. Samples are held for different time periods. Higher temperatures may give fast reactions.	Place all tubes in a 37°C water bath. Have timer set to ring every 5 minutes. Lift and invert one time; then return to bath.	8 Not as important to see difference in buttermilk or negative control. Very important to see any difference between chymosin and rennin.

Chapter

2 Basic Biology for the Biotechnician

A research associate (RA) transfers freshly prepared cultures of genetically engineered mammalian cells to a carbon dioxide (CO_2) incubator.
Photo by author.

If you work in biotechnology, you will be using, studying, or modifying molecules, cells, or organisms. Each is complex and sensitive to even minor changes in the environment. Molecules and most cells are too small to be visualized without the aid of instruments, and technicians must learn to how to handle and study them.

In the following activities, you will learn some of the techniques used to study cells and the molecules they produce. Specifically, you will learn the following:

- how to use indicator solutions and standards to test for the presence of biologically important molecules, such as carbohydrates, proteins, and nucleic acids
- how to grow and monitor cell cultures
- how to use a microscope to measure and study cell structures and cell processes
- how the structure of molecules affects their characteristics

The laboratory methods practiced in this chapter will be applied in later chapters to the manufacture of a protein product made through recombinant DNA (rDNA) technology.

Laboratory 2a　"Dissecting" a "Cell" and Examining Its Components

Background

A bird ovulates a single egg cell at a time. The egg cell is what we call the yolk. As it travels, the egg cell matures and adds some layers of cells (membranes) in preparation for fertilization. Prior to laying the egg, the bird's body adds a shell to protect the egg in case it has been fertilized. The eggs most often purchased at a store are unfertilized.

Most cells and their structures are too small to be seen without the aid of a microscope. However, a few cells, such as bird eggs, are large enough to study macroscopically (without magnification). Although microscopic measurement is presented in an upcoming activity, you can gain an appreciation of how small some cells are by considering their relative sizes. The average cell is approximately 50 micrometers (μm) in diameter, or about one-tenth the diameter of a human hair. Most organelles are even smaller (less than 1 μm) and, certainly, their molecules are extremely small, less than 0.01 μm in diameter. Molecules are too small to be seen even with standard electron microscopes and have only recently been "seen" with a new microscope called the scanning, tunneling microscope.

Since cells are composed of a variety of molecules, a first step in understanding an organism and its components is to analyze its molecular composition. The basic composition of a cell can be determined through separating its structures (fractionation) and testing for the presence of molecules using indicators, which are chemicals that change color when another molecule is present. Phenol red is a common indicator that can be used to indicate the presence of the molecule, carbon dioxide (CO_2), in a solution (see Figure 2.1). When CO_2 is added to a solution, phenol red changes from a red to a yellow color. The color change is due to a drop in the pH (acid/base level).

Some other indicators that are useful in a biotechnology laboratory include Benedict's solution (indicates monosaccharides), iodine (indicates starch), and Biuret reagent (indicates protein). Indicators are mixed with the molecules they are known to indicate. These are positive, standard tests, so we will know a positive test when we see one. Unknown samples are then tested with an indicator. Color changes in the tested unknown samples are compared to the positive control (standards) tests and to negative control (lacking the indicator's target molecule) tests. Through the use of indicators, and positive and negative controls, researchers can detect and sometimes quantify molecules.

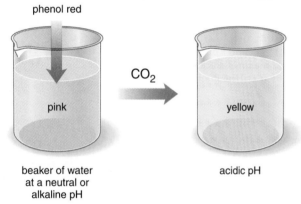

phenol red

pink

CO_2

yellow

beaker of water at a neutral or alkaline pH

acidic pH

Figure 2.1.　Phenol Red Indicator.

Purpose

What are positive indicator tests for proteins, carbohydrates, and fats?
Do parts of an egg test positive for protein, carbohydrate, and/or fat?

Materials

Environmental Health and Safety Officer

Eggs	Tubes, glass, 13×100 mm	Sodium hydroxide
Beaker, 250 mL	Peg racks for 10–13 mm tubes	Cupric sulfate 5-hydrate
White vinegar	Glucose (dextrose)	Oil
Plastic wrap	Benedict's Solution	Sudan III Solution
Slotted spoon	Hot plate stirrer	Scalpel handles, #4
Sodium chloride	Test tube holder	Scalpel blades, #22, for
Distilled water	Starch, soluble	#4 handles
Beaker, 100 mL	Lugol's Iodine Solution	Trays, plastic
Pipets, 5 mL	Vortex mixer	
Pipet pump, green	Gelatin	

Procedure

Part I: Separating Cell Structures

1. Place an uncooked egg into a beaker of white vinegar. Label and cover it with plastic wrap. Leave it for 24 to 48 hours. While the shell dissolves, proceed to Part II.
2. After 24 to 48 hours, the shell should have dissolved in the vinegar (acetic acid). Gently pick up the egg with a slotted spoon and rinse it in water to remove the vinegar. A chemical reaction has happened here. What chemicals were involved as reactants and products?
3. Feel the outer membranes of the cell. The outer membrane, which is different from the membrane around the yolk, provides a good model of a cell membrane. They are thin and flexible. They are permeable to some substances. To verify that water can enter and leave the cell easily, place the egg in a beaker of 5% NaCl solution for 24 hours. Describe the appearance of the egg after 24 hours. What may have caused the change in appearance?
4. Gently rinse off the egg again with water. Then place the egg in a beaker of distilled water for 24 hours. Describe the appearance of the egg after 24 hours. What caused the change in appearance?
5. To retrieve the egg cell, gently slice open the egg's membranes, and let the egg white drip through the slots of the spoon into a 100-mL beaker. Try to get all of the egg white into the beaker without piercing the yolk (egg cell with a clear, flimsy cell membrane around it).
6. Place the egg yolk into another beaker, and set aside the egg membranes.

Part II: Testing Standard Solutions

Following the steps below, test four solutions of known composition (positive controls or standards) with their respective indicator solution. The standards show what a positive test should look like for monosaccharides, starch, proteins, or lipids. Record all data in a data table similar to Table 2.1.

Table 2.1. Results of Standard Molecule Testing Using Different Indicators

Standard (Molecule Tested)	Indicator Used	Description Positive Control (Standard) Test Results	Description Negative Control Test Results
glucose	Benedict's solution		
starch	Lugol's iodine		
protein	Biuret reagent		
fat	none—paper bag test or Sudan III		

100°C

Monosaccharide Indicator Standard Test

1. Test for glucose: In a test tube, mix 2 mL of a 2% glucose (a monosaccharide) solution with 2 mL of Benedict's solution. Heat for 2 minutes in a boiling hot water bath (100 mL of water in a 250-mL beaker at 100°C). Record all color changes and the length of time for each color to appear (refer to Table 2.1).
2. Test for water (negative control): In a test tube, mix 2 mL of deionized water with 2 mL of Benedict's solution. Heat for 2 minutes in a boiling hot water bath (100 mL of water in a 250-mL beaker at 100°C). Record all color changes and the amount of time for each color to appear (refer to Table 2.1).

Starch Indicator Standard Test

1. Test for starch: In a test tube, mix 2 mL of well-mixed starch suspension with 0.25 mL of Lugol's iodine. Gently swirl to mix. **DO NOT HEAT.** Record the color change.
2. Test for water (negative control): In a test tube, mix 2 mL of deionized water with 0.25 mL of Lugol's iodine. Gently swirl to mix. **DO NOT HEAT.** Record the color change.

Environmental Health
and Safety Officer

Protein Indicator Standard Test

Caution: Sodium hydroxide (NaOH) is a strong base, is caustic, and can burn. Wear goggles and gloves. Wipe spills immediately. Flush exposed surfaces with tap water.

1. Test for protein: Place 2 mL of gelatin (protein) solution in a test tube. Wearing goggles and gloves, add 0.5 mL of 10% NaOH and gently vortex to mix. Add 0.25 mL of 5% copper sulfate ($CuSO_4$) and gently mix. The NaOH and $CuSO_4$ mixture is called Biuret reagent. Mix well. Record color change after 30 seconds.
2. Test for water (negative control): Place 2 mL of deionized water in a test tube. Wearing goggles and gloves, add 0.5 mL of 10% NaOH, and gently vortex to mix. Add 0.25 mL of 5% $CuSO_4$, and gently mix well. Record color change after 30 seconds.

Lipid Indicator Standard Test*

1. Test for lipid(s): Place a drop of oil (100% fat) on a piece of brown paper bag. Let it "dry" for 10 minutes. Hold up the paper to light. Record how much light passes through the spot (the percentage of translucence).
2. Test for water: Place a drop of water on a piece of brown paper bag. Let it "dry" for 10 minutes. Hold up the paper to light. Record how much light passes through the spot (the percentage of translucence).

Part III: Molecular Composition of Egg Components

Test each of the egg components for the presence of monosaccharides, starch, protein, and lipid.

1. Conduct each indicator test, as described in Part II, but *substitute* each egg component to be tested for the sugar, starch, protein, or fat in the test. All volumes and test conditions are the same as in Part II; only the item tested (the unknowns) is changed. **Make sure that you do not add any of the standard solutions.**
2. Record the results of testing the egg membranes, the yolk (cell cytoplasm), and egg white for all four molecules on another data table (see Table 2.2).
3. Give a numerical value to each test result using the system described in the key below Table 2.2, which is based on a comparison with the standard tests. Also, include a brief description of color changes.

Table 2.2.   **The Presence and Relative Amount of Organic Molecules Found in Egg**
Key: 3 = very strong / positive test; 2 = strong / positive test; 1 = weak / positive test; 0 = no color change in indicator/negative.

Egg Component Tested	Standard Indicator Reaction				
	Benedict's Solution	Iodine	Biuret Reagent	Paper Bag or Sudan III Test	Comments
egg membranes					
yolk (egg cell)					
egg white					

Data Analysis

Write a conclusion that reports the results of the experiment (check the purpose question) and the chemical nature of the egg. Identify sources of errors in how you carried out the procedures that may lead to false positive or false negative results. Suggest possible variations or extensions of these laboratory procedures. Propose other applications of molecular testing in future experiments or in industry.

*An alternative to the translucence test is to use a lipid indicator, Sudan III. Add 60 μL of Sudan III solution to 2 mL of sample. Gently mix. Red is a negative lipid test and orange is a positive lipid test.

Thinking Like a Biotechnician

1. Describe how you would test kidney bean seeds for the presence of glucose, starch, and protein. Include all reagents, volumes, and testing conditions. Describe the results that you would expect to occur.
2. Which type of molecule(s) tested strongly in all of the egg component samples? Why?
3. If a pea green color resulted for a sample tested with Benedict's solution, what would you conclude about the sugar content? Propose a quantitative method by which the amount of sugar could be determined.
4. An enzyme is thought to have starch-digesting activity. What indicator might you use to show that starch is being broken down to glucose by an enzyme? How would you measure the reaction? What data would you collect?
5. Why is it necessary to have a negative control group for each test (testing water with each indicator)? What does the negative-control result tell you?
6. In what ways are these procedures a "controlled" experiment? List the parameters that must be kept constant to obtain meaningful variations in results.
7. Propose some other use by scientists or consumers for any one of these indicator tests.

Laboratory 2b   The Characteristics of Model Organisms

Millions of species of plants, animals, and microorganisms inhabit the earth. Obviously, scientists cannot study all of them in any great detail. However, a significant amount of evidence from biochemical and physiological studies suggests that the basic operations of all cells and many related organisms are the same. Therefore, after scientists learn a bit about a certain organism's characteristics, they often pick the same organism to study further. This allows the science community to build a large body of information about an organism's growth and behavior. The organism becomes what is called a "model organism," one that is grown and studied as representative of closely related species. Model organisms have the following characteristics:

- relatively easy to grow and maintain in a restricted space (eg, a lab, a field)
- relatively easy to provide necessary nutrients for growth
- relatively short generation time (birth ➔ reproduction ➔ birth)
- relatively well understood growth and development
- closely resembles others organisms or systems (eg, monkeys to humans)

In the animal kingdom, rats and mice are model organisms. Most studies of animal physiology, nutrition, genetics, and cancer are conducted in these mammals. Not only is much known about mice and rats, but they also have other characteristics, such as a large number of offspring per litter, that make them ideal lab animals to study.

In the bacterial world, *Escherichia coli (E. coli)* is the model organism. *It* has been used for genetic studies for more than 50 years. More is known about *E. coli* than any other organism in the world, including its growth requirements, physiology, and genetic code. *It* is easy to grow in the lab on a solid media (agar) or in a liquid (broth) culture. Most biotechnology companies that grow bacteria use *E. coli* bacteria.

A few fungal species act as model organisms, including *Aspergillus,* a type of bread mold, and both baker's and brewer's yeast. *Aspergillus* is a multicellular fungus with a well-understood life cycle (see Figure 2.2). Its fuzzy body is easy to grow on agar in the lab, and its prominent reproductive spores make studying reproduction easy. Yeast (*Saccharomyces cerevisiae*) is a unicellular fungus. Like *E. coli,* yeast is easy to grow on solid or liquid media. Because of their size, yeast cells are easy to observe using a microscope.

To grow and study an organism in a laboratory, one should know the environmental preferences of the species. Maintaining an organism at less than optimal light intensity, temperature, or oxygen level, for example, may put the organism under stress, possibly affecting its growth or other processes.

Purpose

What are the temperature preferences shown by three model organisms (*E. coli, Aspergillus niger,* and baker's yeast) grown in the biotechnology lab?

Figure 2.2. *Aspergillus*, **a Type of Bread Mold, Growing on an Agar Petri Dish.**
Photo by author.

Materials

Laminar flow hood	LB broth base	*Aspergillus sp,* plate culture
Lysol® disinfectant	Loop, inoculating, sterile	Scalpel handles, #4
Petri dishes, 60×15 mm, sterile	Bleach solution, 10%	Scalpel blades, #22,
LB agar base	Plastic beaker, 1L	for #4 handles
Media bottle, 600 mL	Incubator ovens	Yeast
E. coli JM109, overnight culture	Potato dextrose agar, 125 mL	Glucose
Tubes, 50 mL, sterile	Culture tube and caps,	Flask, Erlenmeyer, 250 mL
Tube racks for 50 mL tubes	38×200 mm	

General Safety Precautions

Environmental Health and Safety Officer

- If possible, do all bacteria work in a sterile laminar flow hood or disinfected countertop that is protected from air currents.
- Do *Aspergillus* work in a clean, disinfected chemical fume hood with the fan off and protective shield down. Do not inhale *Aspergillus* spores. When the work is done, turn on the fume hood fan for several minutes to remove airborne spores.
- Use all standard precautions with the Bunsen burner, including tying back hair and using goggles, etc.
- Dispose of any bacteria- or fungus-contaminated products in autoclave bags or soak them in a 10% bleach solution for 30 minutes.

Procedure

Part I: Growing *E. coli* Cells

PreLab
- If a laminar flow hood is available, use it for the sterile work. Run it for 10 minutes before using.
- Disinfect all surfaces prior to transferring bacteria.
- Wash hands before and after handling bacteria.

1. Label the bottom of an LB agar Petri plate. Labels should be small, but readable, and placed at the outer edge of the bottom plate (see Figure 2.3). Include your initials, the date, the media type (LB), and the sample identification (*E. coli*).

2. Using a sterile, plastic 1-μL inoculating loop, collect a loopful of *E. coli* broth culture.

3. Streak the bacterial broth culture onto a sterile LB agar Petri plate (see Figure 2.3).
   a. Streak the broth back and forth across the agar on the top one-fourth of the plate. Discard the plastic inoculating loop into a 10% bleach solution. Consider this first set of streaking to be the "1st Z."

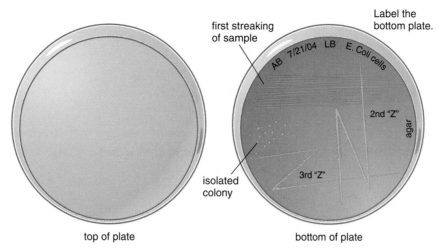

Figure 2.3.   Triple Z Streaking Method.

b. Rotate the plate 90°. Streak a new sterile inoculating loop at a right angle through previous streak. You should go through the first streak only once to pick up the fewest bacteria cells possible. Make a "Z"-shaped streak. This is the "2nd Z." Discard the plastic inoculating loop into a 10% bleach solution.

c. Rotate the plate another 90°. Streak another sterilized loop at a right angle through the first "Z" streak. You should go through that streak only once to pick up the fewest bacteria cells possible. Make a "Z." This is the third "Z." Discard the plastic inoculating loop into a 10% bleach solution.

d. Replace the lid onto the Petri plate. Place your inoculated LB plate **upside down** in one of the incubation ovens designated by the instructor.

e. Be careful to hold the top of the Petri plate over the bottom to minimize contamination.

4. Each person will streak and monitor one plate. Several plates will be incubated in each of the following conditions:

4°C in the dark   room temperature in the dark   30°C in the dark
37°C in the dark   42°C in the dark

Part II: Growing *Aspergillus*

- If a chemical fume hood is available, use it for the *Aspergillus* work. Do not inhale *Aspergillus* spores.
- Disinfect all surfaces prior to the transfer of fungi.
- Wash hands before and after handling fungi.

1. Label the *Aspergillus* racing tube containing potato dextrose agar with a small piece of labeling tape containing your initials, the media, the sample identification, and the date (see Figure 2.4).

2. Using a sterile scalpel, cut a wedge of *Aspergillus* fungus mycelium (fuzzy body), 1 cm by 1 cm, out of the stock plate (see Figure 2.5).

Environmental Health and Safety Officer

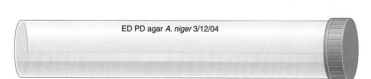

ED PD agar *A. niger* 3/12/04

Figure 2.4.   *Aspergillus* Tube Culture.

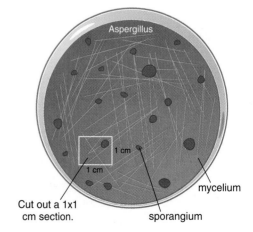

Figure 2.5.   *Aspergillus* Plate Culture.

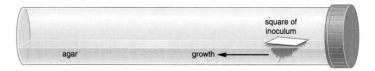

Figure 2.6. *Aspergillus* **Growth Tube.**

3. Transfer the fungus, using the sterile scalpel as a spatula, fungus side down, to the potato dextrose agar just inside the lip of the tube. Press it down lightly to make sure it sticks (see Figure 2.6).
4. Each person inoculates and monitors one tube with *Aspergillus*. Several tubes will be incubated in each of the following conditions:

4°C in the dark	room temperature in the dark	30°C in the dark
37°C in the dark	42°C in the dark	

Part III: Growing Yeast Cells

- Use sterile technique and a laminar flow hood, if available, for sterile work.
- One hour prior to use, each group of four lab partners should prepare a yeast broth culture using a package of yeast, 0.5 g of glucose, and 100 mL of dH_2O. Incubate for 1 hour at 37°C (see Figure 2.7).

1. Using a sterile, plastic 1-μL inoculating loop, collect a loopful of yeast broth culture.

2. Streak the yeast broth culture onto a sterile yeast malt agar Petri plate, using the "triple Z" technique described above.

3. Each person inoculates and monitors one plate of yeast. Several plates of yeast will be incubated in each the following conditions:

4°C in the dark	room temperature in the dark	30°C in the dark
37°C in the dark	42°C in the dark	

Part IV: Data Collection and Analysis

1. Observe each sample after 24 hours.
2. Record the amount and type of growth on each plate, or in each tube, in a data table similar to Table 2.3. Devise a method to quantify the amount of growth seen on the plates or in the tubes, and write a description of your method in your notebook.
3. Collect data from your own cultures as well as from two other technicians in your group. Average each set of data.

Data Analysis

Write a conclusion that reports the results of the temperature of incubation experiment and the variations in the growth of each organism. Identify sources of error in the techniques that may lead to erroneous results. Suggest possible variations or extensions of these laboratory procedures. For each organism, identify one other environmental factor that might be tested. Discuss the reasons that testing growth rate and environmental preferences may be important to genetic engineers and biotechnologists.

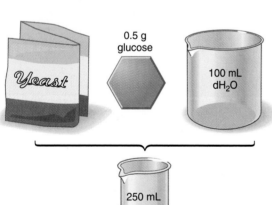

Figure 2.7. **Yeast Culture.**

Table 2.3. **The Amount of Growth Observed in Three Model Organisms in Different Temperatures**

Temperature (Degrees Centigrade, °C)		Amount of Growth		
		E. coli	*Aspergillus*	Yeast
room temperature (20°C)	Trial 1			
	Trial 2			
	Trial 3			
	Average			
30°C	Trial 1			
	Trial 2			
	Trial 3			
	Average			
37°C	Trial 1			
	Trial 2			
	Trial 3			
	Average			
42°C	Trial 1			
	Trial 2			
	Trial 3			
	Average			

Thinking Like a Biotechnician

1. In this experiment, you averaged the results of three technicians' individual experiments. Based on your analysis of the growth data, discuss the advantages and disadvantages of using multiple replications from different technicians.
2. In this experiment, potential biohazards were used (*E. coli* – although you used a safe laboratory strain, *Aspergillus*, and yeast). Describe the measures that should be taken by a lab technician or lab manager to protect workers and the public from biohazard contamination.
3. In addition to temperature, many other variables will affect *E. coli*'s growth and reproduction. Consider three other variables that could be varied and tested to determine their effect on *E. coli* growth. For each variable you suggest, describe the way an experiment would be conducted to test response to the variable. Include the measuring instruments to be used and the type of data to be collected. Report the variables to be tested, experiment plan, and data collection on a chart.
4. *Aspergillus* sp, like many fungi, is light sensitive. Design an experiment to test the effect of different light levels on *Aspergillus* growth. Propose step-by-step instructions on how to conduct the experiment. Include materials and quantities for each, and data that should will be collected.

5. In this activity, *E. coli* was grown on a solid culture medium (agar). To grow large amounts of *E. coli* broth culture (liquid), large fermentation tanks are used. Search the Internet to find a picture of a fermentation tank that is used to grow large amounts of bacteria. Print an image of the tank, and label it with the reference (Web site URL). Propose a different environmental condition that should be varied and tested when growing *E. coli* in broth instead of on agar.

6. Suppose a biotechnology company is growing cells to make a protein product to sell. Describe the possible impact on a company of growing cells in less-than-optimum conditions.

Laboratory 2c Using a Compound Light Microscope to Study Cells

Background

All living things are made up of one or more cells. Most cells are very small, averaging between 10 and 30 μm in diameter. A micrometer is 0.001 millimeter (mm), and there are 1000 μm in a millimeter. To picture cell size, imagine the sharpest pencil point and consider that it would make a mark about 100 μm in diameter.

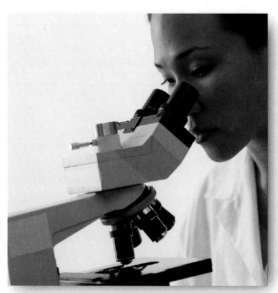

Figure 2.8. A light or compound microscope uses light, and two or more lenses to enlarge and focus an image. The lens at the top is called the eyepiece, or the ocular lens. The ocular lens usually magnifies by 10 times (10X). By rotating an objective lens of 4X, 10X, 40X, or 100X into position, you can achieve magnifications of 40X, 100X, 400X, and 1000X, respectively. To see a significant amount of detail in prokaryotic cells, you need a magnification of 1000X.
© Corbis.

Scientists and technicians learn how a cell functions by studying its structure and biochemistry. Cells are most commonly observed with a light microscope that allows a look inside of all but the tiniest cells (see Figure 2.8). To see even smaller cell structures, one must use an electron microscope.

Some cells appear to have a simple organization. Prokaryotic cells, such as bacteria and blue-green algae, lack a nucleus or membrane-bound organelles. Prokaryotic cells are about 1 μm in size. Cells can be complicated in their organization, containing many specialized organelles; these types of cells are called eukaryotic. A cell's structure is related to its environment and function(s). This is why a nerve cell from the brain looks so different from a red blood cell (RBC).

All cells have certain structures in common: a cell membrane, cytoplasm, and one or more chromosomes. The presence and number of other organelles depend on the type of cell. Cells can be superficially grouped together as bacteria-like, plant-like, or animal-like, depending on the type of structures present, such as cell walls or chloroplasts.

Since most organelles are very small, many will not be visible through a light microscope. When observing cells, one should consider which organelles might be seen. A magnification of 450 times (450X) will resolve (distinguish clearly) to about 2 μm. Review the list below and separate the organelles/structures into two groups: 1) those large enough be seen in cells using compound microscopes (with a maximum magnification of 1000X), and 2) those that are only visible through an electron microscope. Use photos on the Internet to make your predictions.

Some Cellular Structures

mitochondria	nuclei	lysosomes
Golgi bodies	chromosomes	cell walls
ribosomes	vacuoles	endoplasmic reticula
chloroplasts		

It is very important to learn how to handle and use a microscope properly to make accurate observations, avoid damage to lenses, and reduce frustration. For the microscope in your laboratory, identify the following parts:

eyepiece/ocular lens
objectives/objective lens: low power, medium power, high power, oil immersion
focus adjustment knobs: coarse adjustment, fine adjustment
light diaphragm
light source
stage
neck (arm)
base

When using a microscope, take care to follow the rules below:

Rules for Microscope Use

1. Carry the microscope by holding it by both the neck and the base. Place the microscope on a flat surface away from the edge. Place the arm of the scope opposite the user (see Figure 2.8).
2. Do not touch the lenses with anything except lens paper.
3. To focus the microscope on an image, place a slide on the stage with the object centered over the light path. Start with the low power objective (4X) in position and the coarse adjustment knob turned so that the objective lens is close to the stage. Slowly turn the coarse adjustment knob to bring the objective up until the image is in focus. Center the image and focus with the fine adjustment knob. If desired, bring the medium-power objective (10X) into position, and use the fine adjustment knob to focus. Center the image and, if desired, bring the high-power objective (40X) into position, and use the fine adjustment knob to focus. Do not use the coarse adjustment while using the 40X objective. To get the best contrast between structures, adjust light to the lowest level that gives the sharpest focus. Before removing the slide, reset the low-power objective over the slide.

Part I: Observing Prepared Slides

Purpose

What details can be seen in prepared slides of silk, blood, and bacteria?

Materials

Prepared slides (silk, blood, bacteria)
Microscope, compound, with 100×

Procedure

1. Using lower power, focus the silk thread slide so that all three threads of silk are centered and in sharp focus. Move the medium power objective into place and center the specimen and focus the image using the fine adjustment knob.
2. Observe, draw, and label the threads so that their color, depth, and size are clear and accurate in the microscopic field of vision.
3. Center the human blood slide over the light. Focus on RBCs, first on low power, then on medium power, and then on high power. Observe, draw, and label the RBCs, WBCs, and platelets, so that the color, depth, and size are accurate. Is a nucleus visible in any of these cells?
4. Focus the bacteria slide (*E. coli* or *Bacillus (B.) subtilis*) on high power, after focusing with the low- and medium-power objectives. The bacteria are very, very tiny and will appear as tiny specks of dust on low and medium power. Observe, draw, and label the bacteria so that their color, shape, and size are clear and accurate in the microscopic field of vision. The shapes of bacteria include rods, spheres, and/or spirals. Your diagram should show enough detail to identify the bacteria as one or more of these shapes.

Part II: Preparing and Observing Wet Mount Slides

Purpose

What structures are visible in various cells using a light microscope?

Materials

Environmental Health and Safety Officer

Microscope, compound, with 100×
Microscope slides
Microscope slide coverslips, glass
Transfer pipets, 3 mL
Toothpicks

Methylene Blue Stain, 1%
Elodea densa
Onion
Lugol's Iodine Solution
Mixed algae culture
Prepared slides, onion root tip
Tomato

Paramecium caudatum culture
Protozoan culture (cereal media)
Aspergillus sp, plate culture
Digital camera, Moticam 1000
Gooseneck stand for digital camera

Procedure

Use clean, dry slides and coverslips. To the center of the slide, add a small drop of water. Add a small amount of sample. Gently place a coverslip on the slide, so that one edge touches the edge of the liquid on the slide. Next, gently lower the coverslip to press out any air bubbles. The coverslip should appear perfectly flat on the slide.

1. Make a stained, wet mount of human cheek cells adding the smallest drop of methylene blue. Gently scrape the inside of your check for cells. Observe, draw, and label on 400X.
2. Make a wet mount of a *tiny* piece of *Elodea* leaf. Look on the edge of the leaf for individual cells showing moving cytoplasm. Observe, draw, and label on 100X.
3. Make a stained, wet mount of onion epidermis (skin from the leaf in the bulb) adding iodine as the stain. Observe, draw, and label on 100X.
4. Make a wet mount of a *tiny* bit of green algae. Observe, draw, and label on 400X.
5. Observe a prepared slide of dividing cells (*Allium* root tip). Make sure you are observing cells about 40 cells back from the growing tip. Observe, draw, and label on 400X.
6. Make a wet mount of a *tiny* bit of tomato pulp. Observe, draw, and label on 100X.
7. Make a wet mount of a *tiny* drop of the protozoa culture. **Do not add a coverslip.** Observe, draw, and label on either 100X or 400X, depending on the size of the protozoa.
8. Make a wet mount of a *tiny* bit of bread mold. Observe, draw, and label on 400X.
9. Make sure that all drawings are accurate in size, color, and detail within the field of vision. Label all visible organelles. Record the sample name and magnification of observation.
10. Prepare a data table to record the structures seen in each of the cell samples. Label cell structures (from page 23) along the top, and label the rows with the sample names. Put a check in a square when you observe a structure in a cell.

Data Analysis

In a conclusion statement, discuss the similarities and differences you saw in the cell structures from the plant or plant-like samples. Discuss the similarities and differences in these cell structures compared with those taken from animal or animal-like samples. Include observations on size, shape, and structure. Describe any difficulties you encountered when trying to focus on cells or cell structures. What might have caused these difficulties?

Thinking Like a Biotechnician

1. What cell structures did you observe in all of the cell samples?
2. What structures were only visible in the *Elodea* cells? What is their function? Why do the other cells not have these structures? What might happen if stain is used (accidentally) on *Elodea*?
3. What is the purpose of using stain to observe cheek cells and onion cells, but not on *Elodea* or the protozoa? What are the advantages and disadvantages to using a stain?
4. Which cells were from multicellular organisms, and which cells were single-celled organisms? What evidence of this do you have from your observations?
5. If you are having trouble getting something into focus on high power, list three things you should do to correct the problem.
6. Identify any samples that were difficult to observe. Describe reasons for the difficulties. Propose changes in the procedures that might result in better wet mounts or observations.

Laboratory 2d   Making Microscopic Measurements

Background

When making observations with a compound microscope, you should record the size of each specimen. If you know the size of the field of vision at a specific magnification, you can estimate the size of a specimen.

In many microscopes used at companies and universities, a ruler called a micrometer is actually built into the objectives. However, many microscopes do not have micrometers, including those used in most introductory biotechnology courses. Instead, you can estimate the size of each field of vision by measuring the low-power field of vision directly with a piece of graph paper.

To measure the diameter of the low-power field, use a wet mount of 1-mm grid graph paper and count the number of millimeters across the center of the field. The value is converted from mm to μm since microscopic measurements are most commonly reported in micrometers. A micrometer (μm) is equal to 1/1000th (0.001) of a millimeter (mm). In other words, there are 1000 μm in a mm. Micrometers are often called microns, and the terms are used interchangeably in a biotechnology lab.

On most microscopes, the medium- and high-power fields are too small to be measured directly. However, the sizes of the medium- and high-power fields can be determined indirectly if you realize that the field is smaller by the same value that the magnification has been increased (see Figure 2.9). For example, if the size of the low-power (40X) field on a microscope is 5 mm or 5000 μm, then the size of the medium (100X) field would be 2-1/2 times smaller, or 2000 μm. Similarly, the high-power (400X) field would be 10 times smaller, or 500 μm.

Once the field size has been determined, cell sizes can be estimated by what percentage of the field they occupy. For example, a human stomach cell is fairly rectangular, and its length fills about one-third of the field (see Figure 2.10). So, since the cell's length takes up approximately one-third of the medium-power field, it is approximately 2000/3 μm long, or 666.7 μm.

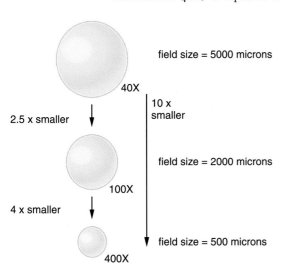

field size = 5000 microns

40X

2.5 x smaller

10 x smaller

field size = 2000 microns

100X

4 x smaller

field size = 500 microns

400X

Figure 2.9.   Sizes of the Fields of Vision on a Microscope.

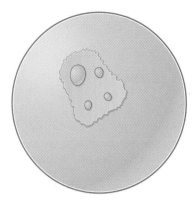

Figure 2.10. **A human stomach cell at 100X occupies about one-third of the field of vision.**

Purpose

What are the diameters of the fields of view on our microscopes at different magnifications? What are the dimensions, in μm and mm, of some familiar materials?

Materials

Microscope, compound
Microscope slides
Microscope slide coverslips, glass
Graph paper, 1-mm grid
Transfer pipets, 3 mL

Human hair
Banana
Lugol's Iodine Solution
Digital camera, Moticam 1000
Gooseneck stand for digital camera

Procedure

1. Make a wet mount of a 10 mm² piece of 1-mm grid graph paper. Count how many 1-mm squares go across the diameter of the low-power field. Convert the diameter measurement from mm to μm. Record the size of this field in both mm and μm in a data table of your own design.
2. Next, do the division, as described above, to determine the sizes of the medium- and high-power fields. Report the values in both mm and μm in the data table.
3. Make a wet mount of a short piece of human hair. Observe, draw, and label on 400X. Determine the width of the hair in mm and μm. Create a second data table to record measurements of this and other samples.
4. Prepare a wet mount of a very small amount of banana cells. Lightly stain with iodine. Observe, draw, and label the specimen on 100X. Determine the width and length of the banana cells in mm and μm. Record these measurements in the data table.
5. Go back and measure any other cells you have observed in previous lab activities. Record their length and width measurements in the data table.

Data Analysis

1. Create and label a line scale (similar to a timeline) that shows measurements between 500 μm (1 mm) and 1 μm (0.001 mm) with every centimeter (cm) representing 50 μm. Put a label on the line for each measurement you have made. Include all the cells you have measured: *Elodea,* banana, human hair, tomato, etc.
2. What patterns do you observe in the size or shapes of the samples you have measured? Explain.

Thinking Like a Biotechnician

1. A technician determines the length of a banana cell at both 100X and 400X. He or she determines the length at 100X is 75 μm, but the length at 400X is 100 μm. Which measurements are more likely to be accurate and why?
2. You may have noticed that the contrast (sharpness) of the image decreases as you increase the magnification of a sample. List a few steps you can take to improve the resolution (ability to distinguish points) of the images at higher magnification.
3. A 100X objective can be used on a compound microscope, bringing the total possible magnification to 1000X. This lens is called an oil immersion lens since a drop of oil is needed

between the objective lens and the coverslip to help gather more light. (The oil corrects for the refractive index of air.) Predict what organelles might be visible if the oil immersion lens is used to view eukaryotic cells. Also, list those organelles you think are so small that even 1000X magnification is not high enough to visualize them.

4. To visualize very tiny organelles, one needs a scanning electron microscope. Go to the Internet and find an electron micrograph (picture from an electron microscope) that shows one or more Golgi bodies. Record the magnification of the micrograph. Record the Web site reference.

Laboratory 2e Variation in the Structure and Properties of Carbohydrates

Background

Every molecule has a distinctive size, shape, and arrangement of atoms. A hydrogen peroxide molecule (H_2O_2), for example, has the same atoms as a water molecule (H_2O), with the exception of one additional oxygen atom. That extra oxygen atom has huge repercussions when it comes to chemical activity and characteristics. Although both are clear liquids, H_2O_2 is an oxidizing agent and will kill cells, while water is nontoxic and is required for life.

The dramatic effects of the composition and arrangement of atoms in a molecule can be seen when one studies carbohydrates. All carbohydrates have the same basic composition of elements, a combination of one carbon atom for every two hydrogen atoms and one oxygen atom (a 1:2:1 ratio), written $C_nH_{2n}O_n$. However, tiny differences in the number and arrangement of these atoms can affect a carbohydrate's taste, texture, and biological activity.

Three factors determine the nature of a particular monosaccharide:

1. The length of the carbon skeleton (ie, four, five, or six carbons), as shown in Figure 2.11.
2. Where its carbonyl (the double-bonded oxygen atom) group is located. If the oxygen is attached at the end of the carbon chain, the sugar is called an aldehyde; 6-carbon aldehydes, such as glucose, make a six-sided ring (attached C1 to C5 through a bond with oxygen). If the oxygen is attached at the middle of the carbon chain, as in fructose, the sugar is called a ketone (C2-C5), as shown in Figure 2.12.
3. The orientation of its atoms around asymmetrical carbons. For example, glucose and galactose are identical, except for the direction of atoms at the No. 4 C (see Figure 2.13).

The number and the type of monosaccharide units also influence disaccharide and polysaccharide characteristics.

Purpose

What are the differences in the structures of some common carbohydrates?
What are the differences in texture and taste of different carbohydrates?
How does their structure affect their characteristics?

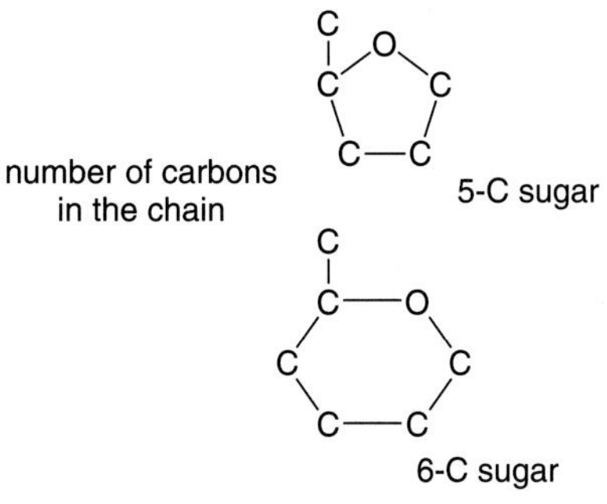

Figure 2.11. Carbon Skeleton Length.

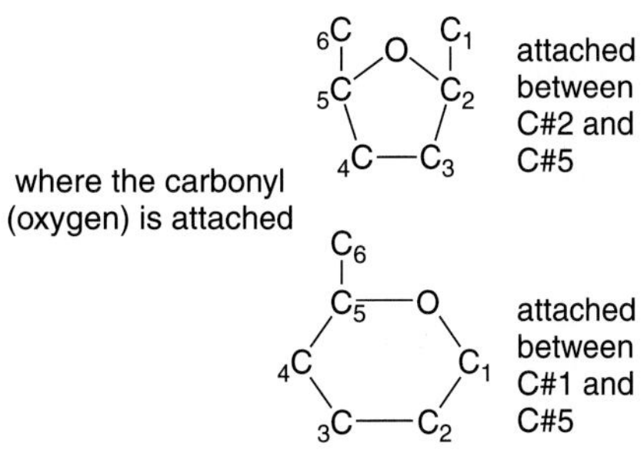

Figure 2.12. Oxygen Atom Position.

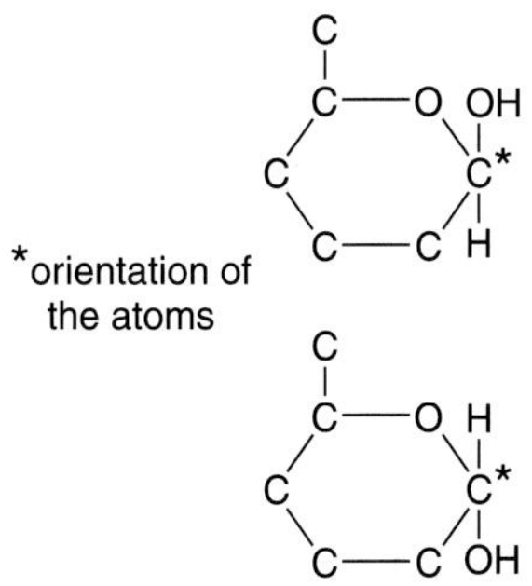

Figure 2.13. Orientation of Atoms.

Materials

Sucrose	Maltose	Petri dishes, 60×15 mm, sterile
Glucose (dextrose)	Lactose	Plastic spoons
Fructose	Starch, soluble	Paper cups
Galactose	Cellulose	Tap water

Procedure

Part I: Gathering Structural Information

1. Use the Internet to find the structure and function of each of the molecules being tested (listed in the "Materials" section). If a structure is labeled "D" or "L," use the D form. If a structure is labeled "right-handed" or "left-handed," use the right-handed form.
2. Draw a structural diagram of each molecule, showing the specific arrangement of atoms in the molecule. Next to each drawing, write a short description of the main functions of the molecule and its distinguishing structure. Also, include bibliographical reference information.

Part II: Comparing the Characteristics of Carbohydrates

Environmental Health and Safety Officer

- **Caution: If you are a diabetic, do not conduct the experiment.**
- Refrain from eating or chewing candy for at least 1 hour before this experiment.
- Rinse your mouth with tap water between taste tests.

1. Scoop a tiny bit of sucrose onto a plastic spoon. Use this sample for the test and then discard the spoon into the trash. Do not return any samples to the stock dishes.
2. Touch your finger to the sucrose. Touch the sucrose to your tongue and take at least 10 full seconds to mentally note its sweetness. Let this amount of sweetness be a standard of 100 on an arbitrary sweetness scale that ranges from 0 to 200. Based on their structure, predict the sweetness of the other carbohydrates. Which do you think will be the sweetest, and which do you think will be the least sweet?
3. Describe the texture of the sucrose.
4. For each of the other carbohydrates, use a new spoon and repeat steps 1 through 3. Rank the sweetness of each sample based on the sucrose standard of 100.
5. Record your data in a data table (see Table 2.4). You may have to use reference materials to determine the function of some of the carbohydrates.

Table 2.4. **Characteristics of Various Carbohydrates**

Carbohydrate Tested	Type of Carbohydrate	Degree of Sweetness	Color	Texture	Function(s)
sucrose	disaccharide	100	white	granular	energy, transport
glucose (dextrose)					

Data Analysis/Conclusion

1. Which carbohydrates were sweetest? Does the number of sugar rings affect how sweet the carbohydrate tastes?
2. Are there any other observed characteristics that appear affected by the number of sugar rings?
3. Did all testers give each sample the same rating? List three reasons why the rating of the same samples could be different for different tasters.
4. Look at the structural formulas for the monosaccharides. Are the structurally similar ones alike in other characteristics? Explain.

Thinking Like a Biotechnician

1. How might carbohydrate structural differences affect how they function in cells and organisms?
2. What causes humans to taste sweetness? Use the Internet to learn how the tongue tastes. Use this information to explain how the tasters could rank the sweetness of the same samples differently.

Laboratory 2f How Molecular Structure Is Affected by Environmental Change

Background

Milk is a watery mixture of many different molecules, including proteins, carbohydrates, and lipids. Casein is the group of proteins in the highest concentration in milk. Casein proteins and fat globules are responsible for most of the white color of milk. Like all proteins, casein is particularly sensitive to changes in temperature and pH.

The range of pH values is from 0 to 14; values below 7 are considered acidic and those above 7 are considered basic. A pH value of 7 is considered neutral. An acid has more H^+ ions (protons) than OH^- ions (hydroxyl ions). The stronger an acid is, the more H^+ ions there are in solution. Acids get 10 times stronger with each pH unit approaching 0. Thus, tomato juice with a pH of 4 has 10 times more H^+ ions than coffee with a pH of 5.0.

A base has more OH^- ions than H^+ ions. The stronger the base is, the more OH^- ions there are in solution. Bases get 10 times stronger with each pH value approaching 14. Thus, Borax® (U.S. Borax Inc) solution, a type of detergent with a pH close to 9.5, has almost 100 times more OH^- ions than blood with a pH close to 7.5.

The extra + or – charges in an acidic or basic solution can affect the structure and function of proteins (see Figure 2.14). The excess charges can interact with the charged areas on a protein and cause it to unwind (denature). In the case of casein, curdling is one indication of a significant change in protein shape. A change in shape can cause a change in protein function. Thus, it is important for a protein to be maintained at an "optimal" pH if it is to function properly.

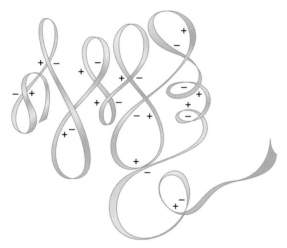

Figure 2.14. **Protein Shape.** A protein has an optimum shape determined by the interactions between different parts of the polypeptide chain. To maintain its function, it must maintain its shape.

Purpose

How much acid or base is necessary to observe an obvious change in structure?

Materials

Environmental Health and Safety Officer

Tubes, glass, 13×100 mm	Micropipet, P-100	Lemon juice
Plug caps for 13×100 mm tubes	Micropipet tips, yellow	1% sodium hydroxide solution
Peg racks for 10–13 mm tubes	pH paper, wide-range 0–14	

*Caution: When using acids and bases, wear goggles and gloves. Wipe spills with a damp paper towel. Flush skin with large amounts of water.

Procedure

Part I: The Effect of Acid on Protein Structure

1. Place 3 mL of milk in a 13×100-mm culture tube. Use pH paper to measure the pH of the milk. Use pH paper to measure the pH of the lemon juice. Record these values in a data table similar to Table 2.5.
2. Add 200 μL of lemon juice (an acid) to the milk. Cap and invert one time to mix. Observe and record any changes in the color or texture of the milk.
3. If no change is apparent, add another 200 μL of lemon juice. Cap and invert one time to mix.
4. Repeat step 3 until there is an obvious change in the consistency (curdling) of the milk.
5. Measure the pH of the solution (point of structural change).
6. Record the pH of the treated milk in the data table along with a description of its appearance (see Table 2.5).

Table 2.5. How Acid or Base Can Affect Protein Structure

Solution Added	pH of Milk before Adding Acid or Base	Volume of Acid or Base Added to Cause Curdling (μL)	pH of Milk after Adding Acid or Base	Physical Appearance of of Solution	Comments
lemon juice (an acid) pH = ___					
1% NaOH (a base) pH = ___					

Part II: The Effect of Base on Protein Structure

Environmental Health and Safety Officer

1. Place 3 mL of milk in a 13×100-mm culture tube. Use pH paper to measure the pH of the milk. Use pH paper to measure the pH of the 1% NaOH (a base). Record these values in the data table.
2. Add 200 μL of 1% NaOH to the milk. Cap and invert one time to mix. Observe and record any changes in the color or texture of the milk.
   Caution: NaOH is a strong base; it is caustic and can burn. Wear goggles and gloves. Wipe spills immediately. Flush exposed surfaces with tap water.
3. If no change is apparent, add another 200 μL of 1% NaOH. Cap and invert one time to mix.
4. Repeat step 3 until there is an obvious change in the consistency (curdling) of the milk.
5. Measure the pH of the solution (point of significant structural change).
6. Record the pH of the treated milk in the data table along with a description of its appearance.

Data Analysis/Conclusion

Describe how, and at what point, the addition of acid or base changed the appearance of the milk. Explain how structural changes could affect the structure and function of a protein. Discuss why it is important for biotechnicians to know the pH of the protein solutions they use. Suggest an experiment to test how temperature affects protein structure.

Thinking Like a Biotechnician

1. A technician checks the pH of an *E. coli* broth culture that is producing the protein insulin. The technician finds that the pH has dropped to 5.7 from the desired pH of 6.5. How can the pH be adjusted back to 6.5?
2. Several proteins will only function within a very specific pH range. Go online and find the optimum pH for the following proteins: pepsin, amylase, and trypsin.

Chapter

3) Basic Chemistry for the Biotechnician

A research associate uses a 50-mL pipet and an automated pipet pump to dispense solution into replicate reaction chambers. The solution has been prepared at a specific volume and concentration.
Photo courtesy of Cell Genesys, Inc.

Virtually every chemical reaction in a lab or manufacturing facility, as in cells, occurs in a watery environment or solution. A lab technician, therefore, must be able to quickly prepare any volume of solution at any concentration of molecules.

Solution preparation (solution prep) is the most basic laboratory skill required of every scientist or technician. Solution prep involves measuring liquid volumes with a variety of instruments, weighing chemicals with a balance or scale, and mixing them together in the correct proportions. In the following laboratory activities, you will learn how to use several instruments to measure ingredients and prepare solutions. The skills you will develop include the following:

- measuring liquid volumes using graduated cylinders, pipets, and micropipets
- measuring solids using tabletop and analytical balances
- performing calculations that determine the amount of solids or liquids needed in a solution
- preparing solutions of varying amounts (concentrations) of solute and solvent
- preparing dilutions of concentrated solutions

When conducting research experiments or manufacturing products, scientists and technicians routinely make hundreds of solutions. Preparing solutions can be challenging at first because of the calculations required. However, with practice, you will master the calculations so that preparing solutions at various concentrations will become second nature to you. In later chapters, you will learn to adjust the acid/base level (pH) of the solutions you prepare, which is another skill required to work as an independent lab technician.

Laboratory 3a Measuring Small Volumes in a Biotechnology Lab

Background

Serological pipets are used to measure volumes from 0.5 mL (500 μL) to 100 mL. The most commonly used pipets are 10-, 5-, 2-, and 1-mL pipets. Pipets are named by the maximum volume they measure. Therefore, a 5-mL pipet measures volumes up to 5 mL.

This activity introduces pipeting technique (see Figure 3.1). As with all fine motor skills, learning how to accurately use a pipet takes practice and determination, but it is essential that you are able to measure volumes with accuracy. The standard practice is to allow for *no more than 10% deviation from the intended value.* In many applications, much less deviation is acceptable. You must also be precise in measurement; that is, you must be able to replicate your measurements repeatedly.

To measure and deliver samples, technicians most commonly use a plastic pipet pump. A blue pump is appropriate for a 1- or 2-mL pipet (see Figure 3.2), and a green pump is appropriate for a 5- or 10-mL pipet (see Figure 3.3). To ensure accurate measuring, operate the pipet pump slowly, and watch carefully as volumes are taken up and dispensed by the pipet. **Mouth pipeting is never allowed.** Other pipet aids may be available, including pipet bulbs or electronic pumps.

Figure 3.1. A pipet is used to measure milliliter (mL) volumes. Pipet at eye level for more accuracy.
Photo by author.

Figure 3.2. Use blue pipet pumps with 1- and 2-mL pipets. Use green pumps with 5- and 10-mL pipets.
Photo by author.

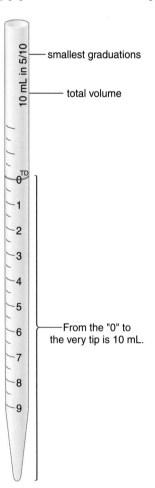

10 mL in 5/10 — smallest graduations

— total volume

From the "0" to the very tip is 10 mL.

Figure 3.3. 10 mL Pipet A 10-mL pipet measures 1 to 10 mL in 0.5-mL increments. Use a green pipet pump with a 10-mL pipet.

Follow these guidelines for correct pipeting technique:

Pipeting Technique Using a Pipet Pump

1. Use a blue pipet pump for 1- or 2-mL pipets. Use a green pipet pump for 5- or 10-mL pipets. Use a red pipet pump for 25- or 50-mL pipets. Make sure you can understand the values of the graduations on the pipet.
2. Insert the pipet into a pipet pump. Gently twist and push the top of the pipet (end with label) into the pump *just until it is held securely.* Do not push too far as this may damage the inside of the pump.
3. Put the pipet tip into the solution. Be careful the sample does not overflow the container due to displacement.
4. Keeping the tip under the surface and holding the container at eye level, roll the pump wheel up to pull solution into the pipet. Pull the solution up until the bottom of the meniscus (the concave surface of the liquid in the pipet) is at the volume value desired.
5. Move the pipet into the recipient container. Roll the pump wheel down (all the way) to dispense solution from the pipet. Touch the tip to the side of the container so that adhesion pulls off any liquid on the side of the pipet. Allow the solution to leave the pipet, but do not force out the last tiny bit. The pipets labeled "TD" measure "to delivery." If the last remaining drop is blown out, a mismeasurement will occur.
6. Remove the pipet from the container. Holding the pipet pump bottom, gently twist and pull the pipet out of the pump. Discard the pipet if it is disposable. Clean it if it is reusable.

Precautions for Using Pipets

- **Use a pipet pump to withdraw and dispense liquids** (see Figure 3.4). Do not pipet by mouth.
- **Hold the bottom of the pipet pump when inserting and removing the pipet.** The bottom part of the pipet pump sometimes sticks to the pipet, and can accidentally be pulled out and thrown away. The pipet pump is useless if this happens.
- **Always keep the pipet in an almost vertical position when there is fluid in the tip.** To avoid contamination, do not allow liquid to accidentally run back into the pipet pump.
- **Use your thumb to roll the pipeting gear up and down. Do not pull or push on top of pipet pump.**

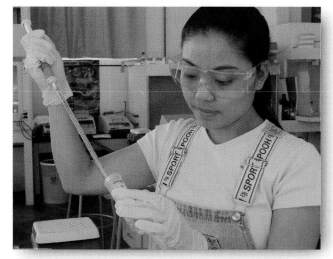

Figure 3.4.   Always use a pipet pump or pipet aid with a pipet. Never pipet by mouth! Keep the pipet almost vertical when pipeting.
Photo by author.

- **Do not pipet a liquid sample into another liquid, unless directed to do so.** Instead, pipet a sample onto the inside of the recipient vessel and allow it to flow down the vessel. This practice minimizes cross contamination of samples. Gently mix by finger flicking, vortexing, or inverting the container. Avoid bubbling.

Purpose

Which pipets are best used to measure specific volumes?
How precisely can you measure using each pipet (1, 2, 5, and 10 mL)?
How accurately can you prepare samples using each pipet (1, 2, 5, and 10 mL)?

Materials

Tubes, glass, 13×100 mm	Green dye (1 mL dye:	Pipets, 5 mL
Plug caps for 13×100 mm tubes	499 mL dH$_2$O)	Pipets, 10 mL
Permanent lab marker pens	Yellow dye (1 mL dye:	Pipet pump, blue
Red dye (1 mL dye:	499 mL dH$_2$O)	Pipet pump, green
499 mL dH$_2$O)	Peg racks for 10–13 mm tubes	Tubes, 50 mL, sterile
Blue dye (1 mL dye:	Pipets, 1 mL	Tube racks for 50 mL tubes
499 mL dH$_2$O)	Pipets, 2 mL	Plastic beaker, 1000 1L

Procedure

1. Using a permanent marker, label four empty 13- × 100-mm tubes with I, II, III, and IV, your initials, and the date.
2. Carefully, study each pipet available for use. What is the maximum amount each pipet can measure? What is the value of the smallest graduation on each pipet? For each pipet, randomly put your thumbnail somewhere on the graduations. If you drew up liquid to that height, what volume would be measured? Record all of this information. Check with your lab colleagues to ensure that you are reading the pipet correctly.
   Also, check to see if there is a "TD" label on the pipet. If there is, that means that the pipet is accurate "to delivery" and that the tiny drop left in the bottom of the pipet after dispensing should not be forced out.
3. Using the smallest pipet possible, measure the following dye solutions into each tube according to the matrix shown in Table 3.1. Unless told otherwise, add the smallest volume first. Add the next volume to the inside of the tube, allowing it to flow down to the bottom. Finger flick the tube to mix the volumes.
4. Compare the No. 1 through 5 tubes with the "key" tubes provided by the instructor. These are the standards for comparison. For each sample tube, check the level of the final volume, the final color (indicative of accurate measurement and thorough mixing), and proper labeling.

Table 3.1.   **Practicing with Pipets Matrix**

Tubes	Solution I	Solution II	Solution III	Solution IV	Solution V
I	6.3 mL	0.5 mL	0.25 mL	- - -	- - -
2	2.4 mL	1.08 mL	- - -	0.19 mL	0.73 mL
3	4.0 mL	1.5 mL	0.5 mL	- - -	- - -
4	3.5 mL	2.0 mL	- - -	0.25 mL	0.2 mL

5. If the volume of any tube is not within one meniscus of the "key" tubes, it should be remade. Keep track of your attempts to prepare the sample tubes. Make a data table to record your evaluation of your tube preparation with all the observations from Procedure steps 3 through 4.
6. Make a table to collect data on how many students in the class had their first Tube 1 samples fall within the one meniscus range of acceptable variation.

Reflection/Analysis

For volumes between 0.1 mL and 10 mL, explain which pipet and pump are appropriate to use for measuring and dispensing. Make three suggestions that other technicians can use to improve their pipeting accuracy. Based on the Tube 1 class data, describe how much precision the students in the class demonstrated in preparing these samples.

Thinking Like a Biotechnician

1. A 250-µL sample is needed from a sterile vessel that is too thin to use with anything but a sterile pipet. Which pipet and pipet pump could be used to withdraw the mL equivalent to 250 µL from the vessel?
2. A 1.75 mL sample is needed for an experiment. Both a 2- and a 5-mL pipet will measure this amount. Which pipet is best to use and why?
3. Practice pipeting dye-solution samples to create the mixtures specified in Table 3.2.
   a. Measure all solutions into 13×100-mm tubes. Label each tube with the tube letter, your initials, and the date.
   b. Although you may help each other, pipeting the samples as independently as possible is better practice.

Table 3.2. **Pipeting Practice Matrix**

Tube Letter	Red Dye Volume (mL)	Blue Dye Volume (mL)	Green Dye Volume (mL)	Total Volume (mL)
A	1.1	1.7	0.33	
B	1.27	0.85	2.9	
C	0.7	2.8	1.8	
D	1.6	1.9	0.66	

- Use the smallest instrument possible for each measurement.
- More than one pipet may be necessary to measure these amounts.
- Evaluation criteria: labels, final volume, and final color/mixing.

Laboratory 3b Measuring Very Small Volumes in a Biotechnology Lab

Inspired by a Gene Connection Lab. Gene Connection is a San Mateo County, California, biotechnology education organization.

Background

Very tiny amounts of chemicals and biological reagents are used in many biotechnology experiments. To measure these minute volumes, technicians use micropipets that measure microliter (µL) amounts.

This activity introduces micropipeting technique. As with all fine motor skills, learning how to use a micropipet takes practice and determination. You must be able to measure these very tiny volumes with accuracy. Operate the micropipet slowly and carefully.

Picking and Setting the Micropipet

1. Check that you have the correct micropipet for the job. Most labs have three sizes of micropipets: a P-10 (for 0.5 to 10 µL), a P-100 (for 10 to 100 µL), and a P-1000 (for 100 to 1000 µL (see Figure 3.5).
   Note: Some laboratories have a P-20 (for 2 to 20 µL) instead of a P-10, or a P-200 (for 20 to 200 µL) instead of a P-100.
2. Dial the desired volume. Do you understand how to read the scale? If not, ask your instructor or review the background information in the text. **Hint:** By knowing the maximum volume of the micropipet, you can figure out what each of the digits on the readout means.
3. Push the end of the pipet into the proper-size tip. The small, white tips are for the P-10; the medium-size, yellow tips are for the P-20, P-100, and P-200; the larger blue tips are for the P-1000. The tips are disposable and usually intended for one use.

100 — plunger
10

ejector

hundreds

tens

ones

!!!

0.2

Use
yellow
tips.

Figure 3.5. **P-100 Micropipet.** Different models of micropipets are operated slightly differently. Make sure you know how to operate and read the micropipet before using it.

How to Take Up a Sample with a Micropipet

4. Before picking up the micropipet, open the cap or lid of the tube from which you are taking fluid. (Or, have your lab partner do this.)
5. Hold the micropipet in one hand, at a 45º angle from vertical. In this way, contaminants from your hands or the micropipet will not fall into the tube. Hold the test tube in your other hand. Both should be almost at eye level.
6. **Depress** the plunger of the micropipet to the **first** stop, and **hold** it in this position.
7. Place the tip into the solution to be pipeted.
8. Draw fluid into the tip by *slowly* releasing the plunger.

How to Expel a Sample from the Micropipet

9. With your other hand, open the cap or lid of the tube you are filling.
10. Hold the micropipet in one hand, at about a 45º angle from vertical. Hold the tube in your other hand. Both should be at about eye level.
11. Gently touch the micropipet tip to the inside wall of the reaction tube into which you want to expel the sample. This creates a tiny surface-tension effect that helps draw the fluid out of the tip.
12. Slowly, depress the plunger of the micropipet to the first stop. Then, continue to the second stop to expel the last bit of fluid, and hold the plunger in this position (see Figure 3.6).
13. Slowly, remove the pipet from the tube, keeping the plunger depressed to avoid drawing any liquid back into the tip.
14. Always change tips for each new reagent you pipet. To eject a tip, depress the ejector button on the top of the micropipet.

Precautions for Using Micropipets

- Set pipet volume *only* within the range specified for that micropipet. Do not attempt to set a volume beyond the pipet's minimum or maximum values.
- When using a micropipet, first apply a tip. Failure to do this will cause liquid to enter into the nose cone. Since a micropipet works by air displacement, its internal mechanism must remain dry.
- Always keep a micropipet in a vertical position when there is fluid in the tip. Do not allow liquid to accidentally run back into the nose cone.
- Use your thumb to control the speed at which the plunger rises after taking up or ejecting fluid. Releasing the plunger too abruptly will cause leakage or bubbles that will trap air and make the measurement inaccurate.

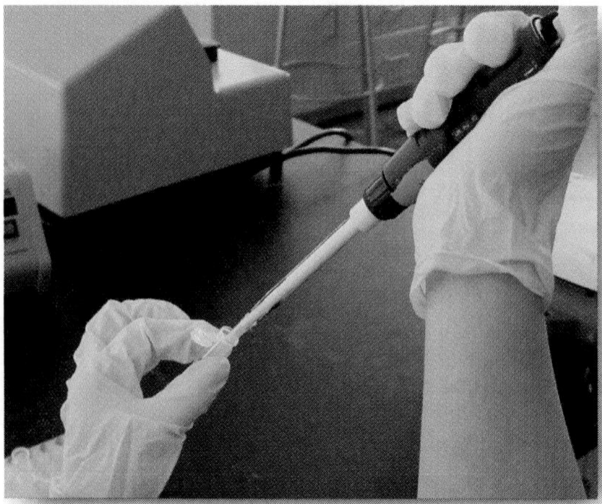

Figure 3.6. **To ensure that the entire sample is released, push the plunger all the way down to the second and final stop as you withdraw the tip from the collection tube.**

Photo by author.

Purpose

Which micropipets are best used to measure specific volumes? How precisely can you measure using each micropipet? How accurately can you prepare samples using each micropipet?

Materials

Tube rack for 1.7 mL tubes
Reaction tubes, 1.7 mL
Permanent lab marker pens
Pack of 4 colors, package of 4
Red dye (1 mL dye:499 mL dH$_2$O)
Blue dye (1 mL dye:499 mL dH$_2$O)
Green dye (1 mL dye:499 mL dH$_2$O)
Yellow dye (1 mL dye:499 mL dH$_2$O)
Micropipet, P-10
Micropipet, P-100
Micropipet, P-1000
Micropipet tips for P-10

Micropipet tips for P-100
Micropipet tips for P-1000
Tubes, 50 mL, sterile
Tube racks for 50 mL tubes
Plastic beaker, 1000 1L
Microcentrifuge
Wax paper

Procedure

Practicing with a P-10 or P-20

1. Using a permanent marker, label two empty reaction tubes with A and B, and your initials.
2. Add the specified amounts of each solution to tube A or B, as listed in Table 3.3. Unless told otherwise, add the smallest volume first. Add each volume to the inside of the tube without letting the drops touch. The drop will stick because of adhesion. When all volumes have been added, bring the drops to the bottom of the tube with a quick wrist flick.

Table 3.3.   **P-10 or P-20 Practice Matrix**

Reaction Tubes	Solution I	Solution II	Solution III	Solution IV	Solution V
A	4.0 μL	5.0 μL	2.0 μL	- - -	- - -
B	6.5 μL	2.5 μL	- - -	- - -	2.0 μL

3. Spin tubes A and B in the microcentrifuge for 1 to 2 seconds to pool the solutions. See the centrifuge instructions at the end of the procedures.
4. After centrifuging, compare your tubes with the standard "key" tubes and other A and B tubes in the class. Both tubes A and B should contain 11 μL. Check the tube volume, color/mixing, and labeling.
5. As an additional check of accuracy, set the micropipet to 11 μL and carefully withdraw all of the fluid in tube A. The contents should *just* fill the tip, with no air space at the bottom of the tip and no leftover fluid in the tube. Repeat with tube B.
6. Is there any liquid left in the microtest tube? If so, determine its volume. What *percent error* did you have in your pipeting of this small volume? Use the equation below to determine the percent error in pipeting this sample:

$$\frac{\text{amount left in test tube}}{\text{total amount pipeted}} \times 100 = \% \text{ error in measurement}$$

Practicing with a P-200 or P-100

1. Label an empty reaction tube C.
2. To tube C, add the solution volumes shown in Table 3.4. Unless told otherwise, add the smallest volume first. Add each volume to the inside of the tube without letting the drops touch. The drop will stick because of adhesion. When all volumes have been added, bring the drops to the bottom of the tube with a quick wrist flick.

Table 3.4.   **P-100 or P-200 Practice Matrix**

Reaction Tube	Solution I	Solution II	Solution III	Solution IV	Solution V
C	22.3 μL	31.6 μL	- - -	44.4 μL	- - -

3. Spin tube C for 1 to 2 seconds. Make sure that you balance the microcentrifuge with another tube that contains the same volume.
4. Check the accuracy of your technique with the P-100 or P-200. Set the micropipet to 98.3 μL and withdraw the contents of tube C. Also, compare your tube with the standard "key" tubes and other "C" tubes. The contents should *just* fill the tip, with no air space at the

bottom of the tip, and no leftover fluid in the tube. Check the tube volume, color/mixing, and labeling.

5. Is there any liquid left in the microtest tube? If so, determine its volume. What percent error did you have in your preparation of this sample?

Practicing with a P-1000

1. Label an empty reaction tube as tube D.
2. To tube D, add the solution volumes shown in Table 3.5.

Table 3.5. **P-1000 Practice Matrix**

Reaction Tube	Solution I	Solution II	Solution III	Solution IV	Solution V
D	253 µL	- - -	- - -	- - -	557 µL

3. Along with a balance tube, spin tube D in the microcentrifuge for 1 to 2 seconds (see Figure 3.7).
4. Check the accuracy of your technique with the P-1000. Set the pipet to 810 µL and withdraw the contents of tube D. Also, compare your tube with the standard "key" tube. Check the tube volume, color/mixing, and labeling.
5. Is there any liquid left in the microtest tube? If so, determine its volume. What percent error did you have in preparing this sample?

Centrifuge Instructions

- Tightly close the caps on all of the tubes to be placed in the microcentrifuge (also called microfuge).

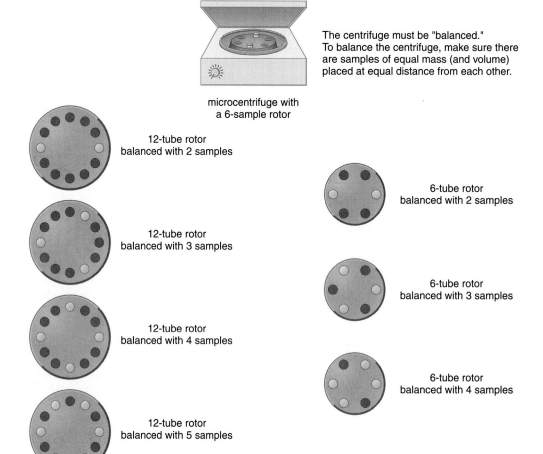

The centrifuge must be "balanced."
To balance the centrifuge, make sure there are samples of equal mass (and volume) placed at equal distance from each other.

microcentrifuge with a 6-sample rotor

12-tube rotor balanced with 2 samples

12-tube rotor balanced with 3 samples

12-tube rotor balanced with 4 samples

12-tube rotor balanced with 5 samples

6-tube rotor balanced with 2 samples

6-tube rotor balanced with 3 samples

6-tube rotor balanced with 4 samples

Figure 3.7. **Centrifuge Basics.**

- The microfuge (sample holder) rotor must always be balanced. You cannot, for example, spin *one* tube in a microfuge. **Spinning in an unbalanced arrangement like this would damage the motor and ruin the centrifuge.**
- The volume and mass of sample in the tubes should be the same. Otherwise, the rotor will spin unevenly (like wet towels spinning out of balance in a washing machine). You can always prepare a "blank" tube with the same volume of liquid to balance a single tube.
- After you have replaced the metal top (if your type of microfuge has a rotor top) and secured the lid of the microfuge, give the tubes a 1- to 2-second pulse. This will mix and pool all the reagents into a droplet in the bottom of each tube.

Reflection/Analysis

For volumes between 1 and 1000 μL, explain which micropipet is appropriate to use for measuring and dispensing. Make three suggestions that other technicians can use to improve their micropipeting accuracy.

Thinking Like a Biotechnician

1. For most experiments, several reagents must be added to the same tube. Propose a method to keep track of the samples that have been added to a reaction tube.
2. Demonstrate the effect of micropipeting incorrectly by doing the following:
   a. Set a P-20 or P-10 to 2 μL.
   b. Purposely, misuse the P-20 or P-10 pipet, and depress the plunger to the second stop.
   c. Suck up this apparent 2-μL volume and release onto a piece of wax paper.
   d. Now, correctly collect a 2-μL volume using the P-20 or P-10.
   e. Release it onto the wax paper next to the other drop. Are the drops noticeably different in size?
   f. How much more is there in the "misused" volume? (Use the pipet to suck up the misused volume in 2-μL increments.)
   g. If a balance or scale is available, and you have been trained to use it, make these measurements on it. Determine the percentage error that would occur if you were to accidentally misuse the pipet in this fashion.
3. Practice micropipeting samples to create mixtures by producing the four tubes in Table 3.6.
   a. Measure all solutions into 1.7-mL microtubes. Label all tubes with the tube number, your initials, and the date.
   b. Although you may help each other, micropipeting as independently as possible is better practice.

Table 3.6. **Micropipeting Practice Matrix**

Tube No.	Red Dye Volume (μL)	Blue Dye Volume (μL)	Green Dye Volume (μL)	Total Volume (mL)
1	27.2	313.0	59.3	
2	555.0	222.0	7.8	
3	133.3	19.8	235.0	
4	9.4	4.1	2.25	

- Use the smallest instrument possible for all measurements.
- Change tips every time.
- More than one pipet may be necessary to measure amounts.
- Total volumes may be checked by using a P-1000.
- Evaluation criteria: labels, final volume, and final color/mixing.

Laboratory 3c Measuring Mass

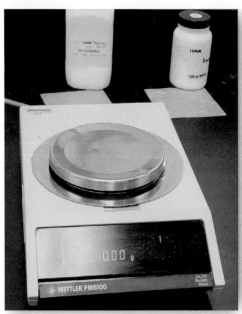

Figure 3.8. This electronic tabletop balance reads to 0.01 g.

Photo by author.

Figure 3.9. This electronic tabletop balance reads to 0.0001 g.

Photo by author.

Background

Using DNA, enzymes, and other reagents in the laboratory requires weighing small amounts, or masses, of these chemicals. Measurements must be made using precision instruments. In a biotechnology laboratory, mass measurements are performed on electronic balances or scales. There are several different kinds of balances with different features, depending on the manufacturer and the cost.

Basically, electronic balances come in two forms: 1) tabletop/portable (see Figure 3.8) ranging from $300 to $1500 each, and 2) analytical balances, beginning in price at about $1500 each (see Figure 3.9).

The tabletop (top-loading) balances vary in the precision they measure, and each balance has a maximum mass that may be measured. Some measure to within 1 g, some measure to within 0.1 g, and some measure to 0.01 g. The last decimal place is an approximation.

Each balance is used in a similar fashion. The weighing protocol that follows ensures that the balance is used properly and is not damaged.

Weighing Protocol

Note: Wear goggles and gloves when using chemicals.

1. Set the balance on a clean, dry, flat surface.
2. If there is a leveling apparatus, level the balance.
3. Check that the power cord is plugged in properly. Press the "ON" button. The balance will undergo a series of self-checks.
4. Check to make sure that the balance is displaying a "g," to show that it will be measuring in grams. If it is not displaying the "g," press the "MODE" button until it does.
5. Make sure that the weigh pan is clean.
6. Press the "TARE" or "zero" button to zero the balance.
7. Add a weigh boat or a piece of weigh paper. **Never place chemicals directly on the weighing pan. Weigh boats and weigh paper are single-use-only items.**
8. Press the "TARE" button again to zero the balance.
9. Using a clean scoop, add the chemical to be weighed to the weigh boat until the desired mass is obtained. Keep the stock bottle directly over the weigh boat to minimize spills.
10. Remove the weigh boat/paper. Close bottles and return them to the chemical stock area. Clean any spilled chemicals.

In this activity, you will prepare and test glucose solutions using Diastix® (Bayer Diagnostics) brand glucose test strips. The test strips, which detect the presence of glucose in urine and other solutions, measure in mg/dL. One dL, or deciliter, is equal to 0.1 L, or 100 mL. Using the B ← → S Rule, one can convert between dL and mL.

Purpose

To measure small amounts of glucose on an appropriate balance.
To make glucose solutions with a given mass of glucose in a specified volume.
To verify mass and volume measurements.

Materials

Balance, analytical	Glucose (dextrose)	Permanent lab marker pens
Balance, tabletop milligram	Lab scoops	Pipets, 10 mL
Weigh paper, 7.6×7.6 cm	Tubes, 15 mL, sterile	Pipet pump, green
Weigh boat, 3.5"×3.5"	Tube racks for 15 mL tubes	Glucose test strips

Procedure

1. Measure the required mass of glucose to prepare the solutions listed in Table 3.7. Use an electronic balance for the first two solutions and the analytical balance for the third.

2. Prepare each solution in a 15-mL conical tube. Mix well to dissolve. Label each tube with the name and concentration in mg/dL of the sample, your initials, and the date.

3. Obtain a Diastix® glucose test strip. Follow the directions on the package, except allow the solution to react for a total of 90 seconds.

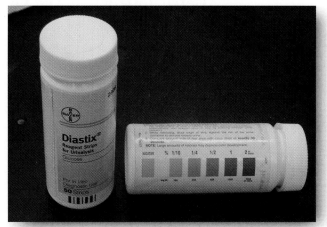

Figure 3.10. **The indicator squares on the glucose test strips are matched to the key on the back of the bottle. Glucose concentrations are reported in % and mg/dL.**
Photo by author.

4. Determine the concentration of the prepared samples by matching the color of the test strips to the standard concentration key on the Diastix® package (see Figure 3.10). Record the Diastix® data for each sample in a data table similar to Table 3.7.

5. Determine how closely the measured concentration is to the expected concentration. What do the data say about your mass measuring technique?

Table 3.7. **Glucose Mass Testing**

Solution to be Prepared (mg/dL)	Equivalent Concentration (g/mL)	Final Volume (mL)	Mass of Glucose (g)	Diastix Test Result (mg/dL)	Diastix Value (g/mL)	Comments
250.0	0.0025	10	0.025			
100.0	0.001	10	0.01			
50.0	0.0005	10	0.005			
0	0	10	0			

Data Analysis/Conclusion

Does it appear that your measurements and the solutions were made correctly? Give evidence for your statements. Identify two technical errors that could be made that would result in inaccurate concentration readings.

Thinking Like a Biotechnician

1. In this activity, what is the value of the "0 mg/dL" glucose tube?
2. In your opinion, how precise are the test strips in measuring glucose concentration? Give evidence.
3. Suggest how the glucose test strips might be used for some other application.
4. Complete the Metric Instrument and Conversion Review Sheet that follows.

Metric Instrument and Conversion Review Sheet

Convert each unit and select the appropriate instrument for its measurement.

Instrument Choices

graduated cylinder	10-mL pipet	5-mL pipet
2-mL pipet	1-mL pipet	tabletop balance
P-1000	P-200	P-100
P-20	P-10	analytical balance

1. example 75.34 mg = <u>0.07534 g</u> <u>analytical balance</u>	8. example 7.34 mL = <u>0.00734 L</u> <u>10-mL pipet</u>	15. example 7.534 g = <u>7534 mg</u> <u>tabletop balance</u>
2. 4.3 mL = _____ μL _____	9. 0.34 g = _____ mg _____	16. 5.034 L = _____ mL _____
3. 0.111 mL = _____ μL _____	10. 34.0 g = _____ kg _____	17. 34 mg = _____ μg _____
4. 440.3 mL = _____ L _____	11. 0.004 L = _____ mL _____	18. 15.4 mg = _____ g _____
5. 66 mg = _____ μg _____	12. 80.34 μL = _____ mL _____	19. 1308 g = _____ kg _____
6. 3.33 g = _____ μg _____	13. 4.67 μL = _____ mL _____	20. 99.1 g = _____ mg _____
7. 330.2 mL = _____ L _____	14. 0.022 g = _____ mg _____	21. 0.23 mL = _____ μL _____

Laboratory 3d Checking the Accuracy of Micropipets Using a Balance

Background

A balance can be used to determine if a micropipet is measuring within an acceptable range. Since 1 mL of water weighs 1.0 g, you can estimate the expected mass for any volume of water (see Figure 3.11). For example,

1.5 mL of water should weigh 1.5 g.
0.25 mL of water should weigh 0.25 g.
150 μL (= 0.15 mL) of water should weigh 0.15 g.

1 milliliter of water takes up a cubic centimeter
of space and weighs 1 gram.

Figure 3.11.   **Mass/Volume Equivalents.**

Water dispensed by a micropipet can be weighed on a balance. By comparing the actual observed mass to the expected mass, you can make an error determination. For any measurement, calculate the % error using the following equation:

$$\frac{(\text{observed mass} - \text{expected mass})}{\text{expected mass}} \times 100$$

Purpose

To measure small volumes of water on an appropriate balance.
To check the accuracy of a micropipet measurement.

Materials

Balance, analytical	Micropipet, P-1000
Balance, tabletop milligram	Micropipet tips for P-10
Weigh paper, 7.6×7.6 cm	Micropipet tips for P-100
Micropipet, P-10	Micropipet tips for P-1000
Micropipet, P-100	Tap water

Procedure

1. Review the use of pipets, pipet pumps, micropipets, and electronic and analytical balances. Specifically, check the following:
    a. Make sure you can read and set the micropipets.
    b. Make sure that you are withdrawing and dispensing volumes properly. Remember to check the feel of the first and second stops on the micropipets.

c. Review the proper way to set up (zero/tare) and read the electronic and analytical balances.

d. Review the proper way to convert between metric units, specifically mL and µL (ie, use the B ← → S Rule).

2. For each micropipet, measure the specified volume of tap water onto a piece of weigh paper on a "tared" balance. In a data table similar to Table 3.8, record the mass of the volume of water measured. Record the type of balance used.

Table 3.8. **Pipeting Precision: Mass versus Volume**

Micropipet	Volume (µL)	Volume (mL)	Expected Mass (g)	Actual Mass (g)	% Error	Acceptable Error (%)	Type of Balance Used
P-1000	1000.0					3	
P-1000	500.0					3	
P-1000	257.0					3	
P-100	100.0					5	
P-100	53.0					5	
P-100	20.0					5	
P-10	20.0					10	
P-10	13.7					10	
P-10	2.0					10	

3. Determine if the micropipet is measuring within the acceptable range of error. Calculate and record the percentage error for each micropipet delivery using the % error equation:

$$\frac{\text{amount left in test tube}}{\text{total amount pipeted}} \times 100 = \%\ \text{error in measurement}$$

Data Analysis

For any error that is outside of the acceptable range, remeasure. Make sure that you are using the instruments (balances and micropipets) correctly. Get help if necessary. If you still getting measurements outside the range of acceptable error, the pipet may be out of calibration. Make the measurement with another student's pipet in order to check the calibration of your pipet. Record comments. Notify your instructor or lab supervisor of any equipment that does not appear to function correctly.

Thinking Like a Biotechnician

Suppose another lab technician in your group is dispensing 100 µL volumes into 10 1.7-mL tubes. On inspection of the samples, several are visibly different from the others and not within the acceptable range of error.

1. Suggest one thing that the technician could do in his operation of the micropipet to improve his pipeting technique.

2. Suggest something that the technician could do to ensure that the micropipet is measuring correctly.

Laboratory 3e Making Solutions of Differing Mass/Volume Concentrations

Background

Solutions are prepared with a certain mass of solute in a certain volume of solvent, similar to the glucose solutions made in the previous activity. Any metric mass in any metric volume is possible, but the most common units of mass/volume concentrations are as follows:

g/mL	grams per milliliter
g/L	grams per liter
mg/mL	milligrams per milliliter
µg/mL	micrograms per milliliter
µg/µL	micrograms per microliter
ng/L	nanograms per liter
ng/µL	nanograms per microliter

Although concentrations can be reported in any mass/volume units, these 7 mass/volume units are the most common in biotechnology applications. The prefix "nano-" means one-billionth. A nanogram is equal to 0.001 µg, and there is 1000 ng in 1 µg.

To determine how to prepare a certain volume of a solution at a certain mass/volume concentration, use the equation that follows. Make sure units that are used can be cancelled and convert any units, if necessary.

Mass/Volume Concentration Equation

concentration desired × total volume desired = mass of solute in the total volume desired.
(for example, g/mL)   (for example, mL)   (for example, g)

Suppose that a technician needs 50 mL of 15-mg/mL pepsin solution for an experiment. Pepsin is a protein-digesting enzyme that is produced and functions in the stomach. Using the concentration in mass/volume equation,

$$50 \text{ mL} \times 15 \text{ mg/mL} = 750 \text{ mg} = 0.75 \text{ g pepsin}$$

Notice how the mL units cancel out during multiplication so as to leave the answer in mg to be weighed out. Since the balances measure in grams, the mg must be converted to g. To make this solution, 0.75 g of pepsin is measured and put into a graduated 50-mL tube. Solvent (deionized water or buffer) is added to reach a total volume of 50 mL (see Figure 3.12).

Reminder: The math is easiest if the units of measurement are the same. Use the B ← → S Rule to convert between units. Here are the units of metric measurement:

$$L \leftarrow \rightarrow mL \leftarrow \rightarrow \mu L$$
$$km \leftarrow \rightarrow m \leftarrow \rightarrow cm \leftarrow \rightarrow mm \leftarrow \rightarrow \mu m$$
$$kg \leftarrow \rightarrow g \leftarrow \rightarrow mg \leftarrow \rightarrow \mu g \leftarrow \rightarrow ng$$

Purpose

To make copper sulfate ($CuSO_4$) solutions of differing mass/volume concentrations.

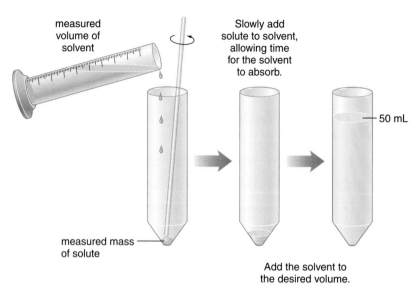

Figure 3.12. **How To Prepare a Mass/Volume Solution.**

Environmental Health and Safety Officer

Materials

Caution: Wear goggles and gloves when measuring chemicals.

Balance, analytical	Cupric sulfate 5-hydrate	Tubes, glass, 13×100 mm
Balance, tabletop milligram	Tubes, 15 mL, capped	Peg racks for 10–13 mm tubes
Weigh paper, 7.6×7.6 cm	Tube racks for 15 mL tubes	Pipets, 5 mL
Weigh boat, 3.5"×3.5"	Deionized water	Pipet pump, green
Lab scoops	Permanent lab marker pens	Spectrophotometer, Spectronic 20 D+

Procedure

- Label all tubes with the sample name and concentration, your initials, and the date.
- Review the use of the balance and weigh boats before beginning.

1. Prepare the solutions in Table 3.9 for tube numbers 1 through 5. Use the Mass/Volume Equation to determine the mass of $CuSO_4$ to measure in order to give the correct concentration at the volume desired for each sample. Create and fill a matrix similar to Table 3.10 that shows which solutions are being made, your mathematical calculations, and a diagram of how to prepare each solution. Be sure to allow adequate space in the column that will contain your drawings.

Table 3.9. $CuSO_4$ Mass/Volume Solution Preparation

Tube No.	$CuSO_4$ Solution To Be Made
1	5.0 mL of 300 mg/mL
2	4.5 mL of 150 mg/mL
3	4.0 mL of 75 mg/mL
4	3.5 mL of 37.5 mg/mL
5	3.0 mL of 18.75 mg/mL

Table 3.10. **Reaction Matrix for CuSO$_4$ Mass/Volume Solutions**

Tube No.	Total Volume (mL)	Concentration (mg/mL)	Calculation of Mass Needed (g)	Diagram of Solution Preparation
1				
2				
3				
4				
5				

2. Prepare the solutions in labeled 15-mL capped, conical tubes, using deionized water as the solvent.
3. Is the difference in concentration of the tubes obvious in one tube versus another? Explain. If any volumes or colors are obviously wrong, dump them out, and remake them. Compare your tubes' colors and volumes to the standard "key" solutions prepared by the instructor and to solutions prepared by other technicians in the lab.
4. Use a spectrophotometer to check your solution preparation following the steps below. A spectrophotometer shines light on a sample and "detects" the amount of light absorbed by the molecules in the solution. If you are using the spectrophotometer correctly, and there are more molecules in one solution versus another, more absorbance of light occurs (the absorbance unit [au] goes up). This is just a brief introduction to spectrophotometry. Spectrophotometers and their use in biotechnology are discussed in detail in Chapter 7.

Using the Spectrophotometer to Check Copper Sulfate Samples

a. Turn on the spectrophotometer (Spec 20D). It needs 15 minutes to warm up.
b. Set the wavelength to 590 nm.
c. Transfer 3 mL of each sample, numbers 1 through 5, to 13×100-mm glass tubes. Label the tubes, along the top, with numbers and initials.
d. Prepare a blank by placing 3 mL of water into a 13×100-mm tube. A blank has everything in the sample except the molecule of interest (in this case, copper sulfate).
e. Calibrate the spectrophotometer.
   • Set the transmittance to 0 (by turning the left knob). The sample holder should be empty and closed.
   • Place the blank into the sample holder. Set the transmittance to 100% (right knob). That means 100% of the light is going through whatever is in the sample holder. Now the spectrophotometer is ignoring the glass tube and solvent.
f. Set the mode to absorbance and read the absorbance of all five sample tubes. Absorbance is measured in au. Since the spectrophotometer is ignoring the glass and solvent, an absorbance reading above 0.02 au is due to the amount of copper sulfate in the sample.
g. Record the absorbance data for each concentration of CuSO$_4$ in a data table. Do the absorbance data make sense for the solution concentrations you prepared? Compare your data to those of other technicians in the lab. Are the data values similar? Why or why not?
h. Using Microsoft® Excel®, prepare a line graph comparing the absorbance of each concentration of sample.
i. Look at the data on the graph. Do they create a straight line (or almost a straight line)? Why is a straight line expected? If most of the data points appear to be in a straight line, but a single data point is not on the line, what can be said about the data or sample? Have the supervisor approve your tubes and graph before you proceed to step 5.

5. Now, add enough deionized water to each of the five tubes to bring the total volume of each to 10 mL. What has happened to the concentration of $CuSO_4$ in the five tubes? Consider how much mass of $CuSO_4$ is dissolved in how much total volume. Create a data table similar to Table 3.11 to show calculations and report data. Report the final concentration in both g/mL and mg/mL.

6. Using the graph, make predictions of what you think the absorbance of each new sample will be. Check your absorbance predictions on the spectrophotometer. Record the absorbance of these samples in the data table.

Table 3.11.   **New Concentrations of the CuSO₄ Solution Tubes**

Tube No.	Total Volume (mL)	Mass of CuSO₄ (g) in Each Tube	New Concentration of Each Tube (g/mL and mg/mL)	Absorbance (au)
1	10 mL			
2	10 mL			
3	10 mL			
4	10 mL			
5	10 mL			

Data Analysis/Conclusion

Observe the tubes prepared in step 4. Do these tubes appear to be the correct concentration for their observed color? Explain. Besides spectrophotometry, suggest a method of checking to see if the concentrations of these tubes are actually accurate. Also, identify the errors that a technician might make that could result in erroneous concentrations. Describe some ways that a technician could minimize his or her solution preparation error.

Thinking Like a Biotechnician

1. Most solutions used in a biotechnology facility are colorless. How can the concentration of a colorless solution be checked?

2. A technician needs to read the absorbance of several samples on a spectrophotometer. But, after calibrating the spectrophotometer for reading the samples, he or she finds that all of the values are over the upper limit of 2.0 au. Why are all of the absorbance readings so high? What might the technician do to be able to use the spectrophotometer to check the samples?

3. Complete the Making Solutions Review Sheet No. 1.

Making Solutions Review Sheet No. I

Convert the values as indicated. Specify the appropriate instrument with which the final measurements should be made. For items 10 through 17, show the calculation (equation and units) for the preparation of each solution. Then, draw a diagram of how to make the solution in an appropriate container.

Instrument Choices

graduated cylinder	10-mL pipet	5-mL pipet
2-mL pipet	1-mL pipet	tabletop balance
P-1000	P-200	P-100
P-20	P-10	analytical balance

1. 3.4 mL = _____ µL _____	4. 73.12 µg = _____ mg _____	7. 10.5 µL = _____ mL _____
2. 43.9 mL = _____ L _____	5. 5.39 g = _____ mg _____	8. 7.503 mL = _____ µL _____
3. 0.17 mL = _____ µL _____	6. 30.6 g = _____ mg _____	9. 33 µg = _____ mg _____

Solution To Be Prepared	Diagram of How To Prepare It
10. 25 mL of 2.5 g/mL NaCl solution	11.
12. 10 mL of 50 mg/mL $CuSO_4$ solution	13.
14. 2 L of 0.5 g/mL dextrose solution	15.
16. 100 mL of 0.005 g/mL NaOH solution	17.

Laboratory 3f   Making Solutions of Differing % Mass/Volume Concentrations

Background

A lab technician must be able to make any solution at any concentration or volume. Most commonly, solutions are made with concentrations reported in one of these three measurements:

Measurement	Example
mass/volume	4 mg/mL salmon sperm DNA solution
% (in mass/volume or volume/volume)	2% sucrose solution
molarity (moles/liter)	0.5 M TRIS solution

Technicians must be able to recognize which chemicals should be measured out, in what amounts, and what math must be done to calculate these amounts. To consistently prepare solutions at the correct volume and concentration takes practice.

Preparation of % mass/volume solutions is presented in this activity. You will prepare several % mass/volume solutions and use some of them as testing reagents. Keep in mind that a 1% solution contains 1 g of solute in a total volume of 100 mL.

Since you will be required to make a variety of % mass/volume solutions at several different concentrations and volumes, use the % Mass/Volume Equation shown below to calculate the mass of each solute needed for a solution at some volume. Notice that as with preparing mass/volume solutions in the previous activity, the math is relatively simple. Multiply concentration desired (in decimals) with the volume needed (in mL).

% Mass/Volume Concentration Equation

Step No. 1

Convert the % to a decimal $\dfrac{\%}{\text{percent value}} = \dfrac{}{\text{decimal value of the g/mL}}$

Step No. 2

$\dfrac{}{\text{decimal (g/mL) of the \% concentration}} \times \dfrac{}{\text{volume (mL)}} =$ grams of solute to measure. Add solvent to solute until the desired volume is reached.

Purpose

To measure out chemicals of differing % concentrations for protein testing solutions.
To prepare different concentrations of gelatin solution for Biuret protein testing.
To prepare Biuret testing reagents and conduct protein tests on several gelatin protein standards of known concentration.

Materials

Environmental Health
and Safety Officer

Caution: Wear goggles and gloves when measuring chemicals.

Balance, analytical	Cupric sulfate 5-hydrate
Balance, tabletop milligram	Tubes, 15 mL, capped
Weigh paper, 7.6×7.6 cm	Tube racks for 15 mL tubes
Weigh boat, 3.5"×3.5"	Permanent lab marker pens
Lab scoops	Gelatin

Sodium hydroxide   **(Caustic solution. Handle with extreme care. Flush skin with water if exposed. Important: Do not touch the NaOH pellets. They are extremely caustic and can burn the skin and eyes. Wear gloves and safety goggles. NaOH is also extremely hygroscopic, meaning it will absorb water for air. Weigh quickly and keep bottle closed tightly.)**

Tubes, glass, 13×100 mm
Plug caps for 13×100 mm tubes
Peg racks for 10–13 mm tubes
Glass rods, 200 mm
Beakers, 250 mL
Hot plate stirrers, 7"×7"
Test tube holder (Stoddard)
Micropipet, P-1000
Micropipet tips for P-1000
Spectrophotometer, Spectronic 20 D+

Procedure

Show all calculations and make labeled diagrams to show how all solutions are prepared.

Part I: Prepare 5 mL of 10% NaOH Solution

Remember not to touch the NaOH pellets. They are extremely caustic and can burn the skin and eyes. Use gloves and safety goggles when measuring. NaOH is also extremely hygroscopic, meaning it will absorb water from the air. Weigh it quickly and keep the bottle closed tightly.

Environmental Health and Safety Officer

1. Calculate the amount of NaOH needed to make 5 mL of 10% NaOH. Show the calculations and create solution preparation drawings.
2. Confirm your math by checking with other lab groups.
3. Use a tabletop electronic balance to weigh out the NaOH.
4. Add 3 mL of deionized water (dH_2O) to a 15-mL conical tube.
5. Add each NaOH pellet, one at a time, to the water in the tube. Cap and gently invert to mix after each pellet. You may feel heat being released during the solution preparation.
6. Slowly, add dH_2O to bring the mixture to a total volume of 5 mL. Make sure the NaOH is dissolved. Wipe any spills with a damp paper towel.
7. Cap the tube. Label it with the sample name and concentration, your initials, and the date.
8. Store at room temperature for up to 2 weeks.

Part II: Prepare 5 mL of 5% CuSO4 Pentahydrate Solution

1. Calculate the amount of $CuSO_4$ needed to make 5 mL of 5% $CuSO_4 \cdot 5H_2O$. Show your calculations and create solution preparation drawings.
2. Confirm your math by checking with other lab groups.
3. Use a tabletop electronic balance to weigh out the $CuSO_4$.
4. Pour the $CuSO_4$ into a 15-mL conical tube.
5. Slowly, add dH_2O to bring the mixture to a total volume of 5 mL. Make sure the chemical dissolves into the water.
6. Cap the tube. Label it with the sample name and concentration, your initials, and the date.
7. Store at room temperature for up to 2 weeks.

Part III: Prepare 5 mL each of 5%, 2.5%, 1.25%, and 0.625% Gelatin Solutions

Note: Proteins are not very soluble. Add water slowly, mixing it to make a paste and then into a solution (see Figure 3.13). Do not shake the solution or it will get bubbly.

1. Calculate the amount of gelatin needed to make each gelatin solution. Show the calculations and drawings of the solution preparations in a table similar to Table 3.14.
2. Confirm your math by checking with other lab groups.
3. Use either a lab top electronic or an analytical balance (where appropriate) to weigh out the gelatin samples.
4. Pour each gelatin sample into the appropriately labeled 13×100-mm tubes.
   Note: It is essential that all mass and volume measurements be as accurate as possible since you are looking for a proportional decrease in concentration.
5. Slowly, add dH_2O to bring the mixture to a total volume of 5 mL in each tube. Place 5 mL of water in an empty tube and mark the bottom of the meniscus. Use this tube as a gauge when filling the other tubes.

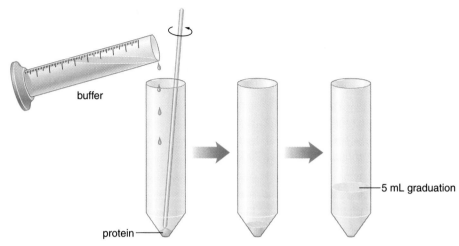

Figure 3.13. **Making Protein Solutions.**

Add water slowly, making a paste.
Avoid shaking, which may denature the protein.

Table 3.14. **Preparation of % Mass/Volume Gelatin Solutions**

Tube Label	Amount of Gelatin (g)	Calculations	Diagram of Solution Preparation
5.0%			
2.5%			
1.25%			
0.625%			

100°C

6. Heat the labeled tubes gently in a **hot** water bath (250-mL beaker with 100 mL of boiling tap water) until the solute dissolves (see Figure 3.14). Gently mix with a stirring rod if necessary.

7. Allow tubes to cool to room temperature before testing. Add a cover or cap and store at 4°C for up to 2 weeks, if not testing on the same day.

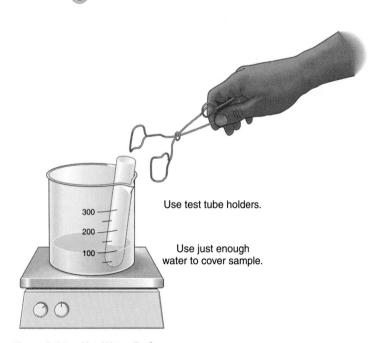

Use test tube holders.

Use just enough water to cover sample.

Figure 3.14. **Hot Water Bath.**

Part IV: Protein Testing Using Biuret Reagent

1. Add 2 mL of the gelatin solution to be tested into a 13×100-mm tube. Save all used and unused samples.

2. Add the 10% NaOH and 5% $CuSO_4$ in a 2:1 ratio as outlined in Table 3.15. First, add the NaOH to the sample, then add the $CuSO_4$ (see Figure 3.15). Thoroughly mix.

3. After 1 minute, record the color changes observed in a data table similar to Table 3.15. Think about the significance of the observed colors and how these data may be useful.

4. If there is no difference in color in the Biuret test results for these concentrations, prepare another 0.625% tube containing 2 mL of solution. Then add an extra 2 mL of water and mix thoroughly. This is a 1:2 dilution (50% sample and 50% water). What is the concentration of this tube now? Label it. Take 2 mL of the sample and dilute again the same way. Repeat again until there are at least three gelatin concentrations lower than the 0.625%.

Table 3.15.   **Color Change from Biuret Testing of Gelatin Samples of Differing Concentrations**

Samples	10% NaOH (μL)	5% CuSO$_4$(μL)	Color	Comments
5.0% gelatin	500	250		
2.5% gelatin	500	250		
1.25% gelatin	500	250		
0.625% gelatin	500	250		

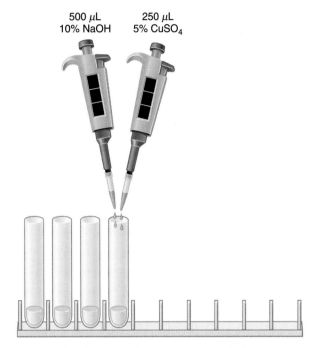

500 μL
10% NaOH

250 μL
5% CuSO$_4$

Figure 3.15.   **Biuret Testing.**   Biuret testing is done using two reagents, 10% NaOH and 5% CuSO$_4$ in a 2:1 ratio.

Conduct a Biuret test on each of these samples and record these additional test results in your data table.

Data Analysis/Conclusion

Describe the results of the Biuret testing of the gelatin solutions of decreasing concentration. Do the colors indicate the expected difference in concentration? How so or not? Describe any errors in technique that could result in misleading data. What might be done to decrease the chances of erroneous data or interpretation? Explain how the results of these Biuret protein tests could be applied to testing of other solutions of unknown concentration.

Thinking Like a Biotechnician

1. The solutions prepared in this activity are reported as % mass/volume concentration. How would the following % mass/volume concentrations be reported in g/mL units?

    10% NaOH = _____ g/mL NaOH
    5% CuSO$_4$ = _____ g/mL CuSO$_4$
    1.25% gelatin = _____ g/mL gelatin

2. Some protein solutions, such as hemoglobin in solution, are colorful. How might the color of hemoglobin impact Biuret indicator testing?
3. Following the protocol in Lab 3e, use the spectrophotometer to check the gelatin solutions' concentration and preparation.
4. Complete the Making Solutions Review Sheet No. 2 that follows.

Making Solutions Review Sheet No. 2

Convert the values as indicated. Specify the appropriate instrument with which the final measurements should be made. For items 10 through 17, show the calculation (equation and units) for the preparation of each solution. Then draw a diagram of how to make the solution.

Instrument Choices

graduated cylinder	10-mL pipet	5-mL pipet
2-mL pipet	1-mL pipet	tabletop balance
P-1000	P-200	P-100
P-20	P-10	analytical balance

1. 0.079 L = _____ mL	4. 9.22 mg = _____ g	7. 0.085 mL = _____ µL
2. 10.72 µL = _____ mL	5. 841 µg = _____ mg	8. 1.223 mL = _____ µL
3. 0.3 mL = _____ µL	6. 3.64 g = _____ mg	9. 0.19 g = _____ µg

Solution To Be Prepared	Diagram of How To Prepare It
10. 40 mL of 6.5 mg/mL CuSO₄ pentahydrate solution	11.
12. 200 mL of 8% NaCl solution	13.
14. 0.75 L of 5% dextrose solution	15.
16. 10 mL of 1.25% NaOH solution	17.

Laboratory 3g   Making Solutions of Differing Molarity Concentrations

The concentration of many solutions is reported as moles/liter (mol/L or M; the M is spoken "molar") or some fraction of those units. This concentration measurement is called *molarity*. Molarity is sometimes a challenging concept to understand. However, with your recently acquired solution preparation skills, you will see that making molar solutions requires only one extra calculation.

To understand how to make a solution of a given molarity, you must know what a "mole" is. A mole of a compound is equal to 6.02×10^{23} molecules, but that is not really a very useful number. So, in biotech, it is easier to use this definition: **The unit "1 mole" is the mass, in grams, equal to the molecular weight (MW),** also called "formula weight" (FW), of the substance (see Figure 3.16). The FW can be determined by using a Periodic Table or by adding the atomic weights of the atoms in the molecule. An easy way, though, is to just read the label of a chemical reagent bottle, which lists the "MW" or "FW." The molecular weight of NaCl is 58.5 atomic mass units (amu) since the Na atom weighs 23 amu, and a Cl atom weighs 35.5 amu.

Figure 3.16.   **Measuring Moles.**   A mole is a convenient method of measuring a large number of molecules (6.02×10^{23}) at one time. A mole of salt (NaCl) is 58.5 g since the molecular weight of NaCl is 58.5 amu.

Molarity concentrations are reported as the number of moles per liter (mol/L or M). If the concentration is very low, then the concentration could be reported in millimoles/liter (mmol/L or mM). If you wanted a 1-M NaCl solution, you would measure out 1 mole of NaCl (58.5 g) and dissolve it in water to a total volume of 1 L. This gives you 1 mole of NaCl per liter of solution, 1 M NaCl.

A liter of solution is a large volume for most research and development purposes. In research and development labs, mL or μL quantities are usually used. To determine how to mix up a smaller volume of a solution of some molarity, follow the example below.

Multiply the volume desired (L) by the concentration (molarity) desired (mol/L), as you did in the mass volume calculations. Then, multiply the result by the compound's molecular weight (g/mol) to account for measuring in moles, as in the following equation:

Molarity Concentration Equation

volume ×	molarity ×	molecular weight	= grams of solute to be dissolved in
wanted	desired	of the solute	solvent to the final desired volume
(L)	(mol/L)	(g/mol)	

Convert smaller or larger units to these as necessary. The "L" units cancel out and the "mol" units cancel out, leaving the mass in grams of the solute needed to make the solution.

Remember that the math is easiest if the units of measure can be cancelled during multiplication. Use the B ← → S Rule to convert between these metric units of measure:

g/mL
g/L
mg/mL
μg/mL
μg/μL
ng/L
ng/μL

Purpose

To make copper sulfate pentahydrate solutions of different volumes and molar concentrations.

Materials

Environmental Health
and Safety Officer

Caution: Wear goggles and gloves when measuring chemicals.

Balance, analytical
Balance, tabletop milligram
Weigh paper, 7.6×7.6 cm
Weigh boat, 3.5"x3.5"
Lab scoops
Cupric sulfate 5-hydrate
Tubes, 15 mL, capped
Tube racks for 15 mL tubes

Deionized water
Permanent lab marker pens
Tubes, glass, 13×100 mm
Peg racks for 10–13 mm tubes
Pipets, 5 mL
Pipet pump, green
Spectrophotometer, Spectronic 20 D+

Procedure

- Label all tubes with the concentration of the sample, your initials, and the date.
- Review the use of the balance and weigh boats before beginning.

1. For tubes numbered 1 through 5, prepare the solutions listed in Table 3.18. Use the Molarity Concentration equation (refer to the discussion at the beginning of this lab activity) to determine the mass of $CuSO_4$ to measure in order to give the right concentration and volume in each sample. Make a reaction matrix to record the volume, mass, and mathematical calculations for each solution (see Table 3.19). Show all units of measure and draw a picture to describe how to make each solution. Be sure to make the "calculations" and the "diagram" columns large enough for their contents.

Table 3.18. **Molar Solutions To Be Made**

Tube No.	Solution To Be Prepared
1	5 mL of 1.0 M $CuSO_4$
2	5 mL of 0.5 M $CuSO_4$
3	5 mL of 0.1 M $CuSO_4$
4	5 mL of 0.05 M $CuSO_4$
5	5 mL of 0.01 M $CuSO_4$

Table 3.19. **Concentrations of the $CuSO_4$ Solution Tubes**

Tube No.	Total Volume (mL)	Mass of $CuSO_4$ (g) to Use	Calculations	Diagram of Solution Preparation
1				
2				
3				
4				
5				

2. Prepare the solutions using deionized water in labeled 15-mL capped, conical tubes. Add the solute first, then add water to the total desired volume. Mix until the solute is dissolved.

Data Analysis and Conclusion

Are the differences in concentration of your five tubes obvious in one tube versus another? Describe any differences and explain why the differences are observed. If any volumes or colors are obviously wrong, dispose and remake them. Compare the colors and volumes of your samples to others in the class. Describe the impact if the final volume is incorrect. What will happen to the concentration of copper sulfate in the samples?

Thinking Like a Biotechnician

1. Each of the tubes in this activity was made "from scratch" by measuring out a specific mass of dry chemical and mixing it with a specified volume of solvent. Suggest a method to make a 0.5-M solution from the 1-M solution. Also, suggest a way to make a 0.1-M solution from the 0.5-M solution.
2. Calculate the mass/volume concentration in each tube and the % mass/volume concentration in each tube and record these data in a table similar to Table 3.20. Be sure to make the "calculations" column wide enough for the equations.

Table 3.20. **Concentration Equivalents**

Molar Concentration of Each Tube	Concentration (g/mL)	Concentration (%)	Calculations
5 mL of 1.0 M CuSO$_4$			
5 mL of 0.5 M CuSO$_4$			
5 mL of 0.1 M CuSO$_4$			
5 mL of 0.05 M CuSO$_4$			
5 mL of 0.01 M CuSO$_4$			

3. Following the protocol presented in Lab 3e, use the spectrophotometer to check the copper sulfate solution's concentration and preparation.
4. Complete the Making Solutions Review Sheet No. 3 that follows.

Making Solutions Review Sheet #3

Convert the values as indicated. Specify the appropriate instrument with which the final measurements should be made. For items 7 through 16, show the calculation (equation and units) for the preparation of each solution. Then draw a diagram showing how to make the solution.

Instrument Choices

graduated cylinder	10-mL pipet	5-mL pipet
2-mL pipet	1-mL pipet	tabletop balance
P-1000	P-200	P-20
P-100	P-10	analytical balance

1. 0.42 g = _____ μg _____	3. 90.22 μg = _____ g _____	5. 0.0285 mL = _____ μL _____
2. 999 μL = _____ mL _____	4. 80.41 mL = _____ μL _____	6. 70.503 mg = _____ g _____

Solution To Be Prepared	Diagram of How To Prepare It
7. 550 mL of 9.5 mg/mL NaOH solution	8.
9. 150 mL of 2% $CuSO_4 \cdot 5H_2O$ solution	10.
11. 3 L of 0.025% dextrose solution	12.
13. 125 mL of 10 M NaOH	14.
15. 75 mL of 0.1 M NaCl	16.

Laboratory 3h   Making Dilutions of Concentrated Solutions

Background

Making dilutions of concentrated solutions is a common practice in a biotechnology lab. A concentrated solution is generally called a "stock solution," and the diluted solution is called the "working solution." Preparing a concentrated stock solution saves a lot of time and is easier to store than large volumes of diluted working solutions. Making a working solution simply requires diluting some volume of stock solution to the concentration needed.

The working concentration of a solution is represented as 1X. A concentrated solution could be represented as 10X if it has 10 times the amount of solute per unit volume compared with the working solution. A 50X stock has 50 times the concentration of solute as a working solution. For example, an enzyme storage buffer may be used at a concentration of 0.01 M TRIS. This is the working concentration of the TRIS solution (1X). But because of shipping costs, a small amount of the enzyme buffer is shipped as a 10X solution with a concentration of 0.1 M TRIS. When the technician is ready to use the buffer, it is diluted with deionized water down to 1X (0.01 M TRIS).

When a number of dilutions must be made, and each is proportionally the same dilution as the one before, it is called a *serial dilution* (see Figure 3.17). Doing a serial dilution makes sense for many experiments when many samples of varying concentrations are needed. A serial dilution is also useful for preparing very dilute solutions that are hard to make from scratch, because the solute masses can be too small to measure on a balance.

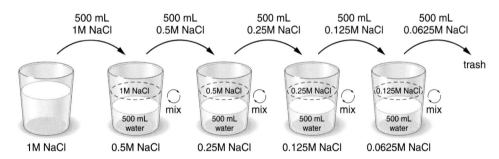

Figure 3.17.   **Serial Dilution.**   Each of these dilutions is one part (previous) sample and one part solvent. This is called a 1:2 dilution, or one part sample in two total parts. This could be read "1 *to* 2," which could erroneously result in a preparation with three parts. In practice, by convention, a 1:2 dilution is actually "1 *in* 2" total parts.

If the technician needs 150 mL of the 0.1 M TRIS, then a dilution of the concentrated 1 M TRIS can be calculated. To figure out how to dilute something from a concentrated solution, we use a simple ratio equation as shown in the following equation:

Diluting Concentrated Solutions Equation

$$C_1 V_1 = C_2 V_2$$

Where C_1 = the concentration of the concentrated stock solution (the starting solution).
V_1 = the volume to use of the stock solution in the diluted sample.
C_2 = the desired concentration of the diluted sample.
V_2 = the desired volume of the diluted sample.

The $C_1 V_1 = C_2 V_2$ equation may be used with any concentration units (ie, mass/volume, %, or molar) as long as the units are the same on each side of the equation (for canceling purposes). Using the equation with the scenario above in which the technician needs 150 mL of the 0.1 M TRIS,

C_1 = 0.1 M TRIS (the starting solution)
V_1 = amount of the concentrate to use for the dilution
C_2 = 0.01 M TRIS (the working solution)
V_2 = 150 mL

$$(0.1\ M)\ (V_1) = (0.01\ M)\ (150\ mL)$$

$$V_1 = \frac{(0.01\ M)(150\ mL)}{0.1\ M}$$

$$(V_1) = 15\ mL$$

Therefore, to make 150 mL of 0.01 M TRIS from the concentrated stock, measure out 15 mL of the concentrated 0.1 M TRIS stock and add 135 mL of deionized water to it and mix well.

Purpose

To make dilutions of concentrated solutions and report their concentration in different ways.

Materials

Caution: Wear goggles and gloves when measuring chemicals.

Environmental Health
and Safety Officer

Balance, analytical	Deionized water
Balance, tabletop milligram	Permanent lab marker pens
Weigh paper, 7.6×7.6 cm	Tubes, glass, 13×100 mm
Weigh boat, 3.5"×3.5"	Peg racks for 10–13 mm tubes
Lab scoops	Pipets, 5 mL
Cupric sulfate 5-hydrate	Pipet pump, green
Tubes, 15 mL, capped	Spectrophotometer, Spectronic 20 D+
Tube racks for 15 mL tubes	

Procedure

- In matrixes similar to those shown in Tables 3.21 and 3.22, record all your calculations and diagrams. Confirm your calculations with another person's calculations before you begin. Draw a diagram to show how each sample is diluted. Use the $C_1 V_1 = C_2 V_2$ equation to make the calculations. Be sure to make the columns the appropriate width for the material they will contain.
- Label all tubes with the name and concentration of the sample, your initials, and the date.

Table 3.21. **Dilutions of the 300X Stock CuSO$_4$**

Volume To Be Made (mL)	Concentration To Be Made (X)	Calculations	Volume of Stock to Use (µL)	Solution Preparation Diagram
5	150X			
7	30X			
5	15X			
5	3X			
4	1X			

1. Prepare 25 mL of 300-mg/mL CuSO$_4$ solution. Mix well. Do not use previously made solutions. **Consider this a 300X stock solution.**

a. Show the calculations for the solution preparation and draw a diagram of how it is made.
b. Determine the % mass/volume for this solution.
c. Determine the molarity of this solution.
Record these values.

2. Make the following dilutions in Table 3.21 from the concentrated stock (300×). Prepare the solutions using deionized water, in labeled 15 mL tubes. Micropipets may be required to make some measurements.

3. Using a matrix similar to Table 3.22, prepare additional dilutions from the more concentrated solutions. Prepare the solutions using deionized water, in labeled 13×100-mm tubes. Make the columns the appropriate width for the material they will contain.

Table 3.22.   **Diluting Samples**

Volume To Be Made (mL)	Starting Concentration (X)	Final Concentration (X)	Calculations	Solution Preparation Diagram
5.0	150X	15X		
2.0	30X	10X		
5.0	15X	1X		
2.5	3X	1X		
2.0	1X	0.5X		

4. Prepare a 1:10 serial dilution (refer to Figure 3.17) of the concentrated (300 mg/mL) stock (see Table 3.23). Prepare the solutions using deionized water, in labeled 13×100-mm tubes. Micropipets may be required to make some measurements.

Table 3.23.   **Dilutions of the 300-mg/mL Stock $CuSO_4$**

Volume To Be Made (mL)	Concentration To Be Made (mg/mL)	Calculations	Volume of Sample (V_1) To Be Used (µL)
3	150.0		
3	15.0		
3	1.5		
3	0.15		

5. Check the absorbances of these solutions on the spectrophotometer following the procedures in Lab 3e.

Data Analysis/Conclusion

Is the difference in concentration within each set of tubes obvious in one tube versus another and as had been expected from the kind of dilution that was made? How so or not? If any volumes or colors are obviously wrong, dump them out and remake them. Compare your tubes' colors and volumes to others in the class. Describe the value of having a 300X solution versus a 1X.

Thinking Like a Biotechnician

Complete the Making Solutions Review Sheet No. 4 that follows.

Making Solutions and Dilutions Review Sheet No. 4

Show the calculation (equation and units) for the preparation of each solution. Then draw a diagram of how to make the solution. Allow extra space in the column for the drawings.

Solution To Be Prepared	Diagram of How to Prepare It
1. 50 mL of 15 mg/mL NaOH solution from 100 mg/mL NaOH	2.
3. 10 mL of 0.5 M CuSO$_4$•5H$_2$O solution from 10 M CuSO$_4$•5H$_2$O	4.
5. 2 L of 5 mg/mL gelatin solution from 1 g/mL gelatin	6.
7. 950 mL of 1X CuSO$_4$•5H$_2$O solution from 25X CuSO$_4$•5H$_2$O	8.
9. 5 L of 0.2 M dextrose solution from 5 M dextrose solution	10.
11. 100 mL of 2.5X NaOH from 50X NaOH	12.
13. 50 mL of 5 mM NaCl from 1 M NaCl	14.

Chapter 4

DNA Isolation and Analysis

A lab technician prepares a buffer to be used in extraction of DNA from bacteria cells. The buffer contains sodium dodecyl sulfate (SDS), a detergent that dissolves cell membranes. When the membranes break up, the cells burst open and release their contents, which include DNA molecules and proteins.
Photo by author.

It has been said of the biotechnology industry that, "DNA is the flash, and proteins are the cash."

This is because isolating and modifying deoxyribonucleic acid (DNA) molecules are some of the newest scientific technologies. By utilizing the new techniques, companies are able to manufacture and market hundreds of new protein products.

In the following lab activities, you will learn some of the techniques used to grow specific cell lines. Working with healthy cell cultures, you will learn how to isolate and analyze DNA from the cells. Some of the new lab techniques in this chapter include the following:

- sterile technique
- growing cells, also called "cell culture"
- cell culture media preparation (media prep)
- bursting cells open, or "cell lysis"
- separation, or precipitation, of DNA, in this case, onto glass rods (spooling)
- DNA analysis by horizontal gel electrophoresis

These are introductory DNA laboratory procedures. In later chapters, you will learn how to introduce foreign DNA into cells to modify their characteristics. This is called genetic engineering, the technology that revolutionized science in the 1970s.

Laboratory 4a Making Solutions for DNA Isolation

Background

For genetic engineering or other work with DNA, a pure DNA sample is required. DNA must be purified from cells, removing all other cellular constituents and contaminant molecules. Many purification protocols include a step to remove protein contaminants using a salt solution.

One of the final steps in DNA isolation is to precipitate DNA, or take the DNA out of solution. In most cases, DNA precipitation is done using alcohol. In the next activity, DNA strands will be precipitated onto a glass rod. To increase the number of DNA strands that will spool around the glass rod, 5 M sodium chloride (NaCl) is added to the solution prior to alcohol precipitation. The Na^+ ions in a NaCl solution bind to the DNA, decreasing its negative charge, allowing DNA molecules to come closer together and spool more easily.

Isolated DNA can be stored for long periods in TE buffer (containing TRIS and EDTA). The TE buffer contains TRIS to maintain the pH of the DNA sample and EDTA to denature any DNases, which might contaminate the sample. In this activity, you will prepare 5 M NaCl solution and TE buffer.

Purpose

To make 10 milliliters (mL) of 5 M NaCl solution.
To make 100 mL of TE buffer: 10 mM TRIS, 1 mM EDTA (DNA storage solution).

Materials

Environmental Health
and Safety Officer

Balance, analytical	Tubes, 15 mL, capped	pH paper, wide/narrow-range
Balance, tabletop milligram	Tube racks for 15 mL tubes	Hydrochloric acid
Weigh paper, 7.6×7.6 cm	TRIS	Sodium hydroxide
Weigh boat, 3.5"×3.5"	EDTA, disodium salt	Glass rods
Lab scoops	Bottle, 125 mL	Filtering flasks, 250 mL, 0.2 μm
Sodium chloride	Graduated cylinder, 100 mL	Vacuum pump and "trap" jar

Procedure

Part I: Preparation of 5 M of NaCl

1. Determine the mass of NaCl to be measured. Remember, you want enough NaCl to give a concentration of 5 M, *but* you only want to make 10 mL of this solution. In your notebook show the calculations and draw a diagram of how the solution will be prepared.
2. Place the NaCl in a 15-mL conical tube. Slowly add dH$_2$O, while stirring, until a final volume of 10 mL is reached.
3. Pour the mixture into a 15-mL capped, conical tube. Cap it. Label it with the sample name, concentration, date, and technician's initials. Store at 4°C until ready to use.

4°C

Part II: Preparation of TE Buffer

Note: The calculations for each ingredient (TRIS and EDTA) are done separately based on a final volume of 100 mL.

1. Determine the mass of TRIS to be measured (from the bottles in the chemical storeroom) to give the correct concentration and volume in the final TE buffer. Show the calculations in your notebook.
2. Determine the mass of EDTA to be measured (from the bottles in the chemical storeroom) to give the correct concentration and volume in the final TE buffer. In your notebook show the calculations and draw a diagram of how the TE buffer solution will be prepared.
3. Measure out the TRIS and EDTA, and add them to a 250-mL beaker.

4. Add 80 mL of deionized water and mix until the chemicals dissolve. Use pH paper to determine the pH. The desired pH is 8.0. If the pH is between 7.5 and 8.5, record the pH on the label and do no further pH adjustment. If the pH is not within this range, slowly mix in small volumes of 1 *M* of HCl to lower the pH or 10% NaOH to raise the pH until it is in range.

5. Add more deionized water until a total volume of 100 mL is reached. If a filter unit is available, filter-sterilize the mixture (see Figure 4.1).

6. If no filter unit is available, pour the buffer into a 125-mL bottle. Cap it. Label it with the sample name, concentration, date, and your initials. Store at 4°C until ready to use.

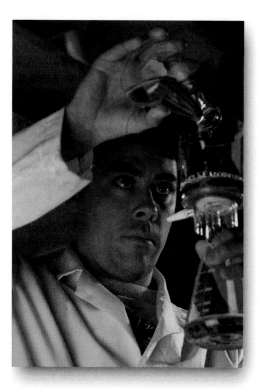

Figure 4.1.   **The top chamber of this filter flask unit has a 0.22-µ*M* filter that will trap bacteria and fungi. It is connected to a vacuum pump that pulls the solution into the bottom sterile chamber.**
© Richard T. Nowitz/Corbis.

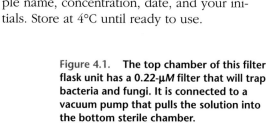

Thinking Like a Biotechnician

1. A 5 *M* NaCl solution is used in several laboratory activities. Show the calculations and a drawing to explain how to prepare 1 liter (L) of 5 *M* NaCl solution.

2. EDTA solution is usually prepared as a concentrated solution and added in small volumes to existing solutions. What volume of 0.5 *M* EDTA should be added to a solution to make it 1 L at a concentration of 1 m*M* EDTA?

3. The TE buffer protocol suggests sterilizing the filter. Why sterilize the TE buffer? Propose another method to sterilize the TE buffer besides filter sterilization.

Laboratory 4b   Pulling DNA out of Solution: DNA Spooling

Background

DNA is arguably the most important molecule in living things. The long, thin fibers in the molecule store *all* of the information needed to produce *all* of the molecules in an organism, either directly or indirectly. The structure of a DNA molecule is related to its function, as it is with all molecules.

To conduct genetic engineering, scientists need DNA in pure form. DNA must be purified out of cells or viruses, isolating it away from other molecular contaminants, such as proteins, carbohydrates, and lipids. Based on its molecular characteristics, DNA can be drawn out of cellular or aqueous solution. These characteristics include the long double-helix shape and the charged phosphate groups on the outer sugar-phosphate backbone. The phosphate groups are repelled by nonpolar solutions, such as alcohol.

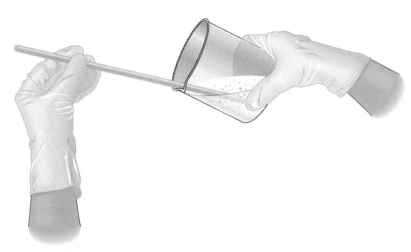

Figure 4.2. **Spooling.** Keep the glass rod almost parallel to the floor when spooling so that it is easier to scoop and twirl DNA molecules around the rod.

In this experiment, DNA molecules are precipitated from solution and spooled onto a glass rod (see Figure 4.2). The DNA has already been isolated from the nuclei of salmon sperm cells. Technicians have collected sperm samples, exploded the sperm cells, separated the contaminant proteins from the DNA, and then pulled the DNA out of the remaining aqueous solution using ethanol to provide the reagent DNA for this experiment.

Purpose

Can DNA be spooled out of solution?
What does DNA look like?
What are some of its many unique properties?
What yield of DNA can be recovered during the isolation?

Materials

Environmental Health
and Safety Officer

Beakers, 50 mL	Micropipet tips for P-1000	Permanent lab marker pens
DNA, salmon testes	Ethanol, 95%	Plastic beaker, 1L tripour
Pipet, 2 mL	Glass rods	**Caution: Alcohol is flamma-**
Pipet pump, blue	Tubes, 15 mL capped	**ble. Keep away from**
Micropipet, P-1000	Tube racks for 15 mL tubes	**flame or ignition sources.**

Procedure

In your notebook, make a data table to record all the data from the observations of DNA at different points in the extraction.

1. Using the TE buffer as the solvent and the $C_1 V_1 = C_2 V_2$ equation, determine how to make 2 mL of 2 mg/mL from a 4-mg/mL salmon sperm DNA solution. In your notebook, record the calculations and a drawing of how to make this dilution.
2. Prepare the diluted salmon sperm DNA solution in a prechilled, clean, 50-mL beaker. You will be using this 2-mg/mL DNA solution in the next step.
3. Describe the appearance, color, viscosity, etc, of the 2-mg/mL salmon sperm DNA. Add these data to the data table.
4. Using a micropipet, add 500 μL of 5 M NaCl solution. Mix by swirling.
5. Keep everything as cold as possible (see Figure 4.3). *Slowly* trickle 4 mL of ETOH down the side of the beaker containing the DNA and NaCl. **Do not mix the alcohol and DNA layers.**
6. Observe the interface between the two solutions. You should see a layer of alcohol on the top of the layer containing the DNA and NaCl. Do not mix the two layers. Describe what the layers look like. Add these data to the data table.

Figure 4.3. Any samples containing DNA, RNA, or protein should be kept cold to decrease the amount of sample degradation.
Photo by author.

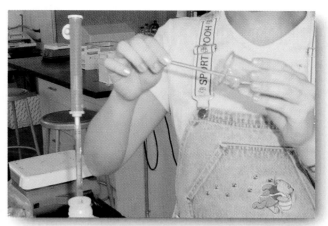

Figure 4.4. Spooling is more like scooping and twirling. Don't let the DNA strands fall off the glass rod.
Photo by author.

7. Place the glass rod at the interface of the two-layered solution. During spooling, you will force ETOH from the top layer down into the bottom DNA layer and pull the DNA out as it moves away from the ETOH (see Figure 4.4).

8. Holding the beaker tilted to the right 45°, wind (spool) the DNA that comes out of solution onto the rod/pipet. These are not single DNA molecules, but thousands of molecules. If you have a partner, be sure to take turns spooling, or each lab partner can spool his or her own samples. Watch the interface as you rotate the rod.

9. For one of the partner's spooled samples, examine and touch the DNA on the rod. Record the appearance of DNA, including color, texture, and other characteristics. Add these data to the data table. Touching the samples exposes it to DNase enzyme, which chops DNA. Record whether or not your sample was touched.

10. Shake the ethanol off the spooled DNA. Touch it to a paper towel. Get rid of as much ethanol as possible without losing the DNA sample.

11. Scrape the spooled DNA into 2 mL of TE buffer in a labeled, capped, conical, 15-mL tube. It is best to prepare the tube to receive the DNA before spooling begins. Record the appearance of DNA in buffer in the data table.

4°C

12. Store at 4°C (refrigerate) for at least 1 week. During that time, the DNA should go back into solution. In the data table, record the appearance of the DNA in buffer after 1 week. At this time, the DNA would be ready to use for indicator testing or gel electrophoresis.

Data Analysis/Conclusion

Discuss how easily the DNA could be pulled out of solution in long, spoolable strands. Did you and your partner have the same results as others? Why or why not? Discuss the value of learning how to separate pure DNA molecules from a known liquid solution. How would this technique be valuable to biotechnologists? Consider where DNA is found naturally.

Thinking Like a Biotechnician

1. In this activity, you precipitated DNA, ordered from a biological supply house, out of a relatively pure solution. Which molecules did the supply company have to remove to purify this DNA?

2. If 100% of the DNA was recovered during spooling and transferred to the 2 mL of TE buffer in step 10, what would the approximate final concentration of DNA be in the tube?

3. Why is the final sample refrigerated?

Laboratory 4c Testing for the Presence of DNA, RNA, and Protein in DNA Extracts

Background

DNA is only one of thousands of molecules found in cells. When attempting to isolate DNA from cells, how can a scientist be sure if he or she has isolated DNA versus, possibly, RNA or protein?

To test for the presence of various chemicals, indicators are used. One indicator of DNA is diphenylamine (DPA) solution. When DNA is present, DPA turns midnight blue. Ribonucleic acid (RNA) is another contaminant of DNA extraction. DPA also is an indicator of RNA, turning green when RNA is present.

Protein also is a common source of contamination in DNA extracts. To test for protein, use Biuret indicator ($NaOH+CuSO_4$). If protein is present in a substance, the Biuret reagent will turn from a medium blue (- protein) to a violet color (+++ protein).

In the experiment that follows, standard solutions (of known composition) are tested. Since it is known what is in each standard, a positive test for the item can be determined. Then, in the future, when other solutions (unknowns) are tested for the presence of a chemical, there is a basis of comparison with the standards.

Purpose

What are positive tests for DNA and protein?
Does the salmon sperm DNA sample test positive for DNA and negative for protein as expected?

Materials

Hood, chemical fume	Acetic acid, glacial	Beaker, 250 mL
Gloves, large	Acetaldehyde	Test tube holder
Glasses, safety	Tubes, glass, 13×100 mm	Hot plate stirrer
Bottle, 1000 mL	Peg racks for 10–13 mm tubes	Gelatin
Diphenylamine (DPA)	DNA extracts (from Lab 4b)	Sodium hydroxide, 10%
Sulfuric acid	DNA, salmon testes	Cupric sulfate 5-hydrate, 5%

Environmental Health
and Safety Officer

Procedure

Test each item of interest for both nucleic acids (DNA and RNA) and protein. Create a data table similar to Table 4.1 to record the results.

DPA test for DNA or RNA

(Conduct this test in an operational chemical fume hood with the fan running.)

 100°C

1. Add 1 mL of DPA solution to a clean, dry test tube.
2. Add 0.5 mL of the item to be tested.
3. Using a boiling hot water bath, heat the test tube contents for 25 minutes in a chemical fume hood.
4. Cool for 5 minutes.
5. Observe color of test tube contents.
6. Assess the amount of DNA or RNA in each sample by the degree of color compared with the positive standard (see Table 4.1).

Biuret Test for Protein

1. Add 0.5 mL of the item to be tested to a clean, dry test tube.
2. Add 0.5 mL of 10% NaOH and 0.25 mL of 5% $CuSO_4 \cdot 5H_2O$ to the test item.
3. Mix thoroughly and observe the color of test tube contents.
4. Assess the amount protein in sample by the degree of color compared with the positive standard.

Data Analysis/Conclusion

Describe the results of the DPA and Biuret testing. Did the known samples behave as expected? Describe. Did the unknown samples act as expected? Discuss the value of having "positive" standard tests when testing DNA extracted from *E. coli* or spinach plants.

Table 4.1. Tests for DNA and Protein with Specific Indicators

Item Tested	DPA Test	Biuret Test	Inferences
2 mg/mL salmon sperm DNA (+ DNA standard)			
2% gelatin solution (+ protein standard)			
salmon sperm DNA extract (unknown)			
water (– control)			

Thinking Like a Biotechnician

1. The spooled DNA was "pure" before spooling and should still be relatively pure after spooling. If the DNA and protein test results are not as expected, what could be contaminating the samples?
2. If a DPA test turns brownish, what may be concluded?
3. If the results of testing a known DNA solution are negative, what might be the reason?

Laboratory 4d EtBr Dot Test: A Quick Test for DNA in Samples

Background

To test for the presence of DNA in a solution, a quick ethidium bromide (EtBr) test can be conducted in a matter of moments. An EtBr test indicates the presence of DNA by glowing a "hot" pink-orange color under ultraviolet (UV) light.

When EtBr is mixed with DNA in solution, the EtBr intercalates (fits between) between the nitrogenous bases of the DNA molecule. This causes the bases to move farther apart and interact with light in a different manner. Shining a UV light on a mixture of EtBr and DNA will reveal glow a pink-orange color. The degree of "glowing" indicates the presence and amount of DNA (see Figure 4.5). Since EtBr can change the shape of DNA molecules, it is a hazard to human cells. It is a known mutagen (can

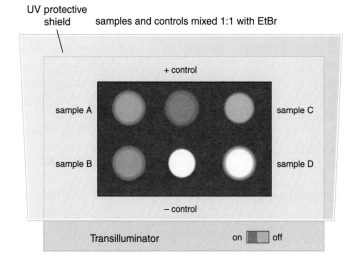

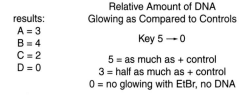

results:
A = 3
B = 4
C = 2
D = 0

Relative Amount of DNA Glowing as Compared to Controls

Key 5 → 0

5 = as much as + control
3 = half as much as + control
0 = no glowing with EtBr, no DNA

Figure 4.5. EtBr Dot Test. When EtBr is mixed with DNA, the mixture glows under UV light. When the sample is compared with the positive and negative standards, one can determine the presence of DNA.

cause changes in the DNA code) and is a suspected carcinogen (cancer-causing agent). Safety precautions, including wearing goggles and gloves, must be taken when using EtBr or when working in an area where EtBr is used.

Purpose

What are positive and negative tests using EtBr as an indicator?
Does the salmon sperm DNA sample test positive for DNA using the EtBr dot test?

Materials

Gel photo imaging system	DNA extracts (from Lab 4b)	Micropipet, P-10
Paper, thermal	Gloves, large	Micropipet tips for P-10
Printer, thermal	Glasses, safety, plastic	
DNA, salmon testes	Ethidium bromide, 0.5 µg/mL	

Environmental Health and Safety Officer

Safety Precautions

- EtBr is a hazardous chemical.
- EtBr is to be prepared and used only by the supervisor.
- Wear goggles and gloves while in an area where EtBr is used.

Procedure

EtBr Dot Test for DNA

a. Clean and dry the inside of a transilluminator light box.
b. Add 10 µL of sample to be tested to the transilluminator glass surface.
c. Add 10 µL of EtBr solution to the sample. Pipet the mixture up and down once to mix.
d. Other samples may be tested at other spots on the illuminator glass surface. Make sure the "dot" of sample is kept apart from other samples.
e. Close the lid and turn on the UV lamp.
f. Observe the amount of color and glowing of each sample compared with the positive (2 mg/mL of salmon sperm stock solution) and negative (deionized water) standards.

1. Using the EtBr dot-test procedures, test each (unknown) sample thought to contain DNA. Also, test deionized water as a negative control, and test 2 mg/mL of salmon sperm DNA solution as a positive control.
2. Photograph and evaluate the results. Use a 5 → 0 scale to assign a numerical rating to the relative amount of DNA in the sample compared with the controls (see Figure 4.5). Record the results on a data table in your notebook.

Data Analysis/Conclusion

Estimate the concentration of the unknown samples. Do this by converting the numerical rating they were given to an estimated concentration (mg/mL) compared with the positive- and negative-control concentrations. Discuss the results of the testing. Are the concentrations of the samples close to the concentrations you expected? If so, why? If not, why not? Suggest applications of the EtBr test in future experiments.

Thinking Like a Biotechnician

1. Why are the positive and negative controls necessary in the EtBr dot test?
2. EtBr is a dangerous chemical. Go online and find a Materials Safety Data Sheet (MSDS) for EtBr. Copy and paste the sections that describe the following:
   • potential health effects (acute and chronic)
   • first-aid measures
3. Suggest a method to better estimate the concentration of DNA in the unknown samples.

Laboratory 4e   Making Media for Bacteria Cell Culture (Media Prep)

Background

In the next several activities, bacteria cells are grown and used as a source of DNA. Bacteria are grown on or in their food source, called media. If the medium is a solid, it is called agar; if it is liquid, it is called broth.

The decision to use one type of medium or another depends on the kind of bacteria to be grown and the intended use. If single, isolated colonies are needed, cells must be grown on agar, usually in Petri plates. Depositing a single cell on the agar surface produces cell colonies. The cell grows and divides hundreds of times resulting in a colony of identical cells. All the cells in a colony are clones of each other. A plate culture is ideal for separating bacteria into individual colonies and isolated, pure, uncontaminated cultures.

Once isolated colonies are grown, a single colony can be transferred to broth culture with the goal of maximizing cell growth and reproduction. In a broth culture, cells have better access to nutrients. They grow, produce molecules, and divide into new cells at a maximum rate. Broth cultures, sometimes as large as tens of thousands of liters, are used in manufacturing to obtain a maximum number of cells to make a maximum amount of protein product.

E. coli bacteria will grow in many kinds of media, but they grow particularly well in Luria Bertani (LB) agar and broth. LB agar is an "all purpose" agar that supports the growth of many types of bacteria and fungi. Other nutrients may be added to the agar for different tests.

Media base (dry mixture of media components) is available for purchase from supply houses. The recipe for making a 1-L batch of agar or broth is printed on most stock media-base containers. Using a simple ratio equation, $\text{Mass}_1/\text{Volume}_1 = \text{Mass}_2/\text{Volume}_2$, you can determine the proper amounts of media for the volume of media needed:

Media Prep Equation

$$\frac{\text{Mass}_1}{\text{Volume}_1} = \frac{\text{Mass}_2}{\text{Volume}_2}$$

M_1 = the mass of media base to use in the original recipe's volume (usually 1 L)
V_1 = the volume of solvent (dH_2O) in the original recipe's volume (usually 1 L)
M_2 = the mass of media base needed for the desired volume
V_2 = the desired final volume of media

For example, suppose the recipe on a media bottle says to use 22 g of media base in 1 L of dH_2O. For an experiment, only 300 mL of prepared media are needed. What amount of media base is needed to make the 300-mL volume?

Convert 1 L to 1000 mL.

$$22g /1000 \text{ mL} = M_2/300 \text{ mL}$$

$$M_2 = \frac{22 \text{ g} \times 300}{1000}$$

M_2 = 6.6 g of media dissolved in dH_2O to a total volume of 300 mL

Prepare and autoclave all media in containers that are at least 2 times the volume of the prepared media volume. This allows room for boiling.

Purpose

To prepare LB agar and LB broth for growing *E. coil* cultures.

Materials

Balance, tabletop milligram	Glass rods	Permanent lab marker pens
Weigh boat, 3.5"×3.5"	Magnetic stir bars	LB broth base
Lab scoops	Hot plate stirrer, 7"×7"	Beaker, 250 mL
LB agar base	Hot hands protector	Media bottle, 125 mL
Beakers, 400 mL	Media bottle, 250 mL	Sterilizer/autoclave

Environmental Health and Safety Officer

Procedure

Note: Recipes can be adjusted for any desired volume of media.

Part I: Preparation of 125 mL of LB agar

- 125 mL of agar is the maximum that can be prepared in the 250-mL media bottles.
- Use $Mass_1/Volume_1 = Mass_2/Volume_2$ to determine the proper amounts of media base to use.

1. Wash a 250-mL media bottle and black cap. Label it with sample name, date, and your initials. (This is for sterilizing the media.)
2. Wash a 400-mL glass beaker. (This is for mixing the media.)
3. Measure out the amount of LB agar base required for the volume of agar desired. Use the $Mass_1/Volume_1 = Mass_2/Volume_2$ equation to calculate the mass needed for the desired volume. Record that mass (M_2) in your notebook along with the calculations. Pour the LB agar base into the clean 400-mL beaker.
4. *Very slowly*, add 90 mL of distilled water, stirring as it is added. The water should, at first, make a thick paste. As you add more water and stir the agar mixture, the LB agar base will eventually become suspended.
   Note: Some agar recipes require the addition of NaOH. If necessary, determine the amount of 1 *M* of NaOH to add to the suspended agar.
5. Add more water until a total volume of 125 mL of suspended agar is achieved.
6. Gently add a magnetic stirrer to the beaker by sliding it down the side of the beaker. Move the beaker of agar suspension onto a stirring, hot plate.
7. Heat on high, gently stirring the entire time, until **just** before it boils. **Do not let it boil.** The agar suspension should become clear.
8. Using bottle holders, carefully remove the beaker from the hot plate and pour the hot agar suspension into the labeled, clean, 250-mL media bottle. **Very loosely cap the bottle with the black cap. The cap should jiggle but still stay on the bottle. This releases pressure without contamination.**
9. Place the media bottle into a pressure cooker or autoclave, along with the rest of the class' bottles (see Figure 4.6). Bolt down the pressure cooker's top or autoclave's door as directed by the instructor, or according to the manufacturer's directions.
10. Heat until the pressure gauge reads 15 pounds of pressure per square inch (psi).
    Caution: Follow all pressure cooker or autoclave instructions.

Environmental Health and Safety Officer

11. Keep the bottles at 15 to 20 psi for 15 to 20 minutes. Cool the agar to 65°C (just barely cool enough to hold bottles). Continue to step 12 if there is time to pour plates. If there is not enough time to pour plates, let the agar cool and solidify. It can be reheated in a microwave at 50% power for about 4 minutes to completely liquefy. Cool to 65°C before pouring.

12. Pour the liquid agar into Petri plates, in a laminar flow hood or disinfected lab tabletop, as directed by your instructor.

Data Analysis/Conclusion

Evaluate your ability to prepare 125 mL of LB agar. Consider the final volume, color, mix, solidity, and labeling of the sample. Describe which of these tasks you performed well, and which you could improve on and how.

Procedure

Part II: Preparation of 50 mL of LB Broth

- 50 mL of broth is an appropriate volume for a 125-mL media bottle.
- Use the $Mass_1/Volume_1 = Mass_2/Volume_2$ to determine the proper amounts of media base to use.

Figure 4.6. A pressure cooker can be used to sterilize media if an autoclave is not available. When using a pressure cooker or autoclave sterilizer, make sure the caps on the bottles are loose enough to release pressure (so they do not explode), but tight enough to stay on. Photo by author.

1. Wash a 125-mL media bottle and black cap. Label it. (This is for sterilizing the media.)

2. Wash a 250-mL glass beaker. (This is for mixing the media.)

3. Measure out the amount of LB broth base required for the volume of broth desired. Record that mass (M_2) in your notebook along with your calculations. Place the LB broth base into the clean 250-mL beaker.

4. Very slowly add 35 mL of distilled water, stirring as it is added. The water should at first make a thick paste. As you add more water and stir the broth mixture, the LB broth base will eventually become suspended. LB broth base goes into solution much more easily than agar base.

   Note: Some broth recipes require the addition of NaOH. If necessary, determine the amount of 1 *M* of NaOH to add to the liquid broth.

5. Add more water until a total volume of 50 mL of suspended broth is achieved.

6. Gently add a magnetic stirrer to the beaker by sliding it down the side of the beaker. If the broth base is not dissolved, move the beaker of broth suspension onto a stirring, hot plate.

7. Heat on high until the broth base has dissolved, gently stirring the entire time. **Do not let it boil.**

8. Using bottle holders, remove the beaker from the hot plate and pour the hot broth suspension into the labeled, clean, 125-mL media bottle. **Very loosely cap the bottle with the black cap.**

9. Place the media bottle into a pressure cooker or autoclave, along with the rest of the class' bottles. Bolt down the pressure cooker's top or the autoclave's door as directed by the instructor or the manufacturer's directions.

10. Heat until the pressure gauge reads 15 psi.
    Caution: Follow all pressure cooker or autoclave instructions.

11. Keep the bottles at 15 psi for 15 to 20 minutes. Cool the broth to room temperature before using.

Environmental Health and Safety Officer

Data Analysis/Conclusion

Evaluate your ability to prepare 50 mL of LB broth. Consider the final volume, color, mix, and labeling of sample. Describe which of these you performed well, and which you could improve on and how.

Thinking Like a Biotechnician

1. After making several batches of sterile LB broth, you see pieces of dust in the broth. Is the broth suitable to use? How could the dust have entered the bottles?
2. Why is it not advisable to heat or sterilize media longer than necessary?
3. Additional compounds can be added to agar before sterilization (or sometimes after). An example of this is "milk agar," in which 2% nonfat powdered milk is added to the agar base. Lactose-digesting bacteria like to grow on milk agar. How many grams of nonfat powdered milk should be added to the 125 mL of LB agar to end up with 2% milk LB agar? Show your calculations.
4. Growing mammalian, fungal, and bacterial cells in or on sterile, prepared media is critical for their study. Each type has specific requirements for growth. Using the Internet, find a media recipe for the fungus *Penicillium chrysogenum*.

    Record the recipe and Web site reference in your notebook. How many more ingredients are necessary for *Penicillium* culture than *E. coli* culture? Suggest reasons why fungus cells have so many more required ingredients in their growth media.

Laboratory 4f   Sterile Technique and Pouring Plates

Background

Sterile technique is used in virtually all biotechnology research applications. When cells, tissues, organs, or organisms are grown in the laboratory, they are maintained in sterile environments. Specimens are grown on sterile solid (agar) or liquid (broth) media. Whichever media is used, it must be sterilized under heat and pressure for at least 15 to 20 min at 121°C and 15 to 20 psi before it is used. Sterile technique is used through media prep and cell culture. Media is prepared and then sterilized in an autoclave. The high temperature and pressure cause the cells and spores of the microorganisms to explode. Media can be prepared, poured into Pyrex® (by Corning, Inc) dishes or bottles, and then sterilized. Alternatively, media can be prepared and sterilized and then poured into sterile containers. Sterile Petri plates may be purchased in sleeves of 20 to 25.

Sterile technique includes all of the things done to one's person or equipment to decrease the possibility of transferring unwanted microorganisms to cultures, such as the following:

- use of disinfectants, including 10% bleach, 95% or 70% alcohol, Amphyl® disinfectant, or Lysol® disinfectant (both manufactured by Reckitt Benckiser, Inc), on surfaces, equipment, or hands.
- use of flame (Bunsen burner) to flame-sterilize bottles, tubes, inoculating loops, etc.
- decrease of air currents into the inoculation area through the use of laminar flow hoods, removing baggy clothing, and tying back long hair. In some facility, employees "gown up" with special protective clothing to protect the product from contamination.

Purpose

To pour a sleeve of Petri plates, under sterile conditions.

Materials

Environmental Health
and Safety Officer

Laminar flow hood	Petri dishes, 100×15 mm, sterile
Lysol® disinfectant	Permanent lab marker pens
Glasses, safety	LB agar base or premade LB agar
Bunsen burner	Microwave oven
Lab gas lighter	

Procedure

Before beginning, do the following:

a. Disinfect working surfaces, hands, and instruments with 10% bleach, 70% ethanol, or a commercial disinfectant.

b. Pouring plates should be done either in a laminar flow hood or on a countertop in an area with few or no air currents (see Figure 4.7).

c. Label Petri plates along the edge of the bottom of the plate with your initials, the date, period, and medium.

d. If the medium is solidified, loosen the cap and heat in a microwave at 50% power until completely liquid (see Figure 4.8). Allow cooling to 65°C (just cool enough to hold bottle comfortably) before pouring.

To pour plates:

1. Turn on the laminar flow hood. Wipe the outside of the bottle of medium and the inside of the laminar flow hood with disinfectant.

2. Stack labeled Petri plates in threes beside the edge of the tabletop or hood top.

3. Remove the medium bottle cap and "flame" the bottle top (pass bottle top through the hot part of the flame three times).

4. Open the bottom Petri plate of the first stack. Pour agar over one-half the height of the Petri plate. Tilt the plate slightly to cover the bottom with agar.

5. Repeat pouring of the other plates and other stacks of plates.

6. Stack groups on top of each other.

Figure 4.7.　Pouring agar plates and transferring the medium in a laminar flow hood is the best practice when sterile technique is important. The safest way to light a Bunsen burner is with an igniter/striker.
Photo by author.

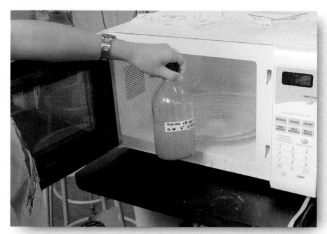

Figure 4.8.　Make sure the cap is loosened, but still attached, when heating a bottle of medium in the microwave oven. If the cap is on too tightly, pressure will build in the bottle and it will explode. The medium should fill no more than one-half of the bottle to allow for boiling.
Photo by author.

7. Leave undisturbed for at least 15 minutes.
8. Allow drying in a clean area, undisturbed, for at least 24 hours before use. Plates are good for about 2 weeks. Store in a cool, dark place.

Data Analysis/Conclusion

Evaluate your ability to pour plates with about 15 to 20 mL of LB agar. Consider the final volume (about 20 mL) of agar in the plate, coverage (equally covering bottom), lumpiness (none), contamination (cloudy or fuzziness in culture), and labeling of the plate. Describe which of these tasks you did well, and which you could improve upon and how.

 *Thinking Like a Biotechnician*

1. Name five things you can do to decrease the chance of contaminating a sample.
2. When pouring plates, you notice that the agar is coming out in lumps. Why is this undesirable and what corrective measures can you take?
3. LB agar plates are needed for several days of lab work. If eight sleeves of Petri plates (20 plates/sleeve) are need, each poured with about 20 mL, what total volume of LB agar should you prepare?

Laboratory 4g   Bacteria Cell Culture

Background

For DNA extraction purposes, it is desirable to use a broth culture of cells. The broth culture must be "started" 1 or 2 days in advance, from a plate culture, to ensure that there is a high density of cells in the culture.

The broth culture is started from a single colony grown on agar plates. Using a single colony of identical cells ensures that all cells in the broth culture are identical (see Figure 4.9).

Materials

Laminar flow hood
Lysol® disinfectant
LB agar plates/broth (from Lab 4f)
E. coli JM109, stock plate
Glasses, safety, plastic
Bunsen burner
Lab gas lighter
Inoculating loop, Ni/Cr wire
Incubator oven, 37°C
Tubes, 50 mL, sterile
Tube racks for 50 mL tubes
Pipets, 10 mL
Pipet pump, green
Water bath, 37°C, shaking

Environmental Health
and Safety Officer

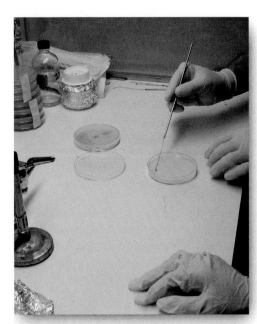

Figure 4.9. **Bacterial cell cultures are started on agar Petri plates. Using a sterile inoculating loop on a sterile bench, a sample is streaked out until some cells are spaced individually on the agar. The cells grow into colonies of identical cells. A colony can be used as a starter for a broth culture.**

Photo by author.

Part I: Growing a Plate Culture
Purpose

To streak and grow a plate culture with isolated colonies.

Procedure

Environmental Health
and Safety Officer

- Do all work in a sterile laminar flow hood or countertop.
- Use all standard precautions with the Bunsen burner, including tying back hair, wearing goggles, etc.
- Dispose of any bacteria-contaminated products in autoclave bags and/or 10% bleach solution.

1. Obtain a Petri plate of LB agar. Label the bottom edge of the plate with your initials, the type of media, the sample identification, and the date.
2. Flame sterilize (as demonstrated by the instructor) an inoculating loop (see Figure 4.10), cool it on a spot of uncontaminated agar, and collect a colony of *E. coli* from the stock plate.

Figure 4.10. **Place the wire in the hottest part of the flame (where the blue and orange meet) and allow it to get hot enough to glow red. Start at the base of the wire and have the loop glow last.**
Photo by author.

3. Streak the bacterial colony onto a sterile LB agar Petri plate (see Figure 4.11).
   a. Be careful to hold the top of the Petri plate over the bottom to minimize contamination.
   b. Streak the sample back and forth across the agar on the top one-fourth of the plate. This is the first set of "Z"s.
   c. Rotate the plate 90°. Flame-sterilize the inoculating loop. Cool on uncontaminated agar.
   d. Streak the loop at a right angle through the previous streak. Go through the first streak only once to pick up the fewest bacteria cells possible. Make a "Z"-shaped streak. This is the second "Z."
   e. Rotate the plate another 90°. Flame-sterilize the inoculating loop. Cool on uncontaminated agar.

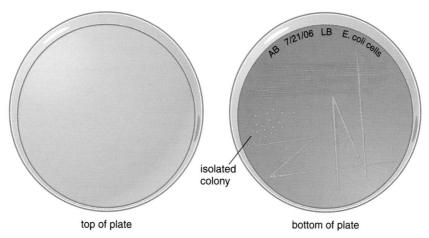

top of plate

isolated colony

bottom of plate

Figure 4.11. **Streaking for Isolated Colonies.** Use the triple-Z method of streaking, flaming between streakings. This method results in a significant decrease in the number of cells spread each time so that isolated colonies result in the last "Z."

37°C

f. Streak the loop again, at a right angle, through the second "Z" streak. Go through that streak only once to pick up the fewest bacteria cells possible. Make a third "Z." Flame-sterilize the inoculating loop. Place on laminar flow hood counter to cool.

g. Replace lid. Place your inoculated LB plate, upside down, in one of the incubation ovens designated by the instructor.

4. Incubate the bacterial plate culture, upside down, for 24 hours at 37°C.

5. Before leaving the lab area, discard any biological waste in the biohazard bag, disinfect your workspace, and wash your hands.

Data Analysis/Conclusion

Evaluate your ability to isolate individual bacteria cells and grow them into isolated colonies. How many isolated colonies are present in the final "Z"? Describe how you might improve the technique next time. Are any of the colonies good candidates for starting a broth culture?

Part II: Starting a Broth Culture
Purpose

To grow a broth culture to use as a source of cells for DNA isolation.

Procedure

Environmental Health and Safety Officer

37°C

- Do all work in a sterile laminar flow hood or on a countertop.
- Use all standard precautions with the Bunsen burner, including tying back hair and wearing goggles, etc.
- Dispose of any bacteria-contaminated products in autoclave bags and/or 10% bleach solution.

1. Obtain a Petri plate of LB agar containing isolated colonies, a 50-mL sterile, conical centrifuge tube, and a bottle of sterile LB broth.

2. Flame-sterilize (as demonstrated by the instructor) the top of the LB broth bottle.

3. Using a sterile 10-mL pipet, transfer 10 mL of LB broth from the bottle to the 50-mL tube.

4. Flame-sterilize (as demonstrated by the instructor) an inoculating loop, cool it on a spot of uncontaminated agar, and collect a colony of *E. coli* from the streaked plate.

5. Holding the tube at a 45° angle, add the colony to the broth, with a twist of the loop, to ensure that most of the colony gets into the broth (see Figure 4.12). Reflame the loop to remove any remaining bacteria.

6. Incubate the broth culture in a shaking hot water bath or a shaking incubator oven at 37°C for 24 hours (see Figure 4.13).

7. Before leaving the lab, discard any biological waste in the biohazard bag, disinfect your workspace, and wash your hands.

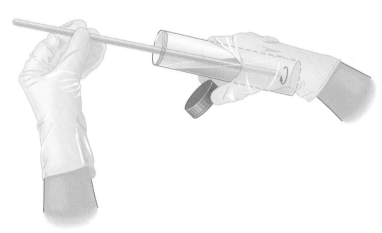

Figure 4.12. Inoculating a Broth Culture. Hold the tube "sideways" to decrease the chance of contaminants falling into the container.

Figure 4.13. In industry, large shaker flask ovens keep cells moving, aerated, and warm, so that they grow and divide at a maximum rate.
Photo by author.

Data Analysis/Conclusion

Evaluate your broth culture. Does it look the way you think it should look? Is it cloudy and obviously full of bacteria cells? How do you know? How can you be sure that there are enough of the right kinds of cells?

Thinking Like a Biotechnician

1. After streaking a plate with a colony of *E. coli* cells and incubating it overnight at 37°C, a technician returns to find no colonies on the plate. List three reasons this could happen.
2. You make 1 L of LB agar and pour it into five media bottles for sterilization. After autoclaving and cooling them, you notice some of the bottles have agar that is not completely solid, while other bottles do have solidified agar, as expected. What should you do? Are any of them usable? If so, which ones?
3. Propose a method to check if a laminar flow hood is still working correctly (filtering out all the bacteria and fungi from the air).

Laboratory 4h   DNA Extraction from Bacteria

Background

Within bacteria cells, DNA and, therefore, genes are found both in the single genomic chromosome and in any extrachromosomal plasmids. Either source of DNA may be a source of genes for genetic engineering or gene therapy purposes.

Isolation of either type of DNA includes bursting open the cells, getting rid of contaminant molecules, and precipitating the DNA out of the solution.

To burst open cells, the cell membrane must be removed. Since the major component of a membrane is a phospholipid bilayer, a detergent can be used to dissolve away this "fatty" layer. Several different detergents may be used depending on the type of DNA to be extracted. For bacteria cells, SDS works well. Even household detergents, such as Dawn® and Ivory® (both manufactured by Procter & Gamble), have been used.

When the cells burst, all the cellular contents are released into the collection vessel. The detergent not only removes the lipids, but also precipitates many of the proteins from the membrane

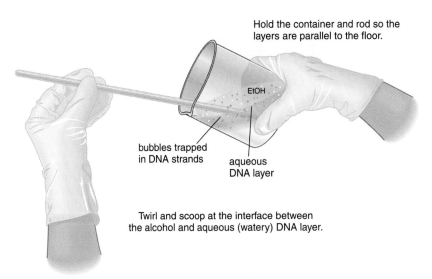

Hold the container and rod so the
layers are parallel to the floor.

EtOH

bubbles trapped
in DNA strands

aqueous
DNA layer

Twirl and scoop at the interface between
the alcohol and aqueous (watery) DNA layer.

Figure 4.14. **Spooling Technique.** When spooling, hold the glass rod almost parallel to the floor. Rotate and revolve through the two layers, scooping the DNA threads out and spinning them around the rod.

and cytoplasm. These proteins drop to the bottom of the vessel and are easy to separate from the DNA. Adding heat speeds the process.

Enzymes may be added to degrade other molecules. For example, RNase is commonly used to decompose RNA contaminant molecules in DNA extractions. Proteases are used to degrade protein contaminants in samples.

Centrifugation can separate the precipitated proteins and degraded cellular debris from the DNA still in solution. The DNA can be drawn out of solution by adding alcohol, usually ethanol (EtOH), or isopropanol. If chromosomal DNA is desired, the DNA can be spooled onto a glass rod (see Figure 4.14). Plasmid DNA is much too small to be spooled. It is precipitated from solution using a series of alcohol washes and centrifugation. Ultimately, plasmid DNA is recovered from one of the pellets left after one of the centrifugations. Plasmid isolation is presented in Chapter 8.

Purpose

Can relatively pure chromosomal DNA be extracted from *E. coli* bacteria cells?

Materials

CleanUp Kit

Environmental Health
and Safety Officer

E. coli broth cultures (from Lab 4h)	SDS, 10%	Ethanol, 95%
Pipets, 10 mL	Water bath, 65°C	Glass rods, 200 mm
Pipet pump, green	RNase, 0.1 mg/mL	TE buffer (from Lab 4a)
Tubes, 15 mL capped	Protease, 0.1 mg/mL	Pipets, 2 mL
Tube racks for 15 mL tubes	5 *M* NaCl (from Lab 4a)	Pipet pump, blue
Permanent lab marker pens	Centrifuge for 15 mL tubes	
	Beakers, 50 mL	

Procedure

65°C

4°C

Safety Precautions
- Do all work in a sterile laminar flow hood or on a disinfected countertop.
- Use all standard precautions with the Bunsen burner, including tying back hair and wearing goggles, etc.
- Dispose of any bacteria-contaminated products in autoclave bags and/or 10% bleach solution.

1. Using sterile technique, add 10 mL of *E. coli* broth suspension to a 15-mL capped, conical, centrifuge tube.
2. Add 0.5 mL of 10% SDS to the tube with *E. coli*. Invert gently five times (5X) to mix.
3. Incubate tube in a 65°C water bath for 15 minutes.
4. Cool on ice for 5 minutes.

4°C

5. If desired, add 0.5 mL of RNase and 0.5 mL of protease to the tube. Invert to mix.

6. Add 0.5 mL of 5 *M* NaCl. Place on ice for 5 minutes.

7. Spin the tube in a tabletop centrifuge for 5 minutes (see Figure 4.15).

8. Gently decant or pipet the supernatant (top layer) to a clean, cold, 50-mL beaker. Observe the color and viscosity of the solution. Create a data table in your notebook to record these and other observations.

4°C

9. Place the beaker containing supernatant on ice for 5 minutes.

10. Layer 5 mL of ice cold 95% ethanol slowly, with a pipet, down the inside of the beaker. Look at the interface between the alcohol layer and the DNA layer. Do you see any evidence of DNA? Observe the color and viscosity of the solutions and interface. Record these observations into the data table.

11. Hold the beaker at a 45° angle and spool the bacterial DNA out of the solution. Slowly rotate a stirring rod clockwise, as well as up and down, and around, through the layers. Rotate and scoop at the interface instead of swirling. Every once in a while, pull up the rod and examine the DNA strands.

12. Try to spool all of the DNA strands. Observe and record the characteristics of the DNA spooled sample in the data table.

13. Blot the excess EtOH off the sample and place the DNA into a sterile, capped, conical centrifuge tube containing 2 mL of TE buffer. Immediately, observe and record the characteristics of the DNA sample in the data table.

mixture before centrifuging

supernatant

precipitant

Heavy sample is pulled down and to the side.

Substances are pulled down based on mass.

Figure 4.15. **Supernatant/precipitant centrifuge results.**

Figure 4.16. **DNA, RNA, and most proteins are temperature-sensitive and may be degraded or denatured by enzyme contaminants (eg, proteases or DNases) at room temperature. To decrease their activity and preserve molecular or cellular samples, most are stored at –20°C or –80°C. This –80°C freezer stores DNA samples for sequencing.**
Photo by author.

4°C

14. Allow the DNA to go back into solution, over several days to a week, before using it for further analysis. After a week, record the sample's appearance in the data table. Store the samples at 4°C for 2 to 3 weeks. Long-term storage of the DNA samples should be at –20°C (see Figure 4.16).

15. Test this sample for DNA, RNA contamination, and protein contamination using EtBr, DPA, and/or Biuret testing. Construct a data table for the DNA, RNA, and protein data collection.

Data Analysis/Conclusion

Describe the quality and quantity of DNA extracted from the bacterial cell sample compared with other DNA samples you have spooled. Discuss how effective the DNA extraction technique is at isolating pure DNA. Give evidence for your statements. Propose variations in the protocol that may lead to improved quantity or purity of the DNA sample.

Thinking Like a Biotechnician

1. Protease is used in this experiment to chop up protein contaminants. There are many different kinds of proteases. One protease that can be purchased at the grocery store is papain, a protease derived from papayas, which is found in meat tenderizers, such as Adolphs® meat tenderizer (by Lawry's). How can one know that 1 mg/mL of papain is the best concentration of the protease to use? Describe a simple experiment to determine the best concentration for protease activity.

2. You used 10% SDS in the experiment to explode the bacteria cells and precipitate protein contaminants. One can purchase 20% SDS commercially. How much 20% SDS would you need to have enough to make 2000 mL of 10% SDS?

3. The genomic DNA that was spooled was considerably less in volume than the salmon sperm DNA spooled in a previous lab experiment. What is the reason for the difference in DNA yield?

Laboratory 4i   Making Agarose Gels for Separating and Analyzing DNA Fragments

Background

Agarose gels are typically used to separate and analyze DNA molecules ranging in length from about 500 to 25,000 base pairs (bp). The ability of a gel to separate molecules is called its "resolving power" and is mainly determined by the concentration of agarose in the gel. Most agarose gels have concentrations between 0.6% and 3.0% agarose in buffer.

Agarose gels are prepared by dissolving powdered agarose in a certain volume of electrophoresis buffer. The agarose-buffer mixture has to be boiled for the agarose to go into solution. Powdered agarose may be purchased from a chemical supply house. The buffer may be prepared in the lab or purchased premade, usually as a concentrated stock solution (see Figure 4.17).

The concentration of agarose used depends on the type of molecules to be analyzed. The longer the molecules in a sample, the less concentrated the gel should be. Too high a concentration may impede the movement of molecules through a gel. The lowest practical working concentration of an agarose gel is about 0.6%, or 0.6 g, of agarose dissolved in 100 mL of buffer. This is used when a sample is composed mostly of long DNA fragments.

As the concentration of agarose in a gel increases, the agarose threads are pushed closer together, making it difficult for larger molecules to move through them. A higher concentration gel separates short DNA fragments well. Gels of 0.8% and 1% are typical for plasmid analysis. Gels of higher concentration, up to about 3%, may be used with smaller DNA pieces. A lower concentration gel resolves long DNA fragments, such as genomic DNA, best.

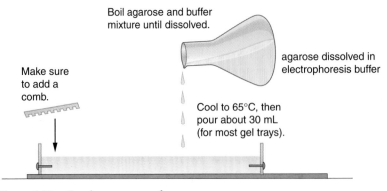

Boil agarose and buffer mixture until dissolved.

agarose dissolved in electrophoresis buffer

Make sure to add a comb.

Cool to 65°C, then pour about 30 mL (for most gel trays).

Figure 4.17.   Pouring agarose gels.

Purpose

To prepare and pour an agarose gel for DNA fragment analysis.

Materials

Environmental Health
and Safety Officer

TAE buffer concentrate, 40X	Lab scoops	Glasses, safety
Beakers, 600 mL	Media bottle, 250 mL	Gel box, horizontal, for
Agarose	Permanent lab marker pens	agarose gels
Balance, tabletop milligram	Microwave oven	Beakers, 50 mL
Weigh boat, 3.5"×3.5"	Hot hands protector	Water bath, 65°C

Procedure

- A 0.8% gel is prepared in the following procedures since that is the appropriate concentration for resolving a variety of DNA fragment lengths.
- Prior to step 1, prepare 500 mL of 1X TAE buffer from the 40X TAE concentrate. This will be used in this and in the following activity.

Use the $C_1 V_1 = C_2 V_2$ equation. Show the calculations and recipe below:

1. Make 100 mL of 0.8% agarose in 1X TAE buffer solution. Determine the recipe for a 0.8% gel, below.

    0.8% of 100 mL = _____ g of agarose in a total volume of 100 mL of 1X TAE

2. Obtain a clean 250-mL media bottle and cap. Label it.
3. Weigh out the required mass of powdered agarose in a weigh boat. Add it to the media bottle.
4. Measure out enough 1X TAE buffer to prepare a total of 100 mL of agarose and buffer mixed together. Add the buffer slowly to the agarose in the media bottle, swirling it to mix.
5. Loosely cap the top of the media bottle. Swirl the flask gently to suspend the agarose in the buffer.
6. To dissolve the agarose in the buffer, microwave the suspension for 4 minutes at 50% power.
7. Wearing bottle holders and safety goggles, lift the beaker toward the light (but away from your face), and very slowly and gently swirl it. **Caution: Do not swirl too fast because it could boil over.** Look to see if all the agarose crystals have dissolved. Agarose crystals that do not dissolve will impede molecular motion through the gel and will affect electrophoresis results. If any agarose crystals are still floating in the buffer, reheat the solution at 50% for 2 minutes more.

Environmental Health
and Safety Officer

65°C

8. Using bottle holders, place the hot dissolved agarose solution on a fireproof lab tabletop.
9. The solution must cool to approximately 65°C before pouring it (see Figure 4.18).
   While waiting for the solution to cool, prepare a gel tray for pouring, following steps 10 through 15.
10. Place about 1 ft of paper towel on the lab tabletop.

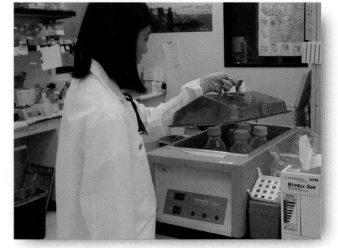

Figure 4.18. If the agarose solution is not to be used immediately, it can be kept hot in a 65°C water bath until it is time to cast the gels.
Photo by author.

11. If the gel tray has gates, secure the gates of the agarose gel tray in the "up" position. Be careful to screw the gates in straight by turning one screw a bit, then the other, and then back to the first screw, etc.

12. Place the tray on the paper towel (if it is a gated gel tray) or into "pouring" position in the gel box if it is a self-sealing gel tray.

13. When the agarose solution is about 65°C (just barely cool enough to hold), pour about 30 mL of it into the gel tray.

14. Quickly place a six-well comb into the notches at the end of the gel tray. Make sure the comb goes into the notches evenly so that all the wells created are of the same size. Check to make sure that no bubbles get trapped on the comb.

15. Leave the gel to cool for 15 minutes.

16. After the gel has solidified, secure the gates into the "down" position for a gated tray. Or, turn the gel into the correct orientation for the self-sealing tray. Be careful that the gel does not slide off the tray.

17. Place the gel (on the gel tray) into the gel box, resting it on the gel tray stand, so that the sample wells created by the comb will be closest to the negative electrode (black) end.

18. Pour 1X TAE buffer into the gel box and over the gel. The gel must be completely submerged and a continuous volume of buffer should cover the gel and the electrodes. This requires about 300 mL of buffer.

19. With the gel covered with buffer, gently pull the comb out of the gel. Pull the comb straight up in one smooth motion.

20. Check to make sure the gel wells are not broken or cracked. The gel can be used immediately, or it can be stored in the gel box overnight at room temperature or in the refrigerator for several days.

Thinking Like a Biotechnician

1. The agarose gel in this lab is prepared with 1X TAE buffer, not water. What is the reason water is not used?

2. A 30-mL gel is recommended for most samples. What are the disadvantages of pouring a gel thicker or thinner than 30 mL?

3. E-gels are commercially prepared agarose gels that will run tiny volumes of samples (see Figure 4.19). They require a special e-gel box setup. Go online and find companies that sell e-gels. What concentrations are available, and how many sample wells do the gels have? How much sample will the wells hold?

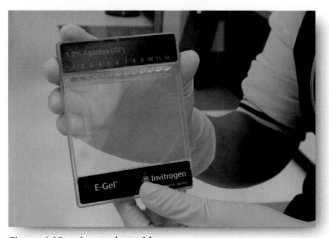

Figure 4.19.   An e-gel cartridge.
Photo by author.

Laboratory 4j   Using Gel Electrophoresis to Study DNA Molecules

Background

Gel electrophoresis is one of several ways that molecules are studied in labs. The technique uses a gel and an electric field to separate molecules based on size, shape, and/or charge. Most frequently, samples of nucleic acids (DNA and RNA) and proteins are analyzed using gel electrophoresis.

DNA molecules in solution have a net negative charge due to their phosphate groups. Because of the negative charge, DNA molecules are attracted to the positive end of a "running" gel box. The agarose gel material acts as a molecular sieve separating longer DNA strands from shorter ones, thus separating the molecules based on their size.

Pieces of DNA of known lengths, called standards, can be run on a gel. Their size determines how far they travel. By running unknown samples and comparing them to the known standards, technicians can deduce the sizes of the unknown pieces.

In this activity, you will load the following types of DNA onto a gel: salmon sperm (animal), *E. coli* (bacterial chromosomal), yeast, plasmid (bacterial extrachromosomal), and lambda (viral). The purpose of running these samples is to try to gain more information on the sizes of the DNA molecules from these organisms and how these types of samples appear on a gel.

Purpose

What is the appearance of different DNA samples on an agarose gel?

Materials

Environmental Health and Safety Officer

Gel box, horizontal, for agarose gels
Prepared agarose gel (from Lab 4h)
TAE buffer concentrate, 40X
Tube rack for 1.7 mL tubes
Reaction tubes, 1.7 mL
Permanent lab marker pens
DNA samples (from previous labs)
Yeast DNA, 50 µg/µL + loading dye

pBR322, 50 µg/µL + loading dye
Lambda DNA, 50µg/µL + loading dye
Other DNA samples + loading dye
Gel loading dye, 10X
Micropipet, P-10
Micropipet, P-100
Micropipet tips for P-10
Micropipet tips for P-100
Microcentrifuge

Lambda/*Hin*dIII, 50 µg/µL + dye
Power supply
Ethidium bromide, 0.5 µg/mL
Gel photo imaging system
Paper, thermal
Printer, thermal
Gloves, large
Glasses, safety, plastic
Weigh boat, 5.5"×5.5"

Procedure

Part I: Preparing the Gel and Gel Box for Loading

1. If using a gated gel tray, carefully secure the gates of the gel tray, containing a 0.8% agarose gel, in the "down" position. Place the gel tray in the gel box in the correct orientation. Be careful to not let the agarose gel slide off the gel tray.
2. Add 300 mL of 1X TAE buffer to the gel box. Gently remove the comb (under buffer) from the gel.

Part II: Preparing the Samples

3. Obtain two 1.7-mL tubes. Label one "SS" for salmon sperm DNA and one "Ec" for *E. coli* DNA.
4. Add 20 µL of the salmon sperm DNA to the SS tube and 20 µL of *E. coli* DNA to the Ec tube. Add 2 µL of DNA loading dye to each (see Figure 4.20). Spin the samples for 2 seconds in a microcentrifuge to pool them on the bottom.

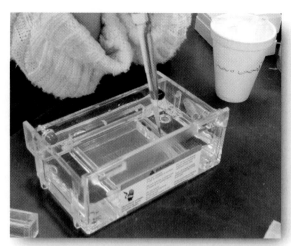

Figure 4.21. **Load above the well, not allowing the tip to enter and possibly puncture the well.**
Photo by author.

Figure 4.20. **Each DNA sample has to have enough loading dye in it so that it will sink into the well. A ratio of about 10:1 DNA to loading dye usually works well.**
Photo by author.

Part III: Loading the Samples

- Position the gel box where it will be "run." Decide which samples should be loaded into which wells, or follow the suggestions in steps 6 through 11.
- Everyone may not be running exactly the same samples in their gels, depending on the available samples. In your notebook, draw a diagram of the gel to show the samples and volumes loaded into each well.

5. Practice loading 15 μL of loading dye into Lanes 1 and 6 (see Figure 4.21).
6. Load all 22 μL of the SS DNA sample into Lane 2 of the gel.
7. Load all 22 μL of the Ec DNA sample into Lane 3 of the gel.
8. Obtain the sample of plasmid DNA sample or uncut Lambda sample (they already have loading dye in them). Load 22 μL of the DNA sample into Lane 4.
9. Obtain the sample of yeast DNA or plant DNA sample (they already have loading dye in them). Load 22 μL of the DNA sample into Lane 5.
10. Obtain the lambda DNA + *Hin*dIII sizing standards (it already has loading dye in it). Load 10 μL of these sizing standards into Lane 6.
11. Obtain the negative control sample (water and loading dye) or the positive control. Load 22 μL of the control sample into Lane 1.

Part IV: Running the Samples

Environmental Health and Safety Officer

12. Connect the electrodes to the power supply (red to red, black to black) and run the gel at 110 V for 45 to 60 minutes, until the front loading dye is halfway down the gel. Make sure the gel box is conducting electricity. There should be a minimum of 25 to 30 mAmp of current, and it should be bubbling at the electrodes. Observe safety precautions for using the gel box and power supply; be sure to turn the power supply off when connecting and disconnecting the electrodes.
13. When the gel has run long enough that the loading dye bands are in the middle of the gel, turn off the power supply and move the gel into a staining tray. The instructor will cover the gel with just enough EtBr to submerge the gel. Stain the gel for 20 minutes. The instructor will pour off the EtBr. Cover the gel with deionized water and swirl for 20 seconds to destain.

Environmental Health and Safety Officer

- Use gloves and goggles when using EtBr.
- The instructor should do EtBr staining.

Part V: Analysis of DNA Fragments

14. Observe the gel on a UV light box (see Figure 4.22). Photograph the gel for analysis. Glue the photo in the middle of a blank notebook page.

15. Label the photograph of the gel data. Label the contents of each well, the size of the standards, and the name and estimated sizes of the bands of unknowns seen in the gel. All bands observed (known and unknown) must be identified. The size of the lambda standard fragments (Lane 6), in base pairs, follows. Estimations of the unknown fragments can be made by comparing their location on the gel to the location of the known lambda DNA fragments.

23130	9416	6557	4361	2322
2027	564	125		

Note: The 125-bp band is difficult to see.

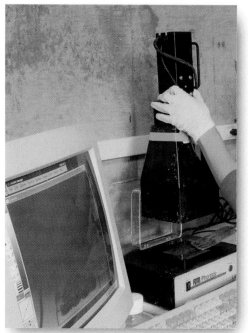

Figure 4.22.   Visualizing of EtBr stained gels is done on a UV light box. Use a camera with a UV filter to photograph the gel.
Photo by author.

Data Analysis/Conclusion

Look for distinct bands and smears of DNA in each lane. Estimate the sizes of the molecules in the bands in each lane by comparing each band to a band of known size in the lambda + *Hin*dIII lane. Do these sizes make sense for what you know about each sample? Explain. Look at other students' gels and data. Are your replications of the extractions and gel running producing results similar to theirs? Why or why not? Of what value is running a sample like this on agarose gels?

Thinking Like a Biotechnician

1. Give plausible reasons for the following results on your gel.
   a. When stained and visualized on the UV light box, other gels have many bands and smears of DNA. Your gel has no bands, smears, or anything on it. What may have caused these results?
   b. A sample that is supposed to give a straight, single band has a big smear of DNA down most of the lane. What may have caused this smearing?
   c. All the bands and smears of samples are located right next to the wells and have not moved very far. What may have caused this?

2. On semi-log graph paper, plot the distance the DNA standard fragments traveled from the wells (in mm) on the horizontal axis versus their size (in base pairs) on the vertical axis. Draw a "best-fit" straight line that represents how DNA fragments of different lengths move through the gel. Use this graph to estimate the sizes of the plasmid bands.

Chapter 5

Protein Isolation and Analysis

A research associate in the Applications Department at Genencor International, Inc tests the activity of a protein, cellulase, on denim material. When a product is manufactured for one use, a company tries to find additional applications and, thus, a larger market.
Photo by author.

The importance of proteins in the biotechnology industry is reflected in the expression, "DNA is the show, but proteins are the dough." For the majority of biotechnology companies, proteins are the product they develop, manufacture, and market. These protein products include pharmaceuticals, industrial enzymes, and proteins that are used in research and diagnostic tools.

Even if a biotech company is not in the protein-making business, it is almost certainly using or modifying proteins as part of the research and development of biotechnology instruments or other agricultural, environmental, or industrial products.

Protein studies are essential. In particular, researchers and scientists work on determining the presence, structure, and activity of a protein or group of proteins for application to protein manufacturing.

In the following activities you will learn some of the basic techniques used to study protein structure and function. Specifically, you will learn the following:

- how to test for an antibody-antigen reaction
- how to test for an enzyme's activity
- how to use indicators to test for the presence and estimate the concentration of proteins in a solution
- how to prepare samples for and conduct a vertical polyacrylamide gel electrophoresis (PAGE) for the purpose of determining protein size
- how to extract proteins from animal cells and analyze them using a PAGE

The laboratory methods practiced in this chapter will be applied in later chapters to the manufacture of a protein product and the use of proteins in diagnostics.

Laboratory 5a   The Specificity of Antibodies: A Simulation

Inspired by a lab developed by Fred Sculco, Noble and Greenough School, Dedham, MA.

Background

Antibodies recognize foreign molecules, called antigens. They tag and aggregate them for removal from the body (see Figure 5.1). All antibody molecules have a specific three-dimensional structure critical to their function of recognizing and clumping antigens. Each type of antibody has a unique variable region that matches only certain antigens.

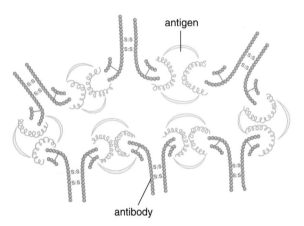

Figure 5.1. **Agglutination.** Antibodies recognize and clump antigens (agglutination), making it easier for white blood cells (WBCs) to remove the invading particles from the body.

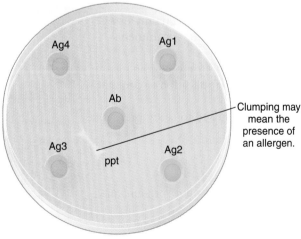

Well punches in the agar are filled with antibody solution (Ab) or a suspected antigen (Ag).

As they diffuse out and meet, if the antibody and antigen match, they bond and clump, forming a white precipitate (ppt).

Figure 5.2. **Ouchterlony Test.** During an Ouchterlony test, a patient's serum (with his or her naturally occurring antibodies) is placed in the center well. Solutions with known antigens are placed in the outer wells. All molecules diffuse. If an antibody molecule finds an antigen, it will clump mand fall out of solution (precipitate).

Antigens may be either free-floating proteins or carbohydrate molecules, such as those that cause allergic reactions. More often, antigens are molecules on the surface of cells or viruses that invade the body. Either way, specific antibodies bind with specific antigens and induce an increase in the number of those specific antibodies in the host organism.

Allergens are antigens that specifically induce the formation of immunoglobulin E (IgE) antibodies. An allergic reaction occurs when an excess of IgE molecules stimulate inflammatory response symptoms, such as swelling, redness, and itchiness. You are allergic to the specific antigens that cause this IgE inflammatory response in your body.

When an antigen binds to an antibody molecule, the complex is too small to be seen. However, when hundreds of antibodies bind to hundreds of allergens, they create a network of many millions of molecules (see Figure 5.1). Researchers have used this knowledge to produce tests to identify when a specific antigen is present in a solution.

One method researchers use to test for antigen-antibody binding is called the Ouchterlony test, or Ouchterlony method (see Figure 5.2). To do an Ouchterlony test, an agar matrix is poured into a Petri plate. A hole (well) is punched in the center of the agar, and an antibody-containing solution is added. Suspected antigens are placed in wells evenly spaced between the center and the edge of the plate. The solutions are allowed to diffuse outward from the center of the well.

When antibodies diffuse into antigens, they bind to them and to each other, causing an agglutination (clumping) reaction. The aggregated antibody-antigen precipitates out of solution and may be visible as a white or colored band at the interface of each diffusion front.

The Ouchterlony method is used in several applications, including allergy testing, to identify a suspected allergen. This test can be used to screen blood serum for the presence of antibodies and, thereby, learn of prior exposure to an antigen. This is what is done, for example, in human immunodeficiency virus (HIV) screening. Ouchterlony testing is also used to identify an antigen in a solution, when assaying for a protein in a mixture. In addition, the test may be used to determine whether an antibody will bind to a particular antigen. This technique would be useful if one were looking for an antibody to use for affinity chromatography, a method of protein purification.

Purpose

Rocky is scratching his skin raw because he has a rash. To which allergens does Rocky's blood serum have antibodies?

Photo by author.

Materials

Environmental Health and Safety Officer

LB agar Petri plates, sterile
Permanent lab marker pens
Transfer pipets, 3 mL
Prepared antigen solutions
Rocky's blood serum antibody solution
Pipets, 1 mL
Pipet pump, blue
Caution: Wear goggles and gloves when using chemicals.

Procedure

1. Obtain three Petri plates containing agar. Label them each with your initials and Trials 1, 2, and 3, respectively.
2. Use a transfer pipet to poke through the agar to plate No. 1 (the bottom plate). Apply a slight suction by compressing it with your fingers (see Figure 5.3). Bore four holes around the edge of the Petri plate (see Figure 5.2). Bore one hole in the middle.
3. Repeat Step 2 with the other Petri plates.
4. Obtain the antibody and antigen solutions, one with Rocky's blood serum (containing antibodies) and four with extracts of suspected puppy allergens (such as flea saliva, Itchless flea powder, Puppystew dog food, Cleantooth dog biscuits, or Fluffy dog shampoo).
5. Using a different sterile, 1-mL pipet for each dispensing, fill the four outer wells with the suspected puppy allergen extracts. Fill the central well with Rocky's blood serum.
   Note: Try to use the same volume of antigen and antibody in each well. However, do not overfill the wells since this will cause the samples to mix on top of the agar. Record which allergen is placed in which well.
6. Leave the plates, undisturbed, overnight. After 24 hours, a precipitin line will appear between one or more of the puppy allergens and Rocky's serum.
7. Record the results of the Ouchterlony test in the form of scale drawings of the Petri plates and a numerical value (5 = strong precipitation; 0 = no precipitation). Calculate average results.
8. Determine which allergens, if any, appear to give a reaction that could cause Rocky's rash.

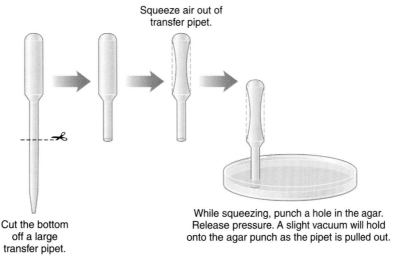

Squeeze air out of transfer pipet.

Cut the bottom off a large transfer pipet.

While squeezing, punch a hole in the agar. Release pressure. A slight vacuum will hold onto the agar punch as the pipet is pulled out.

Figure 5.3. Punching Wells for Ouchterlony Test.

Data Analysis/Conclusion

Based on the results of the Ouchterlony test, what recommendations would be made to Rocky's owner? Give evidence for these recommendations. Identify some of the errors in the experimental procedure that could lead to fallacious data. What can be done to decrease the likelihood of these errors occurring? Discuss how antibody-antigen recognition and binding may be used in other applications besides allergy testing.

Thinking Like a Biotechnician

1. How likely is it that one Ouchterlony test will give results that lead to the understanding of an organism's allergic response? Explain.
2. Why is the speed of agglutination or precipitation not a valuable piece of data in this experiment?
3. Setting up an Ouchterlony test may be time consuming. Why not just mix two solutions together to see if they clump? Suggest an advantage to having the molecules diffuse through and precipitate in the agar.

Laboratory 5b   The Action of Different Enzymes on Apple Juice Production

Inspired by labs by Louann Carlomagno, formerly of Genencor International, Inc.

Background

Many industries use enzymes to create better products (see Table 5.1). As you know, the dairy industry uses enzymes to speed the curdling of milk in cheese production. Both naturally occurring enzymes, such as rennin from calf stomachs, and genetically engineered enzymes (eg, chymosin) are used now. These enzymes create desirable products, which are sometimes cheaper, faster, and of higher quality than uncatalyzed products. Speeding up the changes that occur during the curdling process increases cheese production. Of course, this means increased sales for the cheese company, and greater profits for the owners and shareholders.

As in all industries, apple juice producers want a cheaper, higher-quality product. One goal of juicers is to extract as much juice as possible from every apple. In the 1980s, scientists at the biotechnology company, Genencor International, Inc, found two enzymes that they believed might possibly increase the amount of juice released from apple cells. The enzymes, called pectinase and cellulase, were created in nature by two different fungi. However, neither fungus grew well in the lab. The scientists decided to genetically engineer some fungi, which do grow

Table 5.1.   **Examples of Marketed Biotechnology Enzymes**

amylase	breaks down starch to sugar; used by fabric and beverage industries
pectinase	degrades the cement between plant cells and softens plant fibers; used in making juice
cellulase	decomposes cellulose in plant fiber and breaks down cells; used in the paper industry
subtilisin	protein-digesting enzyme; used in detergents to remove protein stains
Purafect® Prime L protease (Genencor International, Inc)	protein-digesting enzyme
rennin	protein-digesting enzyme; curdles milk for making cheese

Figure 5.4.   Clarified Apple Juice.
Photo by author.

well in the lab, to produce these enzymes on a large scale. The recombinant enzymes had to be tested to determine their effect on juice yield. If results were favorable, Genencor International, Inc could scale up production of the recombinant enzymes, harvest the enzymes, and sell them to juice makers to produce a clear, high-quality product (see Figure 5.4).

The first step in making juice and testing juice enzymes is to mash the apples. Some juice will be released in the mashing process. The mashed apples (chunky applesauce) may then be treated with enzymes to test the effect of each enzyme on the amount of juice that can be extracted.

Purpose

What are the effects of different enzymes on increasing apple juice yield?

Materials

Graduated cylinder, 25 mL
Plastic funnels, short-stemmed
Filter paper, 12.5 cm
Applesauce
Beakers, 50 mL
Lab scoops
Micropipet, P-1000
Micropipet tips for P-1000
Glass rods
Pipets and pipet pumps

For some groups (proteins at 1 mg/mL):
Protease, 1 mg/mL
Cellulase, 1 mg/mL
Rennin, bovine, 1 mg/mL
Pectinase, 1 mg/mL

Procedure

- Each lab group will conduct multiple replications of **one** variation of the experiment. All groups' results will be shared.
- Each group will test three replications of their portion of the experiment.
- To be tested is the amount of each enzyme added to a given amount of applesauce.

1. For each trial set up a juice-o-meter, a funnel resting atop a graduated, 25-mL cylinder (see Figure 5.5).
2. Line each funnel with a filter paper funnel.
3. Mix the stock applesauce well. Then measure 20 mL of applesauce into a beaker.
4. Using a P-1000, add to the applesauce the appropriate volume of the assigned enzyme and water, as shown in the reaction matrix (see Table 5.2). Mix for 10 seconds using a glass rod.
5. Let each mixture sit (incubate) at room temperature for 5 minutes.
6. Pour the mixture of applesauce and enzyme into the filter paper funnel.
7. Allow the mixture to filter for 30 minutes.

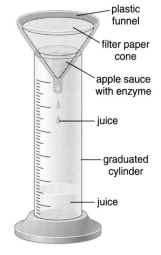

Figure 5.5.   **Juice-o-meter.**

- plastic funnel
- filter paper cone
- apple sauce with enzyme
- juice
- graduated cylinder
- juice

Table 5.2.   Juicing Enzyme Reaction Matrix

Group No.	Enzyme Treatment	Volume of Enzyme Used (μL)	Volume of Distilled Water Added (μL)
1	distilled water	0	800
2	cellulose	200	600
3	cellulose	400	400
4	cellulose	800	0
5	pectinase	200	600
6	pectinase	400	400
7	pectinase	800	0
8	protease	200	600
9	protease	400	400
10	protease	800	0
11	rennin	200	600
12	rennin	400	400
13	rennin	800	0

8. Using a 10-mL pipet (or a smaller one if necessary), determine the volume of juice that has filtered into the graduated cylinder.
9. Repeat Steps 2 through 8 two more times.

Data Analysis

Record the data from **your single experiment** in a data table that you construct, using Microsoft® Excel®. Include each replication that you did and the average volume of juice for your variation. Share your group's data in a class data table, showing the average volume of juice extracted for each treatment. Using Microsoft® Excel®, make a bar graph showing the average amount of juice produced from each treatment.

Conclusion

Assume you have completed this experiment for a company. Write a conclusion statement that describes the results of the experiment, and recommend which enzyme treatment should be used for maximum juice production. Discuss how the type and volume of enzyme affect juice yield. Also, discuss any possible errors that may produce misleading or fallacious data and conclusions. Finally, propose further experimentation to your immediate supervisor as well as applications of this information to industry.

Thinking Like a Biotechnician

1. In any of the trials, did it appear that at some point, adding more of the enzyme did not increase juice yield substantially? Why might that be true?
2. Sketch what a line graph would look like if the data showed that at some point, adding more of the enzyme did not increase juice yield substantially.
3. Suggest a method to determine the optimum temperature for pectinase activity. Include experimental procedures.

Laboratory 5c Developing an Assay for Protease Activity

Background

Protease is a term that describes many enzymes that hydrolyze or break the peptide bonds of proteins. In the presence of a protease, long peptide chains are broken down to shorter peptide chains; they may even be broken down all the way to individual amino acids.

Proteases are used in research, manufacturing, and industrial applications. Some examples include the protease, papain, found in Adolph's® Meat Tenderizer (by Unilever) and the proteases added to detergents to remove protein stains from clothing (see Figure 5.6).

Like many proteins, proteases are colorless; therefore, assays (tests) must be developed to show that they are present and active at the desired concentration. Proteases are used throughout biotechnology research and development.

Figure 5.6. Many meat tenderizers contain the protease, papain, purified from papayas. When papain is sprinkled on meat, it breaks down the protein in the muscle tissue. This makes the meat less stringy and increases its tenderness.
Photo by author.

Purpose

To design a valid experiment that demonstrates the presence of a protease in a sample.

Procedure

1. In teams of four students (or as directed by your instructor), using your previous lab experiences and reagents, plasticware, and glassware commonly found in the laboratory or a grocery store, design a set of experimental procedures to demonstrate the presence of a protease in known solutions. Remember that you are designing a test for protease activity, not proteins in general.

   Before starting, ask yourself, "If protease breaks down protein, what protein will I use as the substrate in the assay?" Make sure that when the protein substrate breaks down, it will give you something to measure.

2. When designing the experiment, make sure you include the following:

   a. Step-by-step instructions, which are short and easy to follow.
   b. All masses, volumes, concentrations, and recipes for reagents.
   c. All the equipment needed for the experiment.
   d. Trials that include a positive control sample.
   e. Trials that include a negative control sample.
   f. Trials that include each variable sample.
   g. Multiple replications of each sample.
   h. Method for collecting measurable, numerical data.

3. Type your experiment plan on a computer so that the procedures can be easily edited when your group is given feedback. Title each version of the plan using this format: TeamName_Protease_V1.doc (V1 = Version 1). Change the version number with each editing. Keep copies of each version. Include all of the following elements in the experimental plan:

   • lab team members
   • a purpose statement of the experiment
   • list of materials
   • procedures (meeting the criteria above)
   • data table (rough draft) to collect the numerical data produced in the experiment

4. Print a copy of the final version of your experimental plan on a transparency, or overhead-projection sheet. Be prepared to present it to the class.

5. Use the protease-assay design rubric (see Table 5.3) to evaluate your own experimental plan and other experimental plans. Two of the plans will be chosen for testing.

Table 5.3. **Protease-assay Design Rubric**

Element	3 Points	2 Points	I Point	0 Points
purpose (objective)	clear, testable purpose statement that leads to measurable data	Purpose statement shows some connection to measurable data.	unclear, untestable purpose statement	No purpose is stated.
materials	list of all ingredients in the experiment	list of most of the ingredients in the experiment	very incomplete or unclear list of ingredients	no list of the ingredients in the experiment
procedures	short, easy-to-follow procedural steps	Some procedural steps are unclear or too long.	Most procedural steps are unclear or too long.	All procedural steps are unclear or too long.
	All volumes, masses, and concentrations of reagents are given.	Some volumes, masses, and concentrations are given.	Most volumes, masses, and concentrations are not given.	No volumes, masses, or concentrations of reagents are given.
	It is clear that everything in each trial is identical, except the variable to be tested.	It is not clear that everything in each trial is identical, except the variable to be tested.	One or two additional variables make it unclear what causes the results of a trial.	Many additional variables make it unclear what causes the results of a trial.
	Trials with either a positive or negative control are included.	A trial with a negative, but not a positive, control is included.	A trial with a positive, but not a negative, control is included.	No trials of positive or negative controls are included.
	There are sufficient (at least three) multiple replications of each trial for each variable tested. These are presented individually and as averages.	There are insufficient replications for data to be averaged for each variable tested.	There are no multiple replications of each trial for each variable to be tested.	Some variables are tested; some are not.
	It is clear what numerical data are to be measured and how they will be measured.	It is clear which data are to be measured, and how they will be measured, but there are no numerical data.	It is not clear which numerical data are to be measured and how they will be measured.	Data to be measured are not stated.
data table (scratch)	The data table is set up correctly (independent variables in the left column, dependent variables in the right columns).	The data table is set up backwards (dependent variables in left column, independent variables in the right columns).	The dependent and independent variables are not clearly shown on the data table.	The data table does not contain independent or dependent variables.
	The data table has a proper title, including the independent and dependent variables, and the subject.	The title is incomplete (missing either the independent or dependent variables, or the subject).	The title is incomplete (missing more than one of the following: the independent or dependent variables, or the subject).	The data table has no title.
	All units of measure are shown.	Some units of measure are shown.	Some units of measure are shown, but may be incorrect.	No units of measure are given (when they should be).
	The data table has cells for individual, as well as average, data.	The data table has cells for individual data, but not for average data.	The data table has cells for average data, but not for individual data.	The data table has no cells for individual or average data.

Laboratory 5d   Testing for the Presence of Protein in Solution

Background

Most proteins are colorless in solution, and all protein molecules are too small to be seen. Chemical indicators may be used to "indicate" whether there are measurable amounts of protein in solution. Several protein indicators are available commercially. A simple protein indicator, Biuret reagent, can be made in the lab. Biuret reagent is a mixture of 10% NaOH and 5% $CuSO_4$ in a 2:1 ratio. In this activity, Biuret reagent is used to test different concentrations of a protein solution.

Purpose

What is the lowest concentration of protein that can be detected with Biuret reagent?

Materials

Environmental Health and Safety Officer

Tubes, 15 mL capped	Bovine serum albumin (BSA)
Tube racks for 15 mL tubes	Cupric sulfate 5-hydrate
Sodium hydroxide	Tube rack for 1.7 mL tubes
Balance, tabletop milligram	Reaction tubes, 1.7 mL
Weigh boat, 3.5"×3.5"	Micropipet, P-1000
Lab scoops	Micropipet tips for P-1000
Tubes, 50 mL, sterile	UV/Vis spectrophotometer
Tube racks for 50 mL tubes	UV spectrophotometer cuvettes
Sodium phosphate, monohydrate	Pasteur pipets, 9"
pH paper	Pasteur pipet bulbs

Safety Precautions

Environmental Health and Safety Officer

Wear goggles and gloves when using chemicals.

Procedure

1. In a labeled, 15-mL, conical tube, prepare 10 mL of a 10% NaOH solution. In your notebook, show your calculations and diagram the preparation of the solution.
2. Prepare 50 mL of a 50-mM sodium phosphate monobasic buffer solution. When preparing the solution, add water only up to 40 mL so that the acid or base level (pH) can be adjusted. Using a piece of pH 0-14 paper, determine the pH. Slowly, add 10% NaOH, 500 μL at a time. Swirl the solution and check the pH. When the pH is between 6 and 7, stop and add water up to 50 mL. If the pH is not up to pH 6 by 50 mL, stop, regardless of the pH at that volume. Record the pH on the label of the tube. This buffer is to be used in the protein solution preparation in the next step. Show your calculations and diagram the preparation of the solution in your notebook.
3. Prepare 5 mL of a 5-mg/mL albumin protein solution in a 50-mM sodium phosphate monobasic buffer. Show your calculations and diagram the preparation of the solution in your notebook.
4. In a 15-mL tube, prepare 5 mL of a 5% $CuSO_4 \cdot 5H_2O$ solution. Show your calculations and diagram the preparation of the solution in your notebook.
5. Prepare a 1:2 serial dilution of the 5-mg/mL albumin stock solution, using the sodium phosphate buffer as the diluent, as follows:

    a. Label six 1.7-mL tubes.
    b. Add 500 μL of buffer to each tube, **except** Tubes 1 and 6.
    c. Add 1 mL of the stock protein (5 mg/mL) to Tube 1.
    d. Remove 500 μL from Tube 1 and add it to Tube 2. Mix gently on the vortex mixer. What is the concentration of Tube 2?

e. Remove 500 µL from Tube 2 and add it to Tube 3. Mix gently. What is the concentration of Tube 3?

f. Remove 500 µL from Tube 3 and add it to Tube 4. Mix gently. What is the concentration of Tube 4?

g. Remove 500 µL from Tube 4 and add it to Tube 5. Mix gently. What is the concentration of Tube 5?

h. Remove 500 µL from Tube 5 so that all tubes have 500 µL of the sample. Save the excess in case you need it for further dilutions.

i. Draw a diagram to show how this serial dilution was accomplished.

6. Prepare a negative control by adding 500 µL of buffer to an empty, labeled, 1.7-mL tube. Remember that the negative control has no protein in it.

7. Conduct the Biuret test by adding 500 µL of 10% NaOH and 250 µL of 5% $CuSO_4$ to each tube. Mix gently.

8. Record the color of each tube in a data table similar to Table 5.4.

9. Examine the results. Determine the concentration at which there is no difference in color between the samples and the negative control. More dilutions may have to be prepared and tested to actually reach a concentration low enough to show this. The concentration that shows no color difference from the negative control is just below the lowest concentration of protein detectable by the Biuret reagent. Place an asterisk in the data table next to the lowest concentration of albumin detectable by Biuret reagent.

10. Conduct a Biuret test on the two albumin solutions of unknown concentration prepared by the instructor. Estimate the concentrations of the unknowns by comparing their colors to the colors of the known concentrations of proteins.

11. If a UV spectrophotometer with a 50-µL cuvette is available, use it to better estimate the concentration of the unknown samples (see the following steps). If necessary, the instructor will demonstrate the UV spectrophotometer's use.

How to Use the UV Spectrophotometer to Check Biuret Test Samples

a. Turn on the UV spectrophotometer. It will go through a series of checks.

b. Set the wavelength to 590 nm.

c. Add the entire negative control/Biuret sample to the cuvette and use it as a "blank." A blank has everything in the sample except the molecule of interest. Follow the instructions on the UV spec to set the absorbance to zero.

d. Remove the blank sample and read the absorbance of each of the albumin-Biuret mixture samples.

e. Record the absorption data for each of the known concentrations of albumin-Biuret mixture in a data table that you construct in your notebook. Does the absorbance data make sense for the solution concentrations you prepared? Compare your data to those of other technicians in the lab. Are the data values similar? Why or why not?

f. Using Microsoft® Excel®, prepare a line graph comparing the absorption to the concentration of each known sample.

g. Look at the data on the graph. Does it create a straight line (or almost a straight line)? Why is a straight line expected? If most of the data points appear to be in a straight line, but a single data point is not on the line, what can be said about the data or the sample?

h. Draw the best-fit straight line through the points. Determine the point at which the absorption of each unknown intersects the line. This is the approximate concentration of each sample. Record these values in your notebook.

Table 5.4.   **The Color of Biuret Reagent during Protein Testing**

Sample	Concentration (mg/mL)	Color after Testing	Protein Detected (Yes or No)	Comments
I	5.00			
2				
3				
4				
5				
C	0			

Data Analysis/Conclusion

Report the best estimate of the concentrations of the unknown samples. Discuss how accurate you think the concentration estimates are. Identify and describe two factors that could impact the accuracy of the concentration determinations. Discuss the applications of the Biuret reagent test in a research facility that isolates or manufactures proteins for sale.

Thinking Like a Biotechnician

1. Discuss the practicality of using Biuret reagent to identify the concentration of protein solutions. Was it a reliable method? Why? Why not?
2. Does a negative Biuret test mean that there is no protein in a sample? Explain.
3. A serial dilution of greater range may be needed for the Biuret standards. Explain how you would create a 1:10 dilution of the albumin for Biuret testing.

Laboratory 5e   Preparing Proteins for Analysis by Vertical Gel Electrophoresis

Background

Most of the proteins found in organisms are in solution. For example, insulin is found in the cytoplasm of pancreas cells and is excreted into blood plasma. In a similar manner, salivary amylase is secreted into saliva from the cytoplasm of salivary gland cells.

When proteins are purified for study, they are extracted in buffer and then either stored in a buffered liquid, or dried and stored in powdered form. In the next several activities, you will study proteins using polyacrylamide gel electrophoresis (PAGE). In this activity, you will prepare a protein solution of a specified concentration in a PAGE running buffer (Laemmli buffer).

Purpose

To prepare 5 mL of a 10-mg/mL protein solution in Laemmli buffer (PAGE running buffer).

Note: For testing protein solutions using indicators, as in the previous lab exercise, use 50 mM of sodium phosphate buffer instead of Laemmli buffer. The sodium dodecyl sulfate (SDS) in the Laemmli buffer interferes with the indicator reactions.

Materials

Environmental Health
and Safety Officer

Balance, analytical
Balance, tabletop milligram
Weigh paper, 7.6×7.6 cm
Weigh boat, 3.5"×3.5"
Lab scoops
Bottle, 1000 mL
TRIS
Boric acid **Caution: Wear
goggles and gloves when
using chemicals.**
SDS, 10%
Pipets, 10 mL
Pipet pump, green

Permanent lab marker pens
alpha-AMYLASE
Cellulase
Rennin, bovine
Lysozyme
Tubes, 15 mL capped
Tube racks for 15 mL tubes
Glass rods
Syringe filter, 0.2 μm
Syringe, plastic, 10 mL

Procedure

Environmental Health
and Safety Officer

1. Prepare 1 L of Laemmli buffer (PAGE running buffer) according to the following steps: Store the unused portions at room temperature.

   a. Measure out the following:

      10 mL of 10% SDS
      (Caution: Powdered SDS is a hazardous inhalant.)
      11 g of TRIS base
      6 g of boric acid

   b. Get a clean, 1-L bottle and cap. Gently add the dry ingredients to the bottle.
   c. Add 800 mL of dH_2O to the dry ingredients. Mix gently, without foaming, until completely dissolved.
   d. Add the SDS. Mix gently, without foaming.
   e. Fill with dH_2O to a total volume of 1 L.
   f. Label the bottle and store it at room temperature.

2. In the next activity, 5 mL of a 10-mg/mL protein solution in Laemmli buffer is needed for the protein gel electrophoresis. Calculate the amount of protein (in grams) to be measured out for 5 mL of a 10-mg/mL protein solution. Record the calculation and diagram the solution preparation in your notebook.

   _____ mL × _____ mg/mL = _____ mg = _____ g

3. The instructor will assign proteins for study. Measure out the protein to be used (on an analytical balance) and add it to a 15-mL conical tube.
4. Stir in the Laemmli buffer slowly making a paste of the protein. Add enough Laemmli buffer to bring the final total volume to 5 mL.
5. Rotate the tube **very slowly** until the protein has dissolved in the buffer (about 5 minutes).
6. Label the tube with the sample name and concentration, date, and your initials. Store for up to 2 weeks at 4°C. For long-term storage, use a syringe filter to sterilize the protein solution (see Figure 5.7).

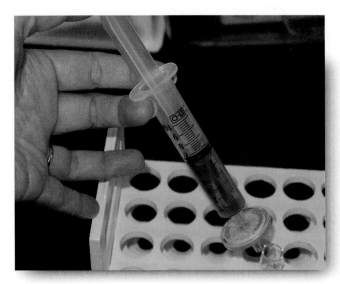

Figure 5.7.   To sterilize small amounts of solution, use a syringe filter. A syringe is filled with the solution to be sterilized. A 0.2-μM filter disc is screwed onto the end of the syringe. A 0.2-μM filter is small enough to separate bacteria and fungi contaminants from the molecules in solution. Gentle pressure pushes the solution though the filter into a sterile tube. If the solution contains proteins, the proteins are small enough to go through the filter, and then the protein solution will be sterile.
Photo by author.

Thinking Like a Biotechnician

1. Laemmli buffer contains TRIS, boric acid, and SDS. What is the function of each ingredient in this buffer?
2. It takes a bit of mixing to get some proteins to go into solution, while other proteins go into solution more easily. Why?
3. If the protein solution needs sterilization for long-term storage, why not autoclave it?

Laboratory 5f   Characterizing Proteins by PAGE

Optimized by Matthew Ho, Rodrick Hilario, Alyssa Lu, and Jonathan Pham, Biotechnology students.

Background

One of the first things to learn about a protein is its size and structure. By running a denaturing sizing gel, one can determine the molecular weight and the number of different polypeptide chains of a protein. Molecular weights are reported in kilodaltons (kD). A dalton (d) is equal to the mass of one hydrogen atom. For example, 1 kD is equivalent to 1000 d. Proteins usually have molecular masses ranging from 10 to 300 kD.

For size determination, a TRIS-glycine (TG) polyacrylamide gel at a given concentration is used. Premade gels can be purchased. The activity below uses gels with a polyacrylamide concentration of anywhere from 4% to 20%. Samples of unknown molecular weight are loaded into wells. Standard proteins of known molecular weight are run in at least one lane.

The gel is run at 35 milliamps (mAmp) for 2 to 3 hours. The SDS in the buffer causes the peptide chains to unravel and linearize. If there is more than one polypeptide in the protein, it separates from the other peptides. Smaller peptides move through the gel faster than larger ones. The peptides "band out" based on size (see Figure 5.8). After staining the peptides, you can size them by comparing the bands of unknown molecular weight to standards of known molecular weight (see Figure 5.9).

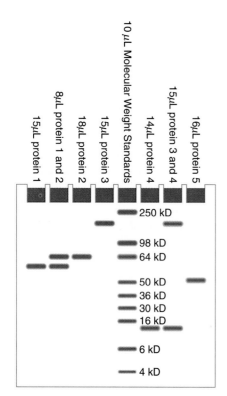

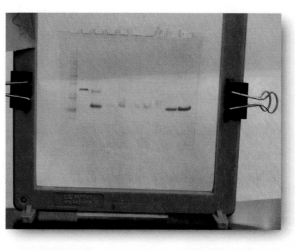

Figure 5.9. Stained PAGE Gel. Coomassie® Blue staining makes peptide bands visible. The standards are in the left lane, and the other nine lanes have one or more peptide bands. A protein composed of more than one polypeptide chain will show a band for each chain. Photo by author.

Figure 5.8. PAGE Gel. Running the gel distributes the samples according to molecular weight. Sizing standards in Lane 5 range from 4 to 250 kD. Through visual inspection, one can estimate the size of unknown bands.

The four proteins studied in this experiment are the enzymes amylase, rennin, cellulase, and lysozyme. Amylase breaks down starch to sugar. Rennin breaks down the milk protein, casein, to produce curds. Cellulase degrades plant cell walls. Lysozyme is found in mucus, saliva, tears, and egg whites. It speeds up the breakdown of bacterial cell walls.

Purpose

What structural characteristics of amylase, pectinase, cellulase, and lysozyme can be determined from running samples on an SDS-PAGE gel? How is the resolution of the polypeptide bands on the gel affected by the concentration of the sample loaded?

Materials

Environmental Health and Safety Officer

Balance, analytical
Balance, tabletop milligram
Weigh paper, 7.6×7.6 cm
Weigh boat, 3.5"×3.5"
Lab scoops
Bottle, 1000 mL
TRIS
Boric acid
SDS, 10%
10 mg/mL protein
   (from Lab 5e)
Permanent lab marker pens
Sucrose
Bromophenol Blue

Bottle, 125 mL
Tube rack for 1.7 mL tubes
Reaction tubes, 1.7 mL
Micropipet, P-100
Micropipet tips for P-100
Micropipet, P-10
Micropipet tips for P-10
Microcentrifuge
Dry block heater/heat block,
   80°C
Gel box, vertical, for PAGE
PAGE gel, 10% TG, 10 well
Transfer pipets, 3 mL
PAGE gel loading tips

Protein sizing markers, 15-
   150 KD
Power supply
Petri dishes, 150×15mm
Ethanol, 95%
Acetic acid, glacial
Coomassie® Blue R-250
Lab rotator, 12×12
White light imaging system
Paper, thermal
Printer, thermal
Gloves, large
Glasses, safety, plastic

Laemmli Buffer (PAGE Running Buffer)

1 L
- 10 mL of 10% SDS
- 11 g of TRIS base
- 6 g of boric acid

Into a 1-L container, gently add 800 mL of dH$_2$O to the dry ingredients. Mix, without foaming, until completely dissolved. Add the SDS and gently stir. Fill with dH$_2$O to a total volume of 1 L. Store at room temperature.

PAGE Sample Prep Buffer (Loading Dye)

50 mL
- 5 g of sucrose
- 0.05 g of bromophenol blue
- 30 mL of Laemmli buffer

Add sugar and bromophenol blue to Laemmli buffer; stir until dissolved. Bring to a final volume of 50 mL. Store tightly covered in a glass or plastic bottle in the refrigerator.

Procedure

Note: Prepare PAGE running buffer and loading dye before beginning.

1. If it has not already been done, prepare 5 mL of a 10-mg/mL protein stock solution using Laemmli buffer as the solvent. Each group is responsible for studying just one type of protein using the stock solution for preparing samples.
2. Dilute the protein stock solution in the following ratios with Laemmli buffer: 1:2, 1:4, and 1:8.

   - Starting with the 10-mg/mL stock, measure out 50 μL and combine it with 50 μL of Laemmli buffer. Mix. This is the 1:2 dilution. It has a concentration of 5 mg/mL. Label this tube "5."
   - Measure out 50 μL of the 5-mg/mL solution and combine with 50 μL of Laemmli buffer. Mix. This is a 1:4 dilution of the original sample. It has a concentration of 2.5 mg/mL. Label this tube "2.5."
   - Measure out 50 uL of the 2.5-mg/mL solution and combine with 50 μL of Laemmli buffer. Mix. This is a 1:8 dilution of the original sample. It has a concentration of 1.25 mg/mL. Label this tube "1.25."
   - Measure out 100 μL of stock solution. It has a concentration of 10 mg/mL. Label this tube "10."
3. For *your* protein, make up four sample tubes for loading. Select **four new** 1.7-mL tubes and label them No. 1, 2, 3, and 4. Add a letter before the number to identify the protein. Place 20 μL of each concentration into the appropriate 1.7-mL tube (see Table 5.5).

Table 5.5. **Sample Preparation Matrix**

Concentration (mg/mL)	Tube No. for Amylase	Tube No. for Rennin	Tube No. for Cellulase	Tube No. for Lysozyme
10	A1	R1	C1	L1
5	A2	R2	C2	L2
2.5	A3	R3	C3	L3
1.25	A4	R4	C4	L4

80°C

4. Add 5 μL of loading dye (sample prep buffer) to each sample. Give each tube a 2-second spin in a microcentrifuge to pool ingredients. Store at 4°C until ready to use.
5. Immediately before loading the samples onto a gel, denature the proteins in the samples by placing the tubes in an 80°C heat block or water bath for 5 minutes. Seal the tubes **tightly**. This step might have to wait if the gel is not ready to be loaded.
6. Set up a vertical electrophoresis gel box as directed in the following steps. Use a TRIS-glycine gel. In your notebook, record the % gel, the lot number, and the expiration date. **Caution: Wear goggles and gloves.**

Vertical Gel Preparation

a. Cut open/drain the preservative from the cassette.
b. Rinse the outside of the cassette 5 times with dH$_2$O.
c. Rinse the edges of the cassette 5 times.
d. Dry front of gel.
e. Label gel. Place a number or dot in the center and a line on the bottom of each well. This makes it easier to see the well boundaries during loading.
f. Pull off the tape at the bottom of the gel cassette.
g. Study the gel box to understand how it is put together and which side is the front (see Figure 5.10). Put the gel(s) in the box with the high side facing out, so that the labeled side faces the front of the gel box.
h. Fill the box with running buffer to the height necessary to cover the wells completely.
i. Gently, remove the comb (that formed the wells).
j. Gently, rinse the wells with at least 3 times their volume of buffer.

Figure 5.10. Two sets of clamps allow two gels to be run at the same time.
Photo by author.

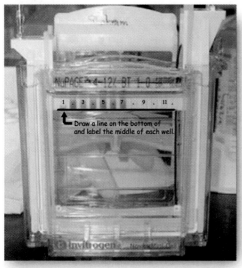

Figure 5.12. Use a permanent marker to number the middle of each well and underline the bottom of the wells. This makes it much easier to see where you are loading a sample.
Photo by author.

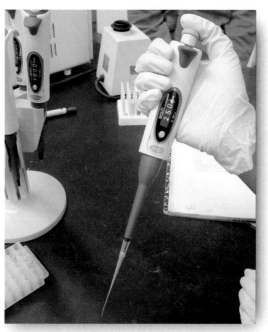

Figure 5.11. Vertical gel loading tips are long and end in a very narrow tip. These long, thin tips fit into the 1-mm gel spacing between the front and back plastic or glass plates that hold the gel.
Photo by author.

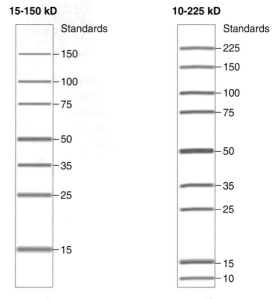

Figure 5.13. **Sizing Standards.** Prestained sizing standards are available from several suppliers. The one shown on the left contains seven polypeptide bands of known size, measured in kilodaltons.

7. Hook up the power supply, and run the empty gel for 10 minutes at 35 mAmp to warm it.

8. Practice loading with sample prep buffer before actually loading samples. Load the gel wells with 25 μL of sample using special, long-tipped PAGE gel loading tips (see Figure 5.11). Be careful to load all of the sample without overflowing into the adjoining wells (see Figure 5.12).

9. Load 5 μL of molecular weight standards to one of the lanes. Researchers commonly use 15-150 kD molecular weight standards if several unknown proteins are being studied (see Figure 5.13).

Environmental Health
and Safety Officer

10. As soon as all samples are loaded, run the gel at 35 mAmp for 1 to 2 hours, until the loading dye reaches the bottom of the gel. Sample preparation buffer/loading dye serves as tracking dye (see Figure 5.14).

11. Remove the gel from gel box. Using a knife, gently separate the two gel plates holding the gel in place. Loosen the entire edge of the gel from the plate using a knife or spatula. Gently, trim off the well fingers and fat edges of the gel.

12. Using water in a Petri plate for adhesion, drop the gel onto the water. Gently remove the water from the plate by decanting or using a vacuum pump.

13. Add enough Coomassie® Blue staining solution (see the recipe below) to just cover the gel. Let it stain for a minimum of 3 hours. Rotating the staining gel on an orbital shaker is desirable for even staining (see Figure 5.15).

Note: Prepare stain/destain in chemical fume hood.

Coomassie® Blue Stain

800 mL of ethanol
200 mL of glacial acetic acid
1000 mL of dH₂O
2 g of Coomassie® Blue R-250

Destain

200 mL of ethanol
150 mL of glacial acetic acid
1650 mL of deionized water

14. Funnel off Coomassie® Blue stain into a "used stain" bottle. Cover gel with destaining or dH₂O solution for at least 7 hours. Change destaining solution several times. Rotating the destaining gel on an orbital shaker is desirable. Destaining can be sped up by microwaving the gel in destain solution at 40% power for 20 seconds and then swirling for 1 minute. Repeat the procedures until the background is light enough to easily distinguish polypeptide bands. The destain may have to be changed periodically (every fifth time).

15. Examine the banding pattern on gel over a white-light box. Use a photo-imaging system to take a photograph of the gel. Make copies for each lab partner. If no photo-imaging system is available, place an acetate sheet over the gel and draw a copy of the gel. Make photocopies for each lab partner.

16. For long-term storage of a gel, dry on gel-drying rack. Follow the directions on the gel-drying kit.

Figure 5.14. Set and maintain the current at 35 mAmp and check for bubbling. If the current goes down, make sure there is enough buffer covering the wells in the back reservoir.
Photo by author.

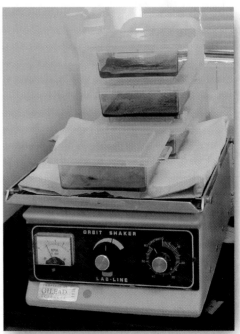

Figure 5.15. Cover the gel with just enough stain for the gel to float and swirl on the orbital shaker.
Photo by author.

17. Glue the gel image into the center of a notebook page. Label the contents of each lane as diagrammed in the background section. Each well, each standard, and each of the sample bands should be labeled with sizes.

Data Analysis/Conclusion

For each protein studied, identify the number of polypeptide chains present, the molecular weight of each polypeptide chain, and the total molecular weight of the protein. Determine the optimum concentration for visualizing the characteristics of each protein studied. Discuss the sources of error in technique that could lead to fallacious data. Describe several ways in which the PAGE technique can be used in industry.

Thinking Like a Biotechnician

1. A technician sets up and starts a PAGE. Current is flowing, and bubbling is visible at the electrodes. After 30 minutes, none of the samples have moved out of the wells. List three things the technician should check.
2. If a gel has a band significantly darker and fatter than all the other bands on the gel, suggest a few reasons for that result.
3. Every amino acid has a different molecular weight because of different R-groups. Using amino-acid data from ProtScale at: http://au.expasy.org/tools/pscale/Molecularweight.html, one can determine that the average molecular weight of an amino acid is about 137 d. Use the average molecular weight of an amino acid and the estimated molecular weight of the polypeptide chains in the protein you studied to determine the number of amino acids in each protein.

Laboratory 5g Separating and Identifying Proteins via SDS-PAGE

Background

The function of a cell, tissue, or organ depends on the proteins and other molecules that make up its structure. So, if scientists are trying to understand the function or behavior of a sample, they need to understand the protein composition. Likewise, if scientists were looking for similarities or differences in tissues, they would compare protein content.

In this activity, you will study tissues from a variety of animal muscle samples to identify similarities and differences in protein content. Since a muscle's function is to contract and relax, certain muscle proteins would be expected in all muscle samples. Since different muscle samples are used in different ways, some protein content differences would also be expected.

Mashing and diluting the animal tissue with sample preparation buffer accomplishes the extraction of protein from cells. Samples are loaded onto vertical polyacrylamide gels containing SDS and are electrophoresed. Proteins are denatured with SDS so they will electrophorese in the gel at a rate proportional to their molecular weight. After the gel is stained, the protein-banding pattern for each sample can be compared to determine how many protein polypeptide chains are present and whether there are differences in the peptides. The molecular weight of the unknown protein bands is determined by comparison with protein standards.

Purpose

What variety of proteins is found in the muscle tissue of some animals?

Hypothesis

Using Internet resources, determine some of the proteins known to exist in muscle cells. Try to find their molecular weights and the number of protein chains for the muscle proteins, so you can predict what to expect on the gel. Record these predictions in your notebook.

Materials

Environmental Health and Safety Officer

Balance, analytical
Balance, tabletop milligram
Weigh paper, 7.6×7.6 cm
Weigh boat, 3.5"×3.5"
Lab scoops
Bottle, 1000 mL
TRIS
Boric acid
SDS, 10%
Permanent lab marker pens
Sucrose
Bromophenol Blue
Bottle, 125 mL
Mortar and pestle
Pipets, 2 mL
Pipet pump, blue

Tubes, 15 mL capped
Tube racks for 15 mL tubes
Permanent lab marker pens
Pipets, 5 mL
Centrifuge, 15 mL tubes
Tube rack for 1.7 mL tubes
Reaction tubes, 1.7 mL
Pipets, 1 mL
Micropipet, P-100
Micropipet tips for P-100
Microcentrifuge
Dry block heater/heat block, 80°C
Gel box, vertical, for PAGE
PAGE gel, 10% TG, 10 well
Transfer pipets, 3 mL

PAGE gel loading tips
Protein sizing markers, 15-150 kD
Power supply
Petri dishes, 150×15 mm
Ethanol, 95%
Acetic acid, glacial
Coomassie® Blue R-250
Lab rotator, 12×12
White light imaging system
Paper, thermal
Printer, thermal
Gloves, large
Glasses, safety, plastic

Procedure

1. Prepare a PAGE running buffer and loading dye before beginning.
2. Use a mortar and pestle (or a test tube with a glass rod) to grind 1 g of animal tissue with 2 mL of cold, deionized water for 1 minute.
3. Add 3 mL of 1X sample preparation buffer/loading dye and mix for 30 seconds.
4. Transfer the mixture to a 15-mL centrifuge tube. The total volume in the centrifuge tube should be 7 mL. Add 1X sample preparation buffer, as needed, to adjust the volume.
5. Repeat Steps 1 and 2 for each animal tissue sample to be studied.
6. Spin the samples for 5 minutes at medium speed in a lab tabletop centrifuge.
7. Transfer 0.5 mL of the supernatant to a 1.7-mL microtube. Prepare three 1:4 dilutions (serial dilution) of the stock sample using the sample prep buffer as the diluent. The diluted samples should each have a final volume of 48 µL per tube. The stock and each diluted sample will be loaded on the PAGE gels. In your notebook, diagram how you will make the dilutions.
8. Store the samples in the refrigerator for up to 5 days.
9. Set up a TRIS-glycine gel (any concentration from 4% to 12%) in a gel box with Laemmli buffer. (see the recipe in the previous lab exercise.)

80°C

10. Denature the proteins in the samples by placing the tubes in an 80°C water bath or heat block for 5 minutes. Seal the tubes **tightly** so they do not open during heating.
11. Load the gel wells. Load 20 µL of the stock (1:4, 1:16, and 1:64 samples) into Lanes 1 through 4, respectively. Add another set of stock and dilutions into Lanes 6 through 9. Use a new tip with each sample.
12. Load 5 µL of protein molecular weight standards into Lanes 5 and 10.
13. Run at 35 mAmp for 1 to 2 hours, until the loading dye reaches just above the bottom vent of the gel cassette. The sample preparation buffer/loading dye serves as tracking dye.

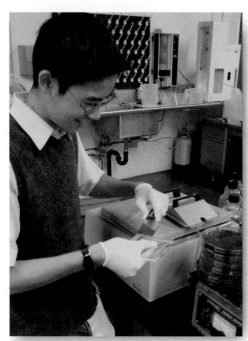

Figure 5.16.   A technician prepares a gel for staining. The two sides of the gel cassette must be gently pried apart without ripping the gel.

Photo by author.

14. Do the following to prepare the gel for staining (see Figure 5.16): Place the larger side of the gel cassette on a tabletop. Use a knife to gently pry the cassette plates apart. The gel will stick to one cassette side or the other. Use distilled water to help detach it from the other plate, if necessary. Gently trim the wells off the gel and loosen the edges of the gel from the plate. Be careful not to rip the gel. Transfer the gel from the cassette into a Petri dish filled with distilled water. Using four gloved fingers, pour off the water while holding the gel in the tray.

15. Cover the gel with Coomassie® Blue staining solution. Stain for a minimum of 3 hours while rotating the gel on an orbital shaker.

16. Remove Coomassie® Blue stain. Cover the gel with destaining solution. Change the destaining solution twice. Leave the destaining solution on the gel for a minimum of 7 hours or use the following accelerated destaining procedure:

   a. Pour off the existing solution.
   b. Add about 50 mL of fresh destain.
   c. Put a paper towel in the microwave.
   d. Put the Petri dish in the microwave.
   e. Microwave for 20 seconds at 40%.
   f. Swirl for 1 minute.
   g. Repeat steps b through f as necessary. Add fresh stain every fifth time.
   h. Pour off the destain and flood with dH_2O.

17. Examine the banding pattern on the gel over a white-light box. Use a photo-imaging system to photograph the gel. Make copies for each lab partner. If a photo-imaging system is not available, place an acetate sheet over the gel and draw a copy of it. Make photocopies for each lab partner.

18. Dry the gels on a gel-drying rack if long-term storage is desired.

19. Glue the gel image into the center of a notebook page. Label the gel. Label the contents of each well. Label the size of each standard. Label the sizes of the bands in each sample.

Data Analysis/Conclusion

For each sample studied, identify the number of polypeptide chains present and their molecular weights. Are any of the bands unique to a sample? Which bands are common to all samples? Are any of the bands expected, based on what is known to be in muscle cells? Give evidence. Are there any bands that are of particular interest? If so, why? Look at other gels. Are all the replications of a sample identical? Discuss possible errors in technique that could lead to fallacious or misleading data. Propose methods of reducing the likelihood of these errors. Describe several extensions and applications of this preliminary experiment. What future experiments would you suggest to your supervisor and why?

Thinking Like a Biotechnician

1. Do you know the concentrations of protein in the muscle extract samples loaded on the gel? How can you find out?

2. Many proteins have bands of the same molecular weight. If you find a protein band that you are fairly confident is a particular protein or polypeptide, how might you confirm that the protein is actually the one you think it is?

3. A lane on a gel has a huge smear in it. What is the most likely cause, and how can the problem be corrected on future gels?

Chapter

6 Assay Development

As cell cultures are grown, they must be assayed, or tested, for the presence, concentration, and activity of protein product.
Photo courtesy of Cell Genesys, Inc.

Most proteins are colorless and all are submicroscopic. How can researchers or production scientists know that the protein they want to produce is present and active? How can the concentration or effectiveness of a protein product be monitored?

Once a protein is selected as a potential product, researchers must develop methods of identifying and quantifying it during production. These tests are called assays. Assay development and the use of assays are of critical importance during research and manufacturing. Assays for a product's presence, activity, concentration, and stability are just some of the many tests developed and conducted during protein production. If at any time, a product is not performing adequately or a manufacturing procedure is not sufficient, manufacture of the product could be halted. This could cost a company a substantial amount of time and money.

A large portion of a company's scientific staff works on assay development and assay application. Depending on the size of the company and the product of interest, assays might be developed and used right on a lab bench in research and development. More commonly, assays are developed in one department of a company (such as Process Development) but then used in another department (such as Assay Services or Quality Control). Technicians growing cultures and purifying product would then send their samples to Assay Services or Quality Control for testing.

In the following activities you will learn some methods of assaying for the enzymes, such as amylase, which is produced by several species. Amylase catalyzes the breakdown of starch to sugar. Specifically, you will learn:

- how to test for the presence of amylase's substrate, starch
- how to test for the presence of the product of amylase activity, the sugar, maltose
- how to assess an enzyme's activity by comparing substrate use and product production
- how isolated compounds from plants for use in activity assays
- how to assay for antimicrobial activity in plant extracts

The assays presented in this chapter are examples of how the presence or activity of a protein product might be tested. In the next chapter, you will conduct an assay for protein concentration. In future chapters, you will apply the assays used and developed in this chapter to recombinant protein production.

Laboratory 6a How Do You Know When You Have Some Amylase?

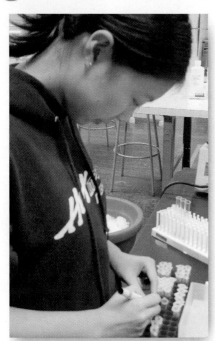

Figure 6.1. Assays take many forms. Here, a technician labels tubes for a colorimetric assay that measures enzymes by the amount of color change in a reaction.

Photo by author.

Background

If Genencor International or another biotechnology company hopes to produce a protein, such as amylase, it must devise a method of identifying amylase in a solution. Scientists must develop tests to show the presence, concentration, and activity of this colorless molecule. The tests are called assays, and assay development is one of the first steps in determining a potential biotechnology product (see Figure 6.1).

Since amylase decomposes starch to sugar molecules, the ability to assay for starch (amylase substrate) or sugar (the result of amylase activity) in a solution is valuable in an amylase production facility.

Purpose

To design an experiment that tests the question: Does a given solution (clear extract) contain the enzyme amylase?

Procedure

1. Spend 10 to 15 minutes with your lab partners discussing how one might test for the presence of amylase. Consider the chemical nature and activity of the enzyme. Review how enzymes have been studied and tested earlier in this course to get some idea of how enzyme-activity experiments are conducted. You may need to go online to find out more about how amylase works, or review information presented in the text, if available. You have all the equipment and supplies in the lab available to you, and most chemicals can be ordered from supply houses if they are not already in stock in the lab.

2. Your group is to produce a laboratory proposal for conducting an experiment that tests the question: Does a given solution (clear extract) contain the enzyme, amylase?

    a. Create a list of procedures that outline in a step-by-step fashion how your experiment will be conducted.
    b. Make sure that the procedures outline the independent variable to be tested. The independent variable is the one factor that will differ from one experimental group to another. For example, in an experiment to measure the effect of nitrogen concentration on grass growth, the independent variable is the amount of nitrogen.
    c. Make sure that the procedures outline the dependent variable and how it will be measured (what equipment and units of measure). The dependent variable(s) is the data collected. In an experiment to measure the effect of nitrogen concentration on grass growth, the length of grass blades in centimeters (cm) might be the dependent variable. The dependent variable changes as a result of the independent variable.
    d. Include a negative control group in your experiment. A negative control group is one that lacks the variable being tested. Often, water or a buffer is used in the negative control group to substitute for a volume of reagent. In an experiment to measure the effect of nitrogen concentration on grass growth, a grass group with no nitrogen, and only water substituting for the nitrogen volume, would be the negative control.
    e. Include a positive control group in your experiment if it is appropriate. In a positive control group, the variable being tested is in a form that will give a positive result. In an experiment to measure the effect of nitrogen concentration on grass growth, a grass group with some "recommended" amount of nitrogen might serve as the positive control.
    f. Design a data table (with a title, labels, and units of measure) into which data from the experiment could be collected.

3. Submit the experiment proposal to your supervisor. If the design is valid and reasonable, it will be approved.

Laboratory 6b   Assaying for Starch and Sugar

Background

An indicator is a chemical that changes color when another chemical is present. Several indicators are used in assays to determine the presence or concentration of a molecule. Some common indicators used in the biotechnology lab include iodine, Benedict's solution, Biuret reagent, phenol red, and Bradford reagent, to name a few.

Iodine (I_3^-) is an indicator of starch molecules (see Figure 6.2). When iodine is caught in long starch molecule coils, it causes a visible color change. Thus, iodine may be used in assays to show the presence of starch in a sample. Iodine can also be used to demonstrate whether starch is being used or removed from the solution.

Benedict's solution is an indicator of some sugars, including glucose and maltose. Benedict's solution contains a copper compound that reacts with the aldehyde group (H-C=O) on open-chain forms of glucose and maltose. These sugars are called aldoses. Depending on the amount of glucose or maltose present, a variety of colors appear during testing.

Since amylase decomposes starch to maltose molecules, the ability to assay for starch and maltose content in a solution is valuable in an amylase production facility.

Figure 6.2. **Starch is the substrate of amylase.** Cornstarch and potato starch are available in grocery stores. For research, soluble starch should be ordered from a chemical supply house, since their product goes into suspension more easily than the other starches.
Photo by author.

Purpose

How does an iodine indicator show the presence of starch?
What happens if you mix iodine with other molecules, such as sugar or protein?
How does Benedict's solution show the presence of sugar?
What happens if you mix Benedict's solution with other molecules, such as starch or protein?

Materials

Environmental Health
and Safety Officer

Balance, tabletop milligram	Maltose	Micropipet, P-1000
Weigh boat, 3.5"×3.5"	Gelatin	Micropipet tips for P-1000
Lab scoops	Tubes, glass, 13×100 mm	Vortex mixer
Starch, soluble	Peg racks for 10-13 mm tubes	Benedict's Solution
Tubes, 15 mL capped	Pipets, 2 mL	Hot plate stirrer, 7"×7"
Tube racks for 15 mL tubes	Pipet pump, blue	Beaker, 250 mL
Glucose (dextrose)	Lugol's Iodine Solution	Test tube holder

Caution: Wear goggles and gloves when using chemicals.

Procedure

1. Prepare 10 mL of 2% starch solution in a 15-mL tube. What amount of each ingredient do you need? In your notebook, show the calculations and a diagram of how to prepare the solution.
2. Prepare 10 mL of 1% glucose solution in a 15-mL tube. What amount of each ingredient do you need? In your notebook, show the calculations and a diagram of how to prepare the solution.
3. Prepare 10 mL of 1% maltose solution in a 15-mL tube. What amount of each ingredient do you need? In your notebook, show the calculations and a diagram of how to prepare the solution.

4. Prepare 10 mL of 2% protein (gelatin) solution in a 15-mL tube. What amount of each ingredient do you need? In your notebook, show the calculations and a diagram of how to prepare the solution.

Starch Assay

a. Place 2 mL of the solution to be tested into a test tube.
b. Add 250 μL of iodine solution to the sample.
c. Mix by vortexing for 1 to 2 seconds.
d. Record color after mixing.

Aldose Assay

a. Place 2 mL of the solution to be tested into a test tube.
b. Add 2 mL of Benedict's solution to the sample.
c. Mix by vortexing for 1 to 2 seconds.
d. Heat in a boiling hot water bath (100 mL of boiling water in a 250-mL beaker) for 2 minutes.
e. Record all the colors that appear while heating in the order they appear.

5. Test the starch solution using the starch and aldose assays.
6. Test the glucose solution using the starch and aldose assays.
7. Test the maltose solution using the starch and aldose assays.
8. Test the protein solution using the starch and aldose assays.
9. Test the water using the starch and aldose assays.
10. In your notebook, create a data table to collect the data from each assay (see Table 6.1). Record the qualitative data in a quantitative (numerical) way. Describe the method used to quantify the data.

Table 6.1. Results of Iodine and Benedict's Test on Sugars, Starch, and Protein Molecules

Molecule Tested	Result(s) of Aldose Assay	Result(s) of Starch Assay	Comments
glucose			
maltose			
starch			
protein			
water (negative control)			

Data Analysis/Conclusion

Discuss how these indicator tests may be used during the production of amylase at a biotech company. Include a discussion of the negative control compared with the test groups. Of what value are these assays? What experimental errors may give misleading results?

Thinking Like a Biotechnician

1. How can you tell if the 2%-starch solution gives the best (most comparable) results for the starch assay?
2. The aldose assay may display up to five color changes in the 2-minute reaction time. Propose an explanation for each of the colors that appear during the assay.
3. Drawing on your experience with sugar testing, is there any other indicator system that could be used to assay for the presence or concentration of sugar in this experiment?

Laboratory 6c   Assaying for Amylase Activity

Background

Amylase is an enzyme that catalyzes starch digestion (see Figure 6.3). It is used commercially in two ways: 1) to eliminate starch in products; 2) to produce sugar from starch. Using amylase to remove starch is a cheap and effective method, but substantial quantities of amylase must be produced if it is to be used commercially. Similarly, amylase is an economical way to obtain sugar for use in beverages and baked goods since sources of starch, for example, cornstarch, are more readily available than sources of sugar (sugar cane).

Some bacteria and fungi cells in nature make amylase. Several herbivorous mammals synthesize amylase as well. In humans, amylase is made in two organs involved in food breakdown. In the mouth, salivary glands produce and excrete amylase (salivary amylase) to break down the starch in food into smaller units (maltose). The pancreas is another organ that makes amylase. Amylase is produced in the pancreas (pancreatic amylase) and excreted to the small intestines where it breaks down starch to maltose. The equation for the reaction catalyzed by amylase is as follows:

$$\textbf{starch} \xrightarrow{\textbf{amylase}} \textbf{maltose + maltose + maltose}$$

How might a biotechnologist know that this reaction is taking place? What assay can be used to test for the activity of this enzyme?

Figure 6.3.   Molecular Structure of Starch.   Amylose is one type of plant starch. The amylose molecule is very long, composed of hundreds of glucose molecules linked together. Amylase breaks the bond between glucose molecules in the chain to produce the disaccharide, maltose.

Purpose

What is the behavior of the human enzyme, salivary amylase, compared with a 10-mg/mL bacterial amylase solution?

Materials

Environmental Health and Safety Officer

Beaker, 100 mL	Micropipet, P-100 and tips	Glucose test strips
24-well microtiter plate	Lugol's Iodine Solution	Tube rack for 1.7 mL tubes
Pipets, 1 mL, and pump	Glass rods	Reaction tubes, 1.7 mL
Balance, weigh boat, lab scoops	alpha-AMYLASE	Benedict's Solution
Starch, soluble	TRIS	Dry block heater/heat block
Micropipet, P-1000 and tips	Calcium chloride	Lid locks for 1.7 mL tubes

Caution: Wear goggles and gloves when using chemicals.

Procedure

(testing for a decrease in starch and an increase in sugar)

1. Collect approximately 5 mL of saliva in a clean 100-mL beaker (see Figure 6.4). Chewing on a rubber band may increase saliva production.
2. Obtain a clean, 24-well plate (see Figure 6.5). Read the rest of the procedures, and label the wells that will be used. Before starting, make a diagram in your notebook of what is to be loaded into each well.

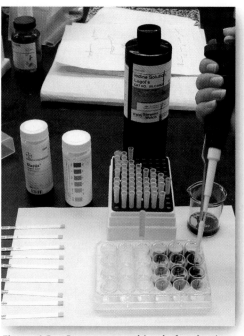

Figure 6.4. **Collecting Saliva.** Human alpha-amylase is found in saliva. Wait 20 minutes after eating or drinking before collecting saliva. When collecting saliva, remember that it is a biohazard that should be treated in a mature, safe fashion. Clean all glassware and spills after use.

Figure 6.5. **Prepare everything before beginning. Be careful to not cross contaminate samples. Change tips with each measurement.** Photo by author.

3. Place 1 mL of 3% starch solution in the first six wells of Rows 1, 2, and 3. **Be sure to mix the starch solution before you take each sample.** How much 3%-starch solution do you have to make? Record the recipe in your notebook.

4. To Columns 1 and 4 of the wells, add 300 µL of human salivary amylase solution to each of the starch-filled wells. To Column 4 of the wells, also add 20 µL of iodine. Mix each for 2 seconds with a clean glass rod. Be careful to not cross contaminate.

5. To Columns 2 and 5 of the wells, add 300 µL of bacterial amylase to each of the starch-filled wells. To Column 5 of the wells, also add 20 µL of iodine. Mix each for 2 seconds with a clean glass rod.

6. To Columns 3 and 6 of the wells, add 300 µL of distilled water to each of the starch-filled wells. To Column 6 of the wells, also add 20 µL of iodine. Mix each for 2 seconds with a clean glass rod.

7. Identify the positive and negative controls in this experiment. Make and record predictions as to what may occur in each well, including the expected color change.

8. Place the 24-well tray on a piece of white paper, out of direct light. Iodine decolorizes in light.

9. **After 24 hours,** in a data table that you create, record data, including individual sample data and average results, on the amount of sugar in the wells of Columns 1, 2, and 3. Although measurements of sugar concentration can be made in percent (%) or milligrams per deciliter (mg/dL), for this activity, record the data in mg/dL. A deciliter (dL) is equal to 0.1 L. Use the glucose test strips as directed on the package; however, wait a total of 90 seconds before reading the sugar concentration (see Figure 6.6).

100°C

   a. The relative amount of sugar (5 ➔ 1 rating) in the wells of Columns 1, 2, and 3 are determined by a Benedict's solution test. Use 300 µL of sample plus 300 µL of Benedict's solution mixed in a 1.7-mL tube. Place a locking cap on the tube, and heat in a 100°C heat block for 2 minutes. Record the color and relative amount of sugar present.

   b. The degree of lightening of the iodine solution from black to a light red-brown or clear color (5 ➔ 1 rating) in the wells of Rows 4, 5, and 6.

Data Analysis/Conclusion

Discuss the results of the experiment, including the behavior of the human salivary amylase compared with the bacterial amylase solution. Discuss possible errors in experimentation that could lead to erroneous or misleading results. Of what value is this type of assay? Where in industry might it be used?

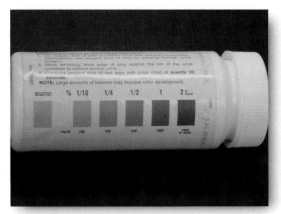

Figure 6.6. Diastix® Test Strips are used to determine the presence and concentration of aldose sugars.
Photo by author.

Figure 6.7. A multichannel pipet speeds setting up the reaction because it allows for pipetting several samples at the same time.
Photo courtesy of Cell Genesys, Inc.

Thinking Like a Biotechnician

1. Which of these assays should give the "best" results?
2. If an assay shows a 100-mg/dL-glucose concentration, what is that value measured in percent (%) of glucose? Show the calculations.
3. Why would the use of a multichannel pipet give "better" results (see Figure 6.7)?

Laboratory 6d Testing Plant Substances as Potential Medicines

Improved with suggestions by Mark Okuda, Bay Area Biotechnology Education Consortium.

Background

In nature, organisms are constantly battling for resources and survival. Plants compete with other plants for light and water. Fast growth, big leaves, and large root systems would be advantageous characteristics. Some plants, such as rhododendrons, actually produce toxic chemicals that drip from their leaves into the soil, killing competing plants around them.

All organisms are infected by viruses or threatened by bacterial disease. Many organisms have defense systems to combat the onslaught of foreign invaders. Numerous plants, fungi, and bacteria produce antimicrobial agents to battle the microbes. Finding and isolating an antimicrobial molecule could lead to a potential therapeutic medicine.

Isolating an active ingredient that actually has antimicrobial activity is not a trivial task. Suspect samples must be collected. One might have to travel to distant places, such as Brazil, to collect samples. Once samples are collected, extraction techniques must be determined and samples processed. Then, samples can be tested for their ability to kill different microbes. When researchers identify a potential antimicrobial agent, they must prove that it does not cause toxic effects in humans.

To test plant extracts for antimicrobial properties, technicians add extract-soaked filter paper disks to bacteria cultures spread on Petri plates. Plant extracts containing compounds effective against bacteria leave clear halos (bacterial death or inhibited bacterial growth) around the soaked disks in the bacteria lawns. The extracts demonstrating these clear areas on Petri dishes are then further purified and screened for the specific ingredients causing the bacterial death. These compounds may include antiseptics, astringents, antibiotics, and toxins.

Purpose

What plant materials, found locally, contain active ingredients that will inhibit the growth of bacteria?

Materials

Environmental Health
and Safety Officer

Balance, weigh boat, lab scoops	Inoculating loop, Ni/Cr wire	Syringe, 10 mL and filter,
LB broth base	Petri dishes, 60×15 mm, sterile	0.2 μm
Media bottles, 250 mL	*E. coli* JM109 (stock plate)	Reaction tubes and rack, 1.7 mL
Sterilizer/autoclave	Plant specimen	Methanol, absolute
Water bath, 37°C, shaking	Mortar and pestle	Pipet, 1 mL and pump
Sterile LB agar	Pipet, 10 mL and pump	Dry block heater/heat block
Laminar flow hood and	Plastic funnels,	Forceps, fine-tipped
disinfectant	short-stemmed	Ampicillin
Glasses, safety, plastic	Filter paper disks,	Glass spreader
Bunsen burner and	5 mm diameter	Incubator oven, 37°C
gas lighter	Beakers, 100 mL	

*Caution: Take care to not work with poisonous plants. Make sure plants are identified and do not use any suspect plants. Wear goggles and gloves when handling plant material.

Procedure

Day 1

Part I: Preparing Agar Plates

1. Prepare a nutrient or LB broth for the *E. coli* at least 24 hours in advance. Using sterile technique, add a colony of *E. coli* culture to the broth medium and incubate, shaking at 37°C for 24 hours.
2. Each lab group needs six Petri plates. Draw a "+" on each plate bottom to divide the plate into quadrants (four sections). Label the quadrants No. 1 through 4. Also, label the dish with your initials and the date.
3. Liquefy sterile LB agar in the microwave at 50% power. Using sterile technique, pour approximately 20 mL of sterile, liquid LB agar into each Petri plate. Let the agar solidify for 15 minutes. Let it dry for at least 24 hours.

Part II: Preparing Plant Extracts (see Caution above)

4. Using a mortar and pestle, grind up 2 g of plant tissue (leaves or bark) with 10 mL of deionized water. Let it sit for 3 minutes. Filter the sample through an 11-cm filter paper funnel. Filter sterilize the filtered sample extract using a syringe filter, as demonstrated by the instructor. Collect 1 mL of extract into a 1.7-mL microtube. Label the sample.
5. Repeat *Step* 4, but replace the water with methanol as the extracting solvent. After the methanol extraction, place the 1.7-mL tube with the 1 mL of methanol extract in a 65°C heat block (caps open) for 24 hours or more, if necessary, to evaporate the methanol. Reconstitute dry matter in the tube with 1 mL of deionized water.
6. For each of the other samples, repeat steps 4 and 5. Label all samples. There should be six tubes of samples.
7. Using sterile forceps (that have been flamed in alcohol) drop three filter paper disks into each tube of filtered extract.
8. Prepare negative control disks, three each, of only methanol and only sterile distilled water.
9. Prepare six positive control disks of ampicillin solution.
10. Allow the disks sufficient time to soak up enough extract to be saturated (perhaps overnight).
11. Close the tubes. Store all samples at 4°C until ready to use.

Day 2

Part III: Setting Up Antimicrobial Plant Extract Assay

12. Using a sterile pipet transfer 1 mL of the *E. coli* broth (made at step 1) to the middle of each Petri dish. Sterilize a spreading loop (using alcohol and a flame), and evenly spread the bacterial culture around the Petri plate. Quickly cover, and allow the culture to soak into the agar for at least 15 minutes.

13. Using sterile forceps carefully place one disk into the middle of each quadrant, about 2 cm from the outer edge of the Petri dish. Blot any excess liquid before placing the disk on the Petri dish. Keep all the methanol-extracted samples on the same dish and all the water-extracted samples on the same dish.

14. Repeat step 13 twice so that you have three replicates of the methanol extraction and three replicates of the deionized water extractions.

15. Place one of the negative control disks, either sterile distilled water or methanol, in the center of the appropriate plate. Place a positive control disk with ampicillin in another quadrant of each plate.

16. You should end up with six Petri plates, each containing a negative control in the middle, a positive control, and three sample disks (see Figure 6.8). **Make sure you have recorded exactly which plant extracts with which solvent went into each quadrant.** Give everything a few minutes to "soak in."

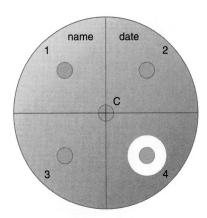

Figure 6.8.   Antimicrobial Screening. With no antimicrobial agent, the *E. coli* bacteria grow in a lawn over the agar. Antimicrobial agents will diffuse out of disks, and kill or inhibit bacterial growth. A halo of no bacteria (No. 4) indicates that something is inhibiting the bacteria growth.

37°C

17. Make sure that the disks are adhering well to the surface of the agar. For incubation, invert the plates and incubate at 37°C for 24 to 48 hours.

18. After incubation, examine the plates with the plant extract disks for zones of inhibition. This is a clear area formed around the disk by the inhibitory action of a substance(s) in the plant material. Photograph or draw the plates, labeling any inhibition of bacterial growth.

19. Create a data table to collect and present data of all the replicates as well as the averages. Include descriptions of the bacterial lawn around each disk. Measure and record the diameter and clarity of any cleared areas around the disks. Give quantitative measurements of your observations.

Data Analysis/Conclusion

Evaluate the performance of each extract as a source of potential antimicrobial medicine. Which, if any, showed significant antimicrobial activity? Give evidence. Discuss possible errors in experiment's design that could give false data. Discuss further experimentation or procedures that could be done. Make recommendations to the supervisor as to which extracts should be the focus of additional investigation as antimicrobial agents.

Thinking Like a Biotechnician

1. If an extract gives a negative result in the antimicrobial assay, does that mean that the extract is not an antimicrobial agent?

2. In preparing the sample disks, some of the methanol extractions smell like alcohol. Why is that a problem?

3. Each extract may have one or more compounds in it. What should be done to begin to identify the exact compound in an extract that is causing the antimicrobial action?

Laboratory 6e   Searching for Native Amylase-Producing Bacteria

This lab was developed by Diane Sweeney of Crystal Springs/Uplands School and modified by Ellyn Daugherty, Pat Seawell of Gene Connection, and David Kane, Biotechnology student.

Background

Biotechnology companies have three options for producing a protein, such as amylase, for market. The potential product may be either extracted from nature, grown in the laboratory from existing sources, or genetically engineered into a production cell line and then scaled-up into larger volumes.

Amylase is a product already present in nature. Several species of decomposition bacteria and fungi present in the soil and on plant surfaces produce the amylase enzyme. The soil or plants may be sampled for the presence of bacteria. If amylase-producing bacteria can be isolated and grown in the lab, then amylase is a potential product for the biotechnology lab. If the bacteria from an existing source can be grown in sufficient quantities for amylase purification and marketing, then R&D costs will be substantially reduced.

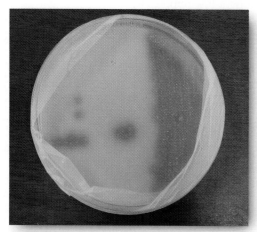

Figure 6.9.   Bacteria colonies growing on starch agar plates. If the cells produce it, amylase diffuses out and breaks down the starch around the colony. The result is clear halos around amylase-producing colonies.
Photo by author.

Manufacturing costs increase as more time and manpower are used to develop new methods of production. Each of the possible methods of manufacturing a protein must be evaluated in light of the production costs. For amylase, the protein must be grown in "the lab," either from existing amylase-producing bacteria or from genetically engineered bacteria. In this activity, native amylase-producing bacteria will be isolated and evaluated for their potential pipeline use.

To assay for amylase-producing bacteria, agar-containing starch can be inoculated with samples suspected of having amylase activity. If amylase is produced by any of the bacteria growing on the starch agar, then clearings (halos) around the bacterial colonies will arise as the starch is broken down into sugar by the amylase enzyme (see Figure 6.9). If an amylase-producing colony can be characterized and scaled-up to large volumes, it can serve as the production host (or cell line) for commercial amylase.

Purpose

Which suspect samples contain amylase-producing bacteria?
Can single, amylase-producing bacteria colonies be isolated from nature?
What are the characteristics of the best amylase-producing bacteria?

Materials

Balance, tabletop milligram	Glass rods	Sterilizer/autoclave
Weigh boat, 3.5"×3.5"	Magnetic stir bars	Laminar flow hood, 3×3×2 ft
Lab scoops	Hot plate stirrer	Lysol® disinfectant
LB agar base	Hot hands protector	Petri dishes, 100×15 mm, sterile
Starch, soluble	Media bottle, 250 mL	Loop, inoculating, sterile
Beakers, 400 mL	Permanent lab marker pens	Incubator oven, 37°C

Procedure

Environmental Health and Safety Officer

Caution: Wear gloves and goggles. No eating or drinking.

1. At least 1 day in advance, prepare 250 mL of 2% starch/LB agar and pour it onto agar plates. (Prepare LB agar as described in Chapter 4, but add 2% mass/volume of soluble starch with the dry LB media mix.)

2. Obtain a 2%-starch/LB agar Petri plate per person. Label (initials and date) the bottom of plate.

3. Using a sterile plastic inoculating loop, sample the plants, soil, or other surfaces for amylase-producing bacteria. Select a sample that seems logical for amylase production. (Remember that bacteria with the capability to produce amylase will probably not do so if no starch is present.) Record the source of your sample and why you chose a sample from that location.

   To obtain a soil or water sample, plunge the inoculating loop into the soil or water. Twist it gently, so as not to break it. Remove it from the soil or water. Shake off any excess dirt or water.

   For a plant bacteria sample, rub the inoculating loop over the plant surface.

37°C

4. Streak the plate with the sample in a "triple Z" arrangement as directed in Lab 4g. Do not "flame" the loop between "Zs. "

5. Place the plate, upside down, in an incubation oven at 37°C.
   Caution: Wear gloves. No eating or drinking.

6. After 24 hours, get the Petri plate and observe bacterial growth. Look for colonies and halos around them. Expect hundreds of colonies, but only a few, if any, colonies with halos. To make halos more visible, chill the Petri plates in a refrigerator for several hours. Iodine may be added to turn the starch areas blue-black. This may kill the colonies or spread bacteria that may be undesirable (if there was interest in keeping the colonies).

7. Draw your plate, making sure it is accurate in size and detail. Label the amylase-producing bacteria.

8. Record the characteristics of each amylase-producing colony on a data table. Record the diameter of the colonies and the width of the halos. Record colors, shapes, and textures of the colonies.

Environmental Health and Safety Officer

Caution: Treat these bacteria with respect. These bacteria are not identified and may be pathogenic. Wear goggles and gloves when handling the plates. Dispose of the plates in the autoclave bag. Wash your hands after handling the plates and disinfect the work surface.

Data Analysis/Conclusion

Determine which colony on your plate, if any, shows amylase production. Is the colony a good candidate for growth as a commercial producer of amylase? Why or why not? Share your data with the colleagues in the class. Pick the three colonies in the class that best show potential for amylase production in the lab. Consider the growth rate and halo characteristics. In a concluding statement, discuss why you have chosen these particular colonies. Also, discuss what the next step in commercial amylase production might be. Finally, discuss the advantages and disadvantages of using these unknown bacteria species as laboratory or manufacturing amylase producers.

Thinking Like a Biotechnician

1. For this assay, which is better: a fast-growing bacteria colony that has a large cloudy halo around it or a slow-growing colony that has a small- to medium-size, very clear halo around it?

2. Propose a method to get any of the bacteria colonies showing the results from question 1 to have additional desirable characteristics?

3. None of these bacteria will be used in our efforts to make large volumes of amylase. Give a good reason and explanation for why these bacteria are less attractive for that purpose than genetically engineering *E. coli* to produce amylase.

Laboratory 6f Testing Plant and Animal Samples for Hydrogen Peroxidase

Developed with the assistance of Tina Doss, Bay Area Biotechnology Education Consortium.

Background

Hydrogen peroxide (H_2O_2) is produced in cells as a byproduct of cellular respiration. Since H_2O_2 is toxic, cells must rid themselves of it rapidly. Within cells there are specific enzymes called peroxidases (hydrogen peroxidase) that are designed to recognize H_2O_2, and break it down into water and oxygen. Hydrogen peroxidase is stored in cells in an organelle called a peroxisome. Hydrogen peroxidase breaks down H_2O_2 to water (H_2O) and oxygen (O_2). The overall equation is as follows:

$$2H_2O_2 \xrightarrow{\text{hydrogen peroxidase}} 2H_2O + O_2$$

Purpose

To find animal or plant samples that have hydrogen peroxidase activity.

Environmental Health and Safety Officer

Materials

Scalpel handles, #4	Carrots	Permanent lab marker pens
Scalpel blades, #22 for	Horseradish root	Pipet, 2 mL
#4 handles	Beef liver	Pipet pump, blue
Apples	Chicken thigh meat	Hydrogen peroxide, 3%
Potatoes	Tubes, glass, 13×100 mm	
Onions	Peg racks for 10-13 mm tubes	

Procedure

1. Use a numerical scale to represent the amount of reaction when a sample's hydrogen peroxidase acts on hydrogen peroxide. Consider, for example, a scale of 1 to 5, where 5 = enough bubbles to overflow the tube, and 0 = no bubbles.
2. Using Microsoft® Excel®, create a data table to report the amount of bubbling for each of the items being tested. Place the table in your notebook.
3. For each item to be tested, use 1-cm³ pieces of sample (cut with a knife or scalpel). Place the square in a 13×100-mm centrifuge tube. Set up a negative control tube with 1 mL of dH_2O.
4. Add 2 mL of 3% H_2O_2 to each 13×100-mm tube.
5. Allow the enzymatic reaction to occur for exactly 60 seconds. Observe the results at 60 seconds. If there is bubbling, H_2O_2 is being broken down.
6. Test each item three times, and determine the average amount of reaction. Record the data in your data table.

Data Analysis/Conclusion

Discuss the results of testing for peroxidase. Which samples had the greatest amount of peroxidase activity and which had the least? Considering what you know about each item and its use in nature, why do you think some samples had less hydrogen peroxidase activity than others. Discuss at least two reasons why individual results might vary from trial to trial. Propose a better way of assaying peroxidase activity than measuring the amount of bubbling. If you wanted a gene for peroxidase to use to genetically engineer *E. coli,* which sample would be the best source? Give an explanation for your recommendation.

Thinking Like a Biotechnician

1. H_2O and H_2O_2 seem similar in structure and function. Compare and contrast the structure and function of these molecules.
2. Enzymes are protein catalysts that may be used over and over again to speed reactions. They are not used up in the reactions they catalyze. How can you test to see whether the enzymes are used in a reaction?
3. Propose a method of extracting hydrogen peroxidase from liver?

Laboratory 6g   Isolation of HRP from Horseradish Root

Based on labs developed by Theo Leung, Biotechnology student, with the advice of Paul Bethke, University of California, Berkeley.

Background

Proteins in plants are potential biotechnology products. To examine proteins for their commercial or research value, researchers must purify them from their source cells. The protein of interest for this activity is horseradish peroxidase (HRP), an enzyme from horseradish root. In cells, HRP breaks down H_2O_2 into safer water and oxygen molecules. The molecular weight of HRP is approximately 40 kilodalton (kD), and it may be visualized through PAGE.

Purpose

Can an active form of HRP be isolated from horseradish root?

Materials

Environmental Health
and Safety Officer

Horseradish root	Micropipet, P-100 and tips	PAGE gel loading tips
Grater	Micropipet, P-10 and tips	Protein sizing markers,
Balance, weigh boat,	Plastic beaker, 1L	15-150 KD
lab scoops	TRIS	Petri dishes, 150×15mm
25 mM Na phosphate buffer,	Boric acid	Ethanol, 95%
pH 7	SDS, 10%	Acetic acid, glacial
Mortar and pestle	Bromophenol Blue	Coomassie® Blue R-250
Graduated cylinder, 25 mL	Sucrose	Lab rotator, 12×12
Cheesecloth	Microcentrifuge	White light photo imaging
Tubes, 15 mL and racks	Gel box, vertical, for PAGE	system
Centrifuge for 15 mL tubes	Transfer pipets, 3 mL	Gloves, large
Acetone	PAGE gel, 10% TG, 10 well	Glasses, safety, plastic
Pipet, 2 mL and pump	Power supply	
Reaction tubes, 1.7 mL	Dry block heater/heat block,	
and racks	80°C	

Procedure

Part I: Preparation of Horseradish Root Sample

1. Prepare 5 g of grated horseradish root and 100 mL of 25-mM NaH_2PO_4, pH 7.0 buffer.
2. Prepare a stock HRP protein sample at approximately 200 mg/mL by mixing 5 g of grated horseradish root with 15 mL of the 25-mM NaH_2PO_4 buffer.

3. Homogenize the stock-root protein sample, grinding with a mortar and pestle until the sample appears as a suspension.
4. Filter the homogenate through three layers of cheesecloth to remove large cellular debris into one or more 15-mL conical centrifuge tubes, placed on ice.
5. Centrifuge the sample tubes for 5 minutes in a 3000X-g centrifuge (or the highest power possible). Make sure the sample tubes have equal volume.
6. After centrifuging the tubes, discard the supernatant and save the pellets. The pellets are cell debris that contains a large amount of proteins. Place the tubes containing pellets on ice to chill them for at least 5 minutes.
7. Prechill about 200 mL of acetone in a freezer (-20°C) for at least 30 minutes.
8. Add acetone to the samples that have been on ice (0°C to 4°C) at a concentration of one part extract for every three parts of acetone (a 1:4 ratio). Finger-flick to mix. Invert to mix three times.
   Caution: Wear goggles and gloves.
9. Centrifuge the samples for 15 minutes in a 3000X centrifuge (or the highest power possible). A pellet containing HRP should appear at the bottom of each the tubes.
10. Gently, decant the supernatant into a trash container. The supernatant contains cellular debris.
11. Redissolve the protein-containing pellet in 2 mL of cold 25-mM NaH_2PO_4 buffer. The sample is now approximately 10 to 20 times more concentrated than the starting sample. Consider this a 20X concentration.

Environmental Health and Safety Officer

Part II: Analyzing Protein Extracts on a PAGE Gel

12. In a 1.7-mL tube, prepare dilutions of the 20X protein samples following the reaction matrix (see Table 6.2).

Table 6.2. **Cell Extract Sample Dilutions**

Tube No., Dilution	Amount of Cell Extract (μL)	Amount of Buffer Diluent (μL)
1:1	40.0	0
1:2	20.0	20.0
1:4	10.0	30.0
1:8	5.0	35.0
1:16	2.5	37.5

13. To prepare samples to load for PAGE, add 6 μL of PAGE loading dye to each of the samples. Pipet up and down once to mix.
14. Set up and prepare a 10-well, 10%-TRIS-glycine PAGE gel for loading.
15. Load one of each sample (35 μL) into adjacent Wells 3 through 7.
16. Put 5 μL of prestained protein standard into Wells 2 and 8.
17. Run the gel at 35 mAmp until the loading dye has run into the bottom quadrant of the gel.
18. Stain the gel in Coomassie Blue stain for a minimum of 3 hours; destain in deionized water for a minimum of 7 hours, or use the microwave quick-destain method.
19. View the gel bands on a white-light box and make a permanent record using a photo-imaging system. Analyze the samples for evidence of the horseradish peroxidase peptides at 40 kD. Label the photo, including sample wells, protein standards, and sample bands.
20. For each of the original samples, conduct a peroxidase activity test following the protocol in the next lab activity.

Data Analysis/Conclusion

Using the PAGE data, describe the variety of peptides found in the samples. What is the likelihood that one or more of the bands is peroxidase? Give evidence. Suggest methods for future peroxidase isolation.

Thinking Like a Biotechnician

1. If large smears of sample appear in some of the lanes, what might be done to improve the resolution of sample in the lanes on the gel?
2. Discuss methods that could be used to determine whether peroxidase is present, and, if so, at what concentration or activity.
3. The samples loaded on the gel are dilutions of the extraction. How can we know the total content of protein in the sample versus the concentration of HRP in the sample?

Laboratory 6h   Testing for the Presence of Peroxidase Using TMB

Background

Hydrogen peroxide (H_2O_2) is a product of cellular metabolism. As cells break down food molecules, some of the reactions liberate H_2O_2. Because H_2O_2 is poisonous to the cells, it can kill them if it is not removed or destroyed. Cells produce the enzyme peroxidase to break down H_2O_2 into safer molecules.

Peroxidase splits H_2O_2 into water and oxygen as shown in the following equation:

$$2H_2O_2 \xrightarrow{\text{Peroxidase}} 2H_2O + O_2$$

As the peroxidase catalyzes the reaction, oxygen bubbles out of the solution. This is one way that the reaction may be observed and monitored.

Another way to test for peroxidase activity is to use an indicator. The indicator used here to test for peroxidase activity is TMB, which stands for 3,3',5,5'-tetramethylbenzidine. The TMB changes to a blue product with the breakdown of H_2O_2 and the transfer of electrons from H_2O_2 to TMB. This is an oxidation-reduction reaction. If a stop solution containing acid is added, the HRP is denatured, and the reaction stops. In the presence of the acid, TMB turns from blue to yellow. The degree of color change is directly related to the amount of peroxidase activity.

In this activity, the horseradish extracts from the last activity will be tested for peroxidase activity. Of particular interest are extracts that showed suspected bands of peroxidase at approximately 40 kD on the PAGE gels.

Purpose

Do the extracts from HRP show peroxidase activity?
What is the lowest concentration of HRP extract to show activity?

Materials

Horseradish peroxidase extracts (from Lab 6g)	96-well micro-titer plate	Micropipet, P-1000
25 mM Na phosphate buffer, pH 7	Micropipet, P-100	Micropipet tips for P-1000
	Micropipet tips for P-100	Hydrochloric acid solution,
	TMB solution, diluted 1:4	0.5 M

Environmental Health and Safety Officer

Procedure

1. Prepare samples for the assay by doing a 1:10 serial dilution of the HRP extract. Use the sodium phosphate buffer as the diluent. Make samples down to 1:1000.
2. Obtain a 96-well, microtiter plate. Label the wells to show where the HRP extract samples will be placed. Test at least three replications of each sample following the instructions in steps 3 and 4. Include negative controls containing sodium phosphate buffer.
3. Add 100 μL of the diluted TMB solution to each well.
4. Do this quickly. Add 100 μL of the appropriate horseradish root extract to each well. Mix thoroughly. Test undiluted starting sample first. Then test 1:10, 1:100, and 1:1000 dilutions. Let stand for 10 minutes.
5. Add 10 μL of 0.5-M HCl (stop solution) to each well.
   Caution: Wear goggles and gloves. Wipe spills immediately.
6. Look for a color change from blue to yellow (see Figure 6.10). If a digital camera is available, photograph the assay results.
7. Dilute the extracts until there is no evidence of a positive TMB assay. Up to 20 dilutions may be necessary.
8. Design a data table to record all the data, including a rating system for the degree of yellow color visible. Include averaged data.

Environmental Health and Safety Officer

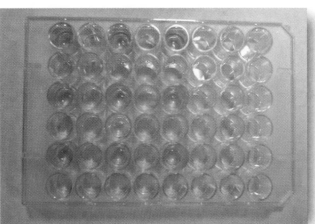

Figure 6.10. **Yellow or yellow-green color indicates that HRP has reacted with TMB.**
Photo by author.

Data Analysis/Conclusion

Compare the results of the unknowns with the negative control. Is there evidence of peroxidase activity in any of the samples? If so, which ones? What is the lowest concentration of extract that shows a positive TMB assay? Explain and give evidence. Discuss the possible errors in this type of experiment. Propose some other applications of this technology and how HRP/TMB might be used.

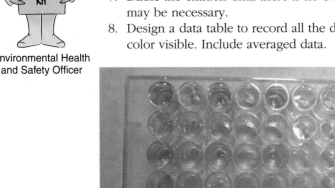

Thinking Like a Biotechnician

1. If the TMB color change is still occurring even at extremely low concentrations of HRP, what might the technician do to make the assay more usable?
2. The HRP enzyme can be linked (conjugated) to an antibody. How might that allow better visualization of the molecules of interest?
3. Explain how an antibody conjugated with HRP might be used in an ELISA.

Chapter 7

Using the Spectrophotometer for Protein Assays

Scientist Dr. Eric Memarzadeh uses an HPLC (high performance liquid chromatography) to identify and test the purity of protein samples. One of the components of the HPLC is an ultraviolet (UV) spectrophotometer. A UV spec measures the absorbance of light by molecules in a sample. A molecule has a characteristic wavelength of light at which it absorbs the most light. This wavelength is used to identify the molecule in a mixture and estimate its concentration.

Photo courtesy of Eric Memarzadeh.

The spectrophotometer (spec, for short) is one of the most valuable instruments in a biotechnology facility. With a spec, a technician can quantify the amount of a molecule in a solution.

A spec works on the principle that every molecule absorbs light energy but not the same amount of the same kind of light. The wavelength at which a molecule absorbs the most light can be used to recognize the molecule in solution. Since more molecules can absorb more light, the amount of molecules in solution (concentration) can be determined based on the amount of light absorbed by a sample, as compared to solutions of known concentration.

In the following activities you will learn how to operate a spectrophotometer and how to use it to determine protein concentration. Specifically, you will learn:

- the parts of a visible spectrophotometer and how changing the wavelength setting changes the color of light on a sample.
- how to determine the wavelength of maximum light absorbance for a sample ($lambda_{max}$)
- how to determine and adjust the pH of a solution
- how to prepare a buffered solution
- how to determine the concentration of an unknown protein solution using a best-fit standard curve
- how to use a UV spectrophotometer to determine the presence and concentration of a colorless protein in solution

Stand-alone spectrophotometers or specs built into instruments, such as an HPLC or ELISA plate readers, allow biotechnologists to keep track of their protein product during research and manufacturing. In future chapters, you will use spectrophotometers to recognize and quantify several of the proteins you will be studying, including those made during recombinant protein production.

Laboratory 7a   Learning To Use the Spectrophotometer

Background

A spectrophotometer uses light (*photo*) to measure (*meter*) molecules. To understand how to use a spectrophotometer, it is helpful to understand something about the nature of light and how it interacts with molecules.

The sun produces a spectrum of several different types of radiant light energy (electromagnetic radiation), including radio waves, microwaves, x-rays, and visible light waves. Sunlight is energy and, therefore, it can be used to "perform work," including reactions, such as photosynthesis in plants, in which sunlight works with water and carbon dioxide molecules to produce carbohydrates. Dye in fabric is another example of how light energy can affect molecules. Think about when you wear a pair of dark blue pants. If you sit outside under a shady tree, the material stays relatively cool to the touch. On the other hand, if you sit in the sun, the dark blue material becomes hot in the sunlight because the blue molecules absorb high-energy light waves.

All types of light energy travel through space in waves. Light waves comes in different forms and colors, including blue light, violet light, ultraviolet light, red light, and infrared light, to name a few. The colored light (waves) that we see is part of the visible light spectrum (VIS). We see light as different colors because of differences in the wavelengths of the light waves (see Figure 7.1). A wavelength is the distance between the crest, or top, of light waves and is measured in nanometers (nm). Wavelengths of 350 to 700 nm make up the visible (you can see them) spectrum. The photoreceptors in our eyes can detect these wavelengths of light. Which of the three wavelengths of light shown in Figure 7.1 would be visible to our eyes?

We cannot see the actual light waves for several reasons, including that the light wavelengths are too tiny. However, we can see color. This is because the nerve cells in our eyes are stimulated by certain colors, or light wavelengths. In other words, each of the wavelengths of light (blue, green, and red, etc) affects our eyes' light detectors differently.

Different wavelengths store varying amounts of energy. The shorter the wavelength, the more energy that particular color of light contains. Think about the waves that hit a beach. If they arrived faster, would they hit you with more, or less, total energy in a minute than waves that were spaced farther apart? Which of the wavelengths of light shown in Figure 7.1 has the most energy?

The visible part of the light spectrum is shown in Figure 7.2. Light that is not visible to the human eye includes x-rays (200 nm), UV light (300 nm), and infrared light (800 nm). Draw the light spectrum in your notebook and include the light that is not in the visible spectrum.

White light contains all the wavelengths of visible light. Colored molecules can either absorb or transmit part or all of this light energy. Substances appear to be a certain color

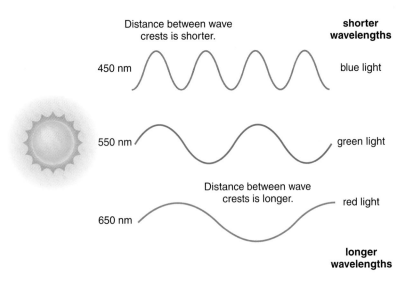

Distance between wave crests is shorter.

shorter wavelengths

450 nm   blue light

550 nm   green light

Distance between wave crests is longer.

red light

650 nm

longer wavelengths

The shorter the wavelength, the more energy in the light.

Figure 7.1.   Light travels in waves.

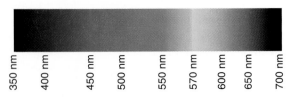

The Visible Spectrum

350 nm   400 nm   450 nm   500 nm   550 nm   570 nm   600 nm   650 nm   700 nm

The wavelength of different colors of light energy

Figure 7.2.   Visible Spectrum.   Wavelengths below 350 nm and above 700 nm are not visible to the human eye, but they may be visible to other organisms, such as bees, which see UV light.

because of the light energy they do *not* absorb. The light bounces off the molecules (transmitted/reflected), hits your eye, and you see it as a certain color. A red T-shirt appears red because dye molecules in the material reflect red wavelengths.

The VIS spectrophotometer can be used to measure the amount and type of colored light (wavelength) absorbed or transmitted by molecules or cells in solution. This can reveal important information about the nature of the molecules being studied. Since the light energy that a molecule absorbs may be used to run chemical processes, such as photosynthesis, absorbance information can also help us understand reactions in cells. In addition, absorbance data are used to determine the concentration of molecules or cells in solution.

In this lab activity, you will learn how the spec works. In subsequent activities, you will use the spec to study molecules in solution.

Purpose

What are the ranges of wavelengths for colors of visible light produced by the spectrophotometer in your lab?

Materials

Spectrophotometer, Spectronic 20 D+
Filter paper, 12.5 cm
Tubes, glass, 13×100 mm

Procedure

Turn on the spec and let it warm up for at least 20 minutes before beginning step 2.

1. To understand how the spectrophotometer works, do the following:

   a. Familiarize yourself with the model of spectrophotometer in your lab.
   b. In your notebook, draw a simplified version of the VIS spectrophotometer available in your facility.
   c. Find and label all the parts: power switch, wavelength control, 0% transmittance knob, 100% transmittance knob, sample holder, display, and the absorbance and transmittance mode settings. If necessary, your instructor will help you find them.

2. Cut a strip of white paper to fit into a spectrophotometer cuvette (13×100-mm spec tube). Then, insert it into the tube. Gently, place the cuvette in the sample holder so that the inside of the fold faces the light source (see Figure 7.3).

3. Set the mode to "transmittance." Leave the sample holder open and cup your hands around the opening. Look through your hands into the sample holder.

4. Have your lab partner set the wavelength at 600 nm and adjust the tube so that you see the maximum amount of orange light on the paper.

5. Turn the wavelength knob slowly **in each direction** and record the range of wavelengths at which you see different colors. Make a data table to record these data.

   a. Do you see other or "in-between" colors?
   b. At which wavelength(s)?
   c. Add these to your data table.

6. Make sure that all partners repeat steps 4 through 5.

Data Analysis/Reporting

Create a graph that shows the range of colors at different wavelengths. Experiment with bar, column, line, and X-Y scatter graphs until you have one that shows your data well.

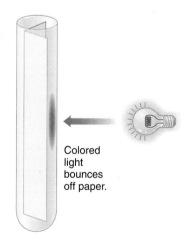

Colored light bounces off paper.

Figure 7.3. Filter paper in cuvette. Light of a specific wavelength reflects off the filter paper. By turning the wavelength knob, you can determine the color of each wavelength.

Make sure that both the wavelength axis and the data plot run continuously from below 400 nm through 700 nm. Color-code the data plot.

Thinking Like a Biotechnician

1. What are the approximate wavelengths of the colors, blue-green, mustard-yellow, and red-orange?
2. The lowest wavelength at which you can see color is the lowest point of the visible spectrum for you. The highest wavelength at which you can see color at is the top of the visible spectrum for you. What is your own personal visible spectrum?
3. Look at another technician's graphs. Are they exact duplicates of yours? Why or why not?

Laboratory 7b   Using the Spectrophotometer to Study Molecules

Background

Some molecules are colored and some are not. Whether or not a molecular solution exhibits color depends on how the molecules interact with light waves. A red hemoglobin solution reacts differently in light than does a green chlorophyll solution.

As a practical example, a blue sweater is blue because the dye molecules in the yarn react with light waves in a certain way. In the case of blue dye molecules, most of the light waves of the visible spectrum are absorbed by the dye molecules, except for the blue ones (around 475 nm). The blue light waves bounce off the dye molecules and hit the nerve cells in your eye, sending a signal to your brain. The result is that you "see" blue.

If a leaf appears green, it is absorbing most of the colors of light, except for the green wavelengths. The leaf uses the absorbed light energy to make food for itself in the reactions of photosynthesis.

When using a spectrophotometer to study molecules, the technician shines light on a sample. The light is either absorbed by or transmitted through the molecules. The transmittance is measured in percentages, which range from 0% to 100%. If a solution's transmittance is 100%, that means that all of the light waves hitting it are transmitted through the solution, and none of the molecules in the solution are absorbing the light energy.

The absorbance of light by molecules in solution is reported in absorbance units (au). The maximum amount of absorbed light that can be detected by a typical VIS spectrophotometer has a value of 2 au. Therefore, all absorbance values fall between 0 and 2 au. The absorbance of a sample is also called the optical density (OD) of the sample. This term is a relic of the days before computerized spectrophotometers determined the concentration of samples automatically. The denser the sample, as with cells growing in broth culture, the higher the absorbance value and OD.

In this activity, three different colored solutions are studied to determine which wavelengths of light they absorb and which of these wavelengths provides the most absorbance ($lambda_{max}$).

Purpose

How much light is absorbed, at different wavelengths, by molecules of different colors?
What are the $lambda_{max}$ and the $lambda_{min}$ (wavelength of minimum light absorption) for each solution?
How is the color of light related to a molecule's ability to absorb light energy?

Materials

Food colorings (1:499 mL dH$_2$O)   Tubes, glass, 13×100 mm
Pipets, 5 mL   Peg racks for 10-13 mm tubes
Pipet pump, green   Spectrophotometer, Spectronic 20 D+

Procedure

1. Place 4 mL of red solution in a cuvette tube.
2. Prepare a "blank" with 4 mL of tap water. A blank has everything the sample contains except the molecule that you are studying. It tells the spec to ignore everything in the sample except the molecules being studied.
3. Use the spectrophotometer to determine the amount of light absorbed by the red solution. Follow the steps below to calibrate (set) and use the spectrophotometer. It is necessary to re-calibrate the spectrophotometer every time the wavelength is changed.

Spectrophotometer Use

a. Make sure the spectrophotometer has warmed up for at least 20 minutes.
b. Set the mode to "transmittance" and the wavelength to 400 nm.
c. Check to see that the sample holder is empty and closed.
d. Use the zero control knob/button (knob on the left) to set the transmittance to 0%.
e. Wipe fingerprints from the blank, insert it, and set the transmittance to read 100% (knob on the right).
f. Wipe fingerprints from the red solution sample tube, insert it, change the mode to absorbance, and read the absorbance value.
g. Repeat steps b. through f. for every 10 nm up to 620 nm.

4. In your notebook, record the absorbance data for the red solution in a data table.
5. Make a line graph to show the absorbance data at different wavelengths. This curve is the absorption spectrum for the red solution.
6. Repeat steps 1 through 5, but use the green food-coloring solution.
7. Add the data for the green solution to your red solution data table and graph.
8. Repeat steps 1 through 5, but use the blue food-coloring solution.
9. Add the data for the blue solution to your red and green solutions data table and graph. You should end up with a data table showing the absorbance of the three different colored solutions at different wavelengths, and a graph with three different colored lines.

Data Analysis/Conclusion

What are the lambda$_{max}$ and the lambda$_{min}$ for each solution? Does each absorbance spectrum make sense for what is expected? How so or not? Explain differences in the lambda$_{max}$ for a solution from one lab group to another. What is the practical value of knowing the lambda$_{max}$ and lambda$_{min}$ for each solution? How can this information be of value in the future to protein researchers and manufacturers?

Thinking Like a Biotechnician

1. Study the peaks and valleys of each absorbance spectrum. Does the red sample absorb non-red light while transmitting red wavelengths? What about the blue and green spectra? Explain.

2. What factors affect the height of a peak on an absorbance spectrum? Sketch a scratch graph showing the pattern you would predict for the relative absorbance spectra for red solutions at 1X, 0.5X, and 0.25X.

3. Sketch an absorbance spectrum that would be expected if you were studying carotene, the orange pigment in carrots.

Laboratory 7c   Measuring the pH of Solutions

Background

The pH of a solution is a measurement of the concentration of hydrogen ions (H^+). The concentration of H^+ ions is reported in moles/liter (M). A solution that has a neutral pH contains 1×10^{-7} M hydrogen ions in solution. It also has 1×10^{-7} M hydroxide ions (OH) in solution. A neutral solution has a pH of 7.0.

Acidic solutions have H^+ concentrations greater than 1×10^{-7} M hydrogen ions in solution. The pH value for an acid is less than 7.0. Basic (alkaline) solutions have H^+ concentrations less than 1×10^{-7} M hydrogen ions in solution. The pH value for an alkaline solution is greater than 7.0.

Measuring the pH involves using pH paper/indicator strips and pH meters. These meters are also used to monitor changes in pH (see Figure 7.4).

Acids and bases can cause serious burns. Use caution when handling them; wear goggles and gloves. Store acids and bases in cabinets designed specifically for them. Use a chemical fume hood, with the fan on, when measuring strong acids or strong bases (see Figure 7.5).

Purpose

What is the pH of some common solutions?

Materials

Environmental Health and Safety Officer

Caution: Wear goggles and gloves when using chemicals. Use a wet paper towel for small spills.

Milk
Orange juice
Cola
Cocoa
Apple juice
White grape juice

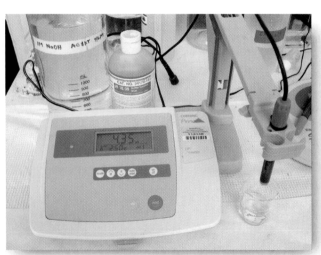

Figure 7.4.   **A pH meter must be calibrated. Calibrating buffers can be purchased. They are often color-coded: pH 7 = yellow, pH 4 = pink, and pH 10 = blue.**

Photo by author.

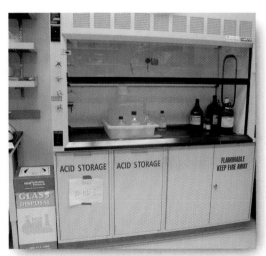

Figure 7.5.   **Acid-Base Cabinet and Fume Hood**

Photo by author.

Materials, continued

Lemon juice
Vinegar, white
Ammonia, household solution, 1%
NaCl, 5M
Alka-Seltzer® in water
NaOH, 0.01%
Tea solution
TAE buffer, 1X
TBE buffer, 1X
pH paper, wide-range pH 0-14
pH paper, narrow-range pH 0-6
pH paper, narrow-range pH 5-10
pH meter and electrode
pH calibrating buffer (pH 7)

Procedure

1. Determine the pH of each solution using wide- and narrow-range pH paper/indicator strips (see Figure 7.6).
2. When you are fairly certain of the pH of each solution, calibrate and use a pH meter to determine and confirm the indicator strip result.

pH Meter Calibration

Although every brand of pH meter is different, the basic methods of calibrating and using a pH meter are the same.

a. Turn on the pH meter. Rinse the electrode with distilled water. Set the temperature knob to room temperature.
b. Place the electrode in the pH 7.0 buffer standard. While swirling the solution, adjust the calibration knob until the display reads "7."
c. Rinse the electrode with distilled water. Place the electrode into the solution to be tested. Swirl the solution until the pH display stops changing. Read the pH value.
d. If the solution is a strong acid or base, use a pH 4.0 or pH 10.0 buffer, respectively, to slope the meter after it has been calibrated to pH 7.0.

3. Report the pH determined by each method in a data table in your notebook.

Data Analysis

Draw a pH line from 0 to 14 to report the relative strength of each acid or alkaline solution. Each solution tested should be added to the pH line. Use the pH determined by the method in which you have the most confidence, either pH paper/indicator strips or a pH meter. Label it as you would a timeline.

Figure 7.6. Dip the pH indicator strips into the solution and immediately remove. Compare the color on the pH strip to the colored key on the packet.
Photo by author.

Thinking Like a Biotechnician

1. Certain substances, including bleach, alcohols, and oils, do not have a "pH" value; they give false readings, or no readings, with the indicator strips or pH meter. What characteristic must a solution have to give it a pH reading?
2. A fermentation tank full of bacterial cell culture needs to be monitored for changes in pH. If the pH becomes too high or too low, the cells could die. Propose a method to monitor and maintain the pH of the culture.

Laboratory 7d   Making an Appropriate Buffer for Protein Storage and Activity

Background

Proteins must be dissolved in buffered solution to maintain their structure and function. Buffers resist changes to pH, and help to maintain protein structure and activity. Different proteins require different buffers in different concentrations.

For the amylase protein, a small number of Ca^{2+} ions must be present in the buffer for it to maintain activity. In addition, the amylase buffer must have a pH between 7.0 and 8.5. A good buffer for amylase activity is TRIS with the following concentration and pH:

$$50 \text{ m}M \text{ TRIS, 5 m}M \text{ CaCl}_2, \text{ pH 7.2}$$

To make this buffer, measure the appropriate amount of the buffering compound, TRIS, and a cofactor, $CaCl_2$. The mass of each of these ingredients is determined by the molarity equation:

$$\text{desired molarity (mol/L)} \times \text{molecular weight (g/mol)} \times \text{desired volume (L)} = \text{needed mass (g)}$$

These are dissolved in water to approximately 75% of the final volume. The pH is adjusted to 7.2, in this case with HCl, using a pH meter, and the volume is raised to the final volume with water.

In this lab activity, you will make the TRIS/CaCl$_2$ buffer and use it to make an amylase solution. The resulting buffered amylase solution will be at a concentration of 10 mg/mL. You will use it in succeeding chapter labs.

Purpose

To make 50 mL of a buffer of 50 mM TRIS, 5 mM CaCl$_2$, pH 7.2.
To make 5 mL of a 10-mg/mL amylase solution in 50 mM TRIS, 5 mM CaCl$_2$ buffer, pH 7.2.

Materials

Environmental Health and Safety Officer

Gloves, large	Beakers, 100 mL	alpha-AMYLASE
Glasses, safety, plastic	pH meter and electrode	Tubes, 15 mL capped and
TRIS	pH calibrating buffer (pH 7)	rack
Calcium chloride, anhydrous	Hydrochloric acid solution,	Permanent lab marker pens
Balances, analytical	1M	Syringe filter, 0.2 μm
and tabletop	Sodium hydroxide, 10%	Syringe, plastic, 10 mL
Weigh paper and weigh boats	pH paper, wide and narrow	
Lab scoops	range	

Safety Precautions

- Wear goggles and gloves when using chemicals.
- Use a wet paper towel for small spills.

Procedure

Part I: Buffer Prep

1. Determine the amount of TRIS needed to prepare 50 mL of a buffer with a 50-mM concentration. Show the calculation in your notebook.
2. Determine the amount of $CaCl_2$ needed to prepare 50 mL of a buffer with a 5-mM concentration. Show the calculation in your notebook.
3. Mix the TRIS and $CaCl_2$ into 75 mL of deionized water until dissolved.
4. Measure the pH of the solution with pH paper. (It is probably fairly alkaline, or basic). Record this value in your notebook.
5. After calibrating a pH meter, adjust the pH up or down by adding 1 M of HCl or 10% NaOH (or 1 M of NaOH) to a pH of 7.2. Mix thoroughly.
   Caution: Wear goggles and gloves when using chemicals. Use a wet paper towel for small spills.
6. Add enough deionized water to bring the total volume to 50 mL. Mix thoroughly.
7. Check the pH again to make sure it has remained at 7.2. Adjust the pH if necessary.

You have just made a buffer! It will maintain a pH of about 7.2 for several weeks to months.

Environmental Health and Safety Officer

4°C

Part II: Addition of Protein

8. Measure out enough amylase to make 5 mL of a 10-mg/mL solution. Show the calculation in your notebook.
9. Add the amylase to a sterile 15-mL tube. Add buffer to the 5-mL graduation. Rotate **gently** to mix. Amylase is not very soluble, so it may take several minutes to go into solution. Do not shake it. Foaming indicates denaturing of protein.
10. Label the tube with the sample name, buffer recipe, your name, and the date. Store at 4°C until ready to use. For long-term storage, filter-sterilize the protein solution using a 0.2-μm filter, as directed by the supervisor.

Thinking Like a Biotechnician

A technician prepares the amylase in a TRIS/$CaCl_2$ buffer, but forgets to store it at 4°C. After a long weekend, the technician finds the sample on the lab bench.

1. Why is the improper storage a problem?
2. How can the sample be tested to determine whether it is still usable?

Laboratory 7e   Demonstration of Buffer Efficacy

Developed with the assistance of Avi Moussa, Biotechnology Student.

Background

Buffers are designed to resist changes to pH within a certain pH range. Different buffers are more effective than others in their ability to maintain the pH of a solution.

Environmental Health
and Safety Officer

Purpose

What is the buffering efficacy of some common buffers?

Materials

Balances, analytical and tabletop	Beakers, 100 mL	Sodium hydroxide, 10%
Weigh paper and weigh boats	Permanent lab marker pens	pH paper, wide and narrow range
Lab scoops	Graduated cylinders, 25 mL	Micropipet, P-100
TRIS	pH meter and electrode	Micropipet tips for P-100
Sodium phosphate, monohydrate	pH calibrating buffer (pH 7)	
	Hydrochloric acid solution, $1M$	

Safety Precautions

- Wear goggles and gloves when using chemicals.
- Use lab matting or a paper towel to cover the lab tabletop while conducting the experiment.
- Use a wet paper towel for small spills.
- If exposed to acid or base, rinse the affected area with large amounts of water.

Procedure

1. Prepare 50 mL of a 0.1-M TRIS buffer at pH 8.0, and 50 mL of a 0.1-M sodium monophosphate buffer at pH 4.5. In your notebook, show all calculations, and draw a diagram of each buffer preparation.
2. Calibrate the pH meter to 7.0.

Buffering Efficacy of Water
3. To a clean 50-mL beaker, add 25 mL of dH_2O.
4. Determine the pH of the dH_2O.
5. Add 20 µL of $1M$ HCl to the dH_2O.
6. Mix well. Determine the new pH of the water solution.
7. Repeat steps 5 and 6, four times, for a total of 100 µL of acid.
8. Repeat steps 2 through 7, using $1M$ NaOH instead of the acid.
9. In your notebook, record the pH of all the water mixtures in a data table.

Buffering Efficacy of a Sodium Monophosphate Buffer
10. To a clean 50-mL beaker, add 25 mL of $NaH_2PO_4 \cdot H_2O$ buffer, pH 4.5.
11. Confirm the pH of the sodium monophosphate buffer.
12. Add 20 µL of $1M$ HCl to the sodium monophosphate buffer.
13. Mix well. Determine the new pH of the sodium monophosphate buffer.
14. Repeat steps 12 and 13, four times, for a total of 100 µL of acid.
15. Repeat steps 10 through 14, using $1M$ NaOH instead of the acid.
16. Add the pH data for all the buffer mixtures to the data table.

Buffering Efficacy of Sodium TRIS Buffer
17. To a clean 50-mL beaker, add 25 mL of TRIS buffer.
18. Confirm the pH of the TRIS buffer.
19. Add 20 µL of $1M$ HCl to the TRIS buffer.
20. Mix well. Then determine the pH of the TRIS buffer.
21. Repeat steps 19 and 20, four times, for a total of 100 µL of acid.
22. Repeat steps 17 through 21, using $1M$ NaOH instead of the acid.
23. Add the pH data for all the buffer mixtures to the data table.

Data Analysis

Using Excel®, graph the data for all three solutions on a three-line, line graph. Put the amount of acid or base along the X-axis and the pH of the sample on the Y-axis. Color-code and label each line on the graph.

Conclusion

Write a conclusion statement discussing the characteristics of each buffer and the evidence for each buffer's efficacy or lack of efficacy. Also, discuss the value of using buffers, instead of water, as the solvent for protein or nucleic acid solutions.

Thinking Like a Biotechnician

1. When preparing a buffer, why is water added in two stages? Why is water not added to the buffering salt up to the desired final volume, all in one step?
2. Look at other results for this experiment. Do the graphs of other groups look the same as yours? Consider two groups that have conducted the TRIS buffer efficacy test. Both groups' graphs are the same shape, but Group 1's entire graph is 1 pH unit lower than Group 2's graph. Explain how this could happen.
3. In March, a buffer is prepared and used. The unused portion is stored at 4°C. In August, a technician wants to use it. On inspection, the technician sees a tiny bit of fuzz in the buffer on the bottom of the bottle. Is the buffer usable? Why or why not? What do you think the fuzz is?

Laboratory 7f   Using the Spectrophotometer to Study the Amylase Protein

Background

Amylase, like other molecules, interacts with light waves and absorbs or transmits light energy of various wavelengths. If set at an appropriate wavelength, a spectrophotometer can detect amylase in a solution as the amylase molecules absorb light energy. The more amylase molecules in solution, the greater the absorbance should be.

Amylase molecules absorb light of some wavelengths better than others (just as the different dye solutions did in Lab 7b). If one is to detect small amounts of amylase in solution, it is best to know at which wavelength the amylase molecules absorb the most light. This wavelength will be the most "sensitive" to the presence of amylase.

Like most proteins, amylase molecules are colorless and, in buffer, they absorb light only in the UV range, actually at 280 nm. Spec 20 D spectrophotometers are VIS specs, and they do not detect in the UV range. To use the Spec 20 D to detect amylase, we mix the amylase with a colored indicator, Bradford reagent. The Bradford reagent reacts proportionally with the protein to give a blue molecule.

To determine the lambda_{max} for amylase (+ Bradford protein reagent), we must produce an absorption spectrum for the Bradford-amylase pair and see where the peak of light absorption is (see Figure 7.7). The lambda_{max} will then be used to detect amylase molecules in solution in future experiments.

A Bradford assay can be used to estimate the approximate protein concentration prior to running protein samples on gels. Bradford reagent contains Coomassie® Blue G250 dye molecules, which react primarily with the arginine amino-acid residues in proteins.

Purpose

What is the absorption spectrum for amylase (+ Bradford protein reagent)?
What is the lambda_{max} for the amylase (+ Bradford protein reagent) mixture?

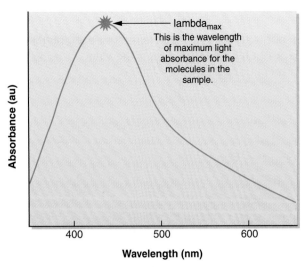

Figure 7.7. Lambda$_{max}$ Graph. For research and manufacturing, knowing the lambda$_{max}$ of a sample is valuable. Once the lambda$_{max}$ has been determined, the spec is set to that wavelength, and used to determine the presence and concentration of the molecule of interest in the sample.

Environmental Health and Safety Officer

Materials

Amylase, 10 mg/mL (from Lab 7d)	Plug caps for 13×100 mm tubes	Permanent lab marker pens
Micropipet, P-1000	Peg racks for 10-13 mm tubes	Bradford reagent, 1X or 0.5X
Micropipet tips for P-1000	Pipets, 5 mL	Spectrophotometer,
Tubes, glass, 13×100 mm	Pipet pump, green	Spectronic 20 D+

Safety Precautions

- Wear goggles and gloves when using chemicals.
- Use lab matting or a paper towel to cover the lab tabletop while conducting the experiment.
- Use a wet paper towel for small spills.
- If exposed to acid or base, rinse the affected area with large amounts of water.

Procedure

1. Prepare tubes to determine the absorption spectrum for amylase as follows:

   a. Prepare a sample tube by placing 0.5 mL of a 10-mg/mL amylase solution into a cuvette. Add 3 mL of 1X Bradford reagent. Mix gently, but thoroughly, and let stand for approximately 3 minutes.

   b. Prepare a blank by placing 0.5 mL of buffer into a cuvette. Add 3 mL of 1X Bradford reagent. Mix gently, but thoroughly, and let stand for approximately 3 minutes.

2. Use the spec to determine the amount of absorbance at each of 17 wavelengths by following the steps at the top of the next page.

3. In your notebook, record the absorbance data for the amylase-Bradford mixture in a data table.

Spectrophotometer Use

1. Make sure that the spec has warmed up for at least 20 minutes.
2. Set the wavelength to 540 nm. Do not read absorbencies at wavelengths lower than 540 nm. Do you know why?
3. Check to see that the sample holder is empty and closed.
4. Use the 0% T control knob to set the amount of transmittance to 0%.
5. Wipe fingerprints from the blank, insert it, and set the transmittance to 100% with the 100% T knob.
6. Wipe fingerprints from the sample tube, insert it, and read the absorbance value.
7. Repeat steps 2 through 6 for every 5 nm up to 620 nm.

Data Analysis/Conclusion

Graph the absorbance data as a line graph. This line is the absorption spectrum for the amylase-Bradford mixture. What is the $lambda_{max}$ for the amylase-Bradford mixture? What is the $lambda_{min}$ for the amylase-Bradford mixture? Of what value are these wavelength data? Describe how and when these data may be used in the R&D or manufacturing of a protein. Discuss any errors in technique that might lead to an incorrect determination of the $lambda_{max}$.

Thinking Like a Biotechnician

1. Instead of a nice, smooth, bell-shaped curve, the absorbance spectrum for a molecule has one point that is "spiked up" to about 0.8 au above the rest of the graph. What might cause this?
2. Amylase is a colorless molecule; thus, Bradford reagent was used in this experiment to make it visible in the Spec 20 D. Name at least one disadvantage to using the Bradford reagent on a suspected amylase sample.
3. Xanthophyll is the yellow pigment in lemons. Sketch the absorbance spectrum that would be expected for a sample of xanthophyll.
4. Propose a method to detect colorless amylase in a sample and still be able to recover it, unaltered, for future use.

Laboratory 7g Determining the Concentration of Amylase in Solution

Background

Often, the goal of a biotechnology company's product pipeline is to manufacture a protein. The company must synthesize enough of the protein to market it at a profit.

The proteins are made in cells, usually ones that have been transformed with recombinant DNA (rDNA). The protein-making cells are grown in huge fermentation tanks. Often, the protein is released into the fermentation broth in which the cells are grown, although sometimes the proteins are held within the cell. Either way, the protein has to be isolated from all the other thousands of proteins made by a typical cell.

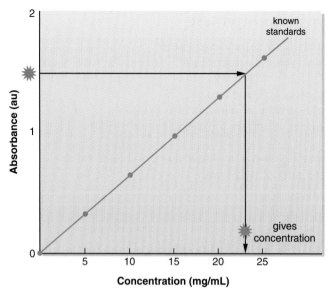

Figure 7.8. Standard Curve of Protein Concentration versus Absorbance. The absorbance of a sample is directly proportional to the number of molecules present (concentration).

Separating a protein of interest from other unwanted molecules is called purification. The biotech company wants purified proteins that are active, stable, and of a relatively high concentration. When proteins are purified from solutions (cytoplasm or fermentation broth, etc), the product must be checked to see whether the protein is present and how much is present. At every step in the manufacture of a protein, the concentration must be determined. Protein concentration is usually measured in milligrams per milliliter (mg/mL) or micrograms per milliliter (µg/mL).

Since the protein molecules are submicroscopic, we must measure them using indirect methods. To determine the concentration of a solution, one produces a standard curve that plots the absorbance of solutions at *known* concentrations. First, the technician prepares solutions of known concentrations and reads their absorbance at a given wavelength. The technician produces a "best-fit" straight line, representing how the concentration affects the absorbance by the molecule being tested. The absorbance of an *unknown* solution is then determined. From the "best-fit" straight-line standard curve, the concentration of the unknown solution is determined based on where the absorbance value intersects the standard curve (see Figure 7.8).

Purpose

What are the concentrations of two unknown amylase solutions?

Materials

Environmental Health and Safety Officer

Amylase stock solution, 10 mg/mL (from Lab 7d)	50 mM TRIS, 5 mM CaCl$_2$, pH 7.2 (from Lab 7d)	Plug caps for 13×100 mm tubes
Tube rack for 1.7 mL tubes	Pipets, 1 mL	Peg racks for 10-13 mm tubes
Reaction tubes, 1.7 mL	Pipet pump, blue	Spectrophotometer,
Micropipet, P-1000	Pipets, 5 mL	Spectronic 20 D+
Micropipet tips for P-1000	Pipet pump, green	
Permanent lab marker pens	Tubes, glass, 13×100 mm	

Caution: Wear goggles and gloves when using chemicals.

Procedure

Part I: Sample Preparation

1. Prepare a serial dilution of the *known* samples starting with the 10 mg/mL of amylase stock solution as follows:

   a. Label five 1.7-mL tubes No. 1 through 5.
   b. Add 0.5 mL of a buffer of 50 mM TRIS, 5 mM CaCl$_2$, pH 7.2 to each of the test tubes No. 2 through 5.
   c. To test tube No. 1, add 1 mL of the stock 10-mg/mL-amylase solution. Mix gently. Record the concentration of this sample in your notebook.
   d. Take 0.5 mL of the protein solution in test tube No. 1 and add it to test tube No. 2. Mix well.
   e. Take 0.5 mL of the solution in test tube No. 2 and add it to test tube No. 3. Mix well. Record the concentration of this sample in your notebook.
   f. Continue making these dilutions with the remaining test tubes. After preparing test tube No. 5, discard the extra 0.5 mL so that all tubes No. 1 through 5 contain the same volume of solution. Record the concentration of these tubes in your notebook. What type of serial dilution have you performed (ie, 1:2, 1:3, 1:4, or 1:5)?

2. Transfer 0.5 mL of each of these known concentrations to a labeled 13×100-mm tube. Add 3 mL of Bradford protein reagent to each. Mix well. Wait 3 minutes.

3. Label two more 13×100-mm cuvettes "unknown No. 1" and "unknown No. 2." Add 0.5 mL of the appropriate unknown amylase solution to each tube. Add 3 mL of 1X Bradford protein reagent to each unknown. Mix well. Wait 3 minutes.

4. In another 13×100-mm cuvette, prepare a blank with 0.5 mL of buffer plus 3 mL of 1X Bradford protein reagent. Mix well. Wait 3 minutes.

Part II: Absorbance Data Collection

5. Read each tube's absorbance at lambda$_{max}$ for an amylase-Bradford reagent mixture (lambda$_{max}$ was determined in the last activity).

6. In your notebook, create a data table to store the absorbance data for all the amylase samples of known concentration (amylase protein standards). In another data table, record the absorbance of the unknown amylase samples.

Data Analysis/Conclusion

7. Make a **very large** graph with concentration on the X-axis and absorbance on the Y-axis. Make a "best fit" straight line of the **known** concentration samples versus their absorbance values. **Note:** If you are creating the graph using Microsoft® Excel®, pull down "Chart" on the "Menu," select "Add Trendline," and select "Linear Regression." It will add a "best-fit" straight line for you. Double-click on the "Best-fit Trendline." Select "Options." Click on "axis through 0" and "show equation of the line." This will determine the "slope of the line" to be used later.

8. Using this best-fit standard curve, estimate the concentration of your "unknowns." Show (draw in) where the absorbance value for each "unknown" intersects the following: the Y-axis, the "best-fit" straight line, and the X-axis (refer to the Background section of this lab). Record these estimates of the "unknown's" concentration in the data table of unknown amylase samples from step 5.

    In industry, the concentration of a sample is calculated mathematically using the linear regression equation below. This method allows technicians to determine the concentrations of many "unknowns" quickly.

$$y = mx + b$$

y = the absorbance of the unknown sample
m = the slope of the best-fit straight line
x = the concentration of the unknown sample
b = the Y intercept

Note: y: For unknown protein solutions, such as those used in amylase R&D, the absorbance is easily measured on a spectrophotometer, as in the steps above.

m: The slope can be determined by using the "Trendline" option described in step 7. The slope of a line also can be determined using data in a Microsoft® Excel® data table as follows.

Highlight two cells. In the first cell, type "slope =." Type the formula, found in the box below, into the second cell. At the "*y values*" prompt, highlight the Y-axis data you want considered. At the "*x values*" prompt, highlight the X-axis data you want considered:

$$=linest(yvalues,xvalues,false,false)$$

Then press "Enter." The "false/false" is telling the program that you want your line to go through "zero." By adding this formula, you are directing the computer to compare the rise of your line with the run of your line. This will give you the value for the slope of the line.

b: In this case, b = 0, because at 0 concentration, you expect the absorbance to be 0.

x: The concentration of an unknown sample can be solved by putting the other numbers into the equation.

Using either method of slope determination, you may now do the mathematical calculations (y = mx + b) to determine the concentration of your unknown protein samples.

Since "b" should be equal to 0, the equation is just y = mx, so, if you know the slope of the standard line and the absorbance of an unknown sample, you can now determine "x," the concentration of the sample.

Using y = mx + b, calculate the concentrations of the unknown samples, and add these data to your data table.

9. Collect the concentration determinations for each unknown (y = mx + b) from the other groups in the class (multiple replications). Put these values into a new data table. Calculate the average concentration of each sample for all the replications of the experiment. These averages are the best guess of the true concentrations of the "unknowns."

How good are your data? Are they accurate, reliable? How well does your data "match" the multiple replications of the experiment? Compare your values to the averages, the mean, and the range of values.

10. In the lab during R&D, if data are within 10% of the value expected, they are often considered "close enough." Determine the amount of deviation your measurements have (in %) from the average values. To do this, use the following equations.

$$\frac{\text{your sample's value} - \text{the class' average for the sample}}{\text{the class' average for the sample}} \times 100 = \underline{\quad}\% \text{ deviation for unknown No. 1 from the class average}$$

$$\frac{\text{your sample's value} - \text{the class' average for the sample}}{\text{the class' average for the sample}} \times 100 = \underline{\quad}\% \text{ deviation for unknown No. 2 from the class average}$$

Is your determination of each "unknown's" concentration "close enough"?

11. Commonly, sample data are analyzed to see how much they deviate from average data. Scientists usually consider data within 1 deviation above or below the average to be valid. Determine the standard deviation (SD) of each group of amylase samples (multiple replications) using the following formula.

$$\text{Standard Deviation} = \sqrt{\frac{\sum (\text{Average} - \text{sample reading})^2}{\text{\# of samples}}}$$

If you are using Microsoft® Excel® for your data table, it is relatively easy to calculate the SD for a group of numbers. Highlight an empty cell, and enter the following equation:

= STDEV (highlight the numbers you want to analyze)

Press "Enter." Add and subtract the SD to your class average. Do your own samples' data fall within the SD?

The range of acceptable concentration determinations is the average, + and - the SD. For example, if the average for a group of data is 4.8 mg/mL, and the SD is 0.7, then the range of acceptable data is 5.5 mg/mL down to 4.1 mg/mL. If a sample does not fit in this range, then the data either do not support the hypothesis or they are erroneous.

Should your individual determinations of the "unknown's" concentration be accepted as valid? The smaller the SD for the collection of samples, the more reproducibility there is in the measurements. With a small SD, you can have confidence that the group of measurements reflects the concentrations of the samples.

Thinking Like a Biotechnician

1. Without using the spectrophotometer, how can you estimate the concentration of amylase in the unknown samples?
2. On the best-fit standard curve, all the points are lined up, except the 10-mg/mL sample. It is much lower than the rest of the line. Why might this be? Should the value be used in the standard curve?
3. A set of proteins is studied in the spectrophotometer. The linear regression ($y = mx + b$) gives a slope of $m = 0.93$. An unknown sample's absorbance is measured at 0.66 au. What is the approximate concentration of the unknown sample?

Laboratory 7h   Comparing Assay Techniques: BCA versus Bradford

Background

Several protein assay methods are available. Some researchers prefer using a BCA (bicinchoninic acid) assay to a Bradford assay when determining protein concentration since it is reported that BCA is more stable and more sensitive. Each of these assays is available for purchase in kit form.

To be certain that an assay is the best choice for a certain application, a technician would design an assay to test the assay.

Purpose

To plan and execute trials to compare the concentration sensitivity of both a Bradford assay and a BCA assay on amylase solutions, using a UV/VIS spectrophotometer.

Materials

Pierce Brand BCA kits	50 mM TRIS, 5 mM CaCl$_2$, pH	Micropipet tips for P-1000
Pierce Brand Bradford kits	7.2 (from Lab 7d)	UV/Vis spectrophotometer
Amylase stock solution,	Tube rack for 1.7 mL tubes	UV spectrophotometer
0.1 mg/mL (diluted from	Reaction tubes, 1.7 mL	cuvettes
Lab 7d stock)	Permanent lab marker pens	Pasteur pipets, 9"
	Micropipet, P-1000	Pasteur pipet bulbs

Procedure

1. Use the User's Manual to learn how to conduct both BCA and a Bradford assays in the UV/VIS spectrophotometer.
2. Read the directions in both the BCA and Bradford assay kits.
3. Design a set of procedures to measure and confirm the concentration of progressively smaller concentrations of amylase in solution, until confidence in measurements is no longer possible. Use BSA as the standard solution. Test each assay kit with enough replications to be confident in your data.

Data Analysis

Report all procedures, raw data, data analysis, error analysis, results, inferences, and applications in your notebook.

Conclusion

Prepare a formal, written laboratory report for your supervisor using Microsoft® Word® and Microsoft® Excel®. Detail the performance of each assay kit, and state your recommendation as to which one should be used for amylase studies. Submit the report to your supervisor.

Laboratory 7i   Using the UV Spec to Study Colorless Protein Samples

Background

Proteins that have color can be visualized in the visible spectrum using almost any spectrophotometer. Determining the lambda$_{max}$ is rather simple and predictable if a protein's color is obvious. Yet, most proteins are colorless. However, if you add an indicator, the protein becomes colored and can be seen with a VIS spec. Most indicators, though, alter the protein so the sample cannot be retrieved for other uses. Being able to visualize a colorless protein is valuable in that the sample can be retrieved unaltered. A UV spectrophotometer is used to measure colorless proteins. Like a VIS spec, a UV spec shines light (wavelengths of 350 nm or less) on a sample and determines the amount of light transmitted through the molecules. A deuterium lamp produces the UV light. Special low-volume, high-quality cuvettes are used in UV specs (see Figure 7.9).

The lambda$_{max}$ for colorless proteins can be determined on a UV spectrophotometer, and the lambda$_{max}$ can be used to determine the concentration of the colorless proteins in solution.

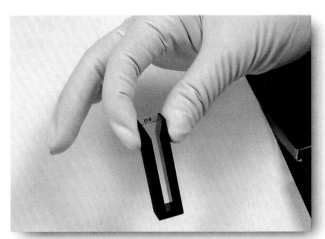

Figure 7.9. **Quartz cuvettes are often used in a spec if DNA is being studied at 260 nm. Quartz, glass, or plastic cuvettes can be used if the measurement is at wavelengths above 280 nm. Since the UV cuvettes hold much less sample than the cuvettes for the Spec 20 D, less sample is wasted. In addition, samples that are studied without indicator solution are retrieved and available for future use.**
Photo by author.

Purpose

To prepare absorbance spectra for different concentrations of the same colorless protein.
To determine the lambda$_{max}$ for the colorless protein.

Materials

Amylase stock solution, 10 mg/mL (diluted from Lab 7d stock)	Tube rack for 1.7 mL tubes	UV/Vis spectrophotometer
	Reaction tubes, 1.7 mL	UV spectrophotometer cuvettes
50 mM TRIS, 5 mM CaCl2, pH 7.2 (from Lab 7d)	Permanent lab marker pens	Pasteur pipets, 9"
	Micropipet, P-1000	Pasteur pipet bulbs
	Micropipet tips for P-1000	

Procedure

Each UV spectrophotometer operates slightly differently. Make sure you know which cuvettes to use and how to clean them. Make sure you know how to "blank" a sample. Familiarize yourself with how to navigate through the dialog box of the spectrophotometer you are using and how to direct the spectrophotometer to collect an absorbance spectrum.

1. Prepare 5 mL of a 1-mg/mL protein solution from the 10 mg/mL amylase solution in 50 mM TRIS, 5 mM CaCl$_2$, pH 7.2 buffer. Prepare a 1:10 serial dilution of the protein solution (two additional tubes) resulting in a total of three different concentrations of the protein. Use the buffer as a diluent.
2. Use the UV spec to determine an absorbance spectrum for each of the protein samples.
3. Collect and record data for wavelengths between 200 and 400 nm (UV light wavelengths) in a data table in your notebook.

Data Analysis/Conclusion

Create a three-line line graph showing the absorbance spectrum for each protein solution. Color-code and label each line. Determine the lambda$_{max}$ for each sample. What can be said about the lambda$_{max}$ for each protein? How are the lines on the graph similar, and how do they differ from each other? Is this expected? Why or why not? How are these determinations important when studying protein samples?

Thinking Like a Biotechnician

1. When analyzing a 1 mg/mL amylase absorbance spectrum, most of the absorbance values peak at 2 au. Why is this a problem in determining the lambda$_{max}$ of the sample? What should be done?
2. When analyzing the 1 mg/mL amylase absorbance spectrum, most of the absorbance values peak at under 0.2 au, and most are under 0.02 au. Why is this a problem in determining the lambda$_{max}$ of the sample? What should be done?

Chapter 8

Recombinant Protein Production

Using a microscope, a biotechnologist checks the health of cells in liquid media. Genetically engineered mammalian cells, such as those growing in these cultures, are used to grow complex human proteins. Bacteria cells can be engineered to produce simpler proteins.

Photo courtesy of Cell Genesys, Inc.

Advances in molecular biology in the early 1970s, including the ability to create and transfer recombinant DNA (rDNA) molecules into cells, revolutionized both science and industry. Using special enzymes and special cell-culture techniques, scientists could create new combinations of genes and place them into specific cell lines that would produce proteins coded by the newly inserted DNA. New and improved cells and organisms, with hundreds of new agricultural and pharmaceutical benefits, were and are still being created.

The first genetically modified organisms were bacteria that made rather simple proteins of pharmaceutical interest, such as growth hormone and insulin. Later, scientists used genetically engineered fungi and mammalian cells to manufacture complex enzymes and antibodies. In the 1980s, several plants were transformed with rDNA giving them traits that improved yield and quality.

In the following activities, you will learn how to use rDNA molecules to transform bacteria into protein factories. Specifically, you will learn how to:

- use restriction enzymes to characterize an rDNA sample
- transform bacteria cells into amylase producers
- distinguish between transformants (genetically engineered cells) and nontransformants
- grow and monitor a cell culture of transformed cells
- extract rDNA plasmids from transformed cells

Once cells are transformed, they must be grown in large enough volumes to yield marketable amounts. This occurs in manufacturing during fermentation, scale-up, and protein purification. These manufacturing techniques are presented in lab activities in the next chapter. Although bacterial transformations are performed in these activities, many of the transformation techniques are similar to those involved in the genetic engineering of other organisms.

Laboratory 8a Restriction Analysis of the Lambda Phage DNA Sequence

Background

Lambda (λ) phage DNA, cut using the *Hin*dIII restriction enzyme, is universally used as a DNA sizing standard. The uncut lambda DNA is 48,502 bp long. When *Hin*dIII is used to digest, or cut, the lambda DNA molecule, eight restriction fragments result with lengths shown in Table 8.1.

Seven of the eight fragments produced during the lambda/*Hin*dIII restriction digestion are easily visualized on an agarose gel (see Figure 8.1). Since the standard bands are of known size, the sizes of other unknown DNA fragments can be estimated by comparing the distance they travel on a gel to the distance traveled by the lambda/*Hin*dIII restriction fragments on the same gel.

Table 8.1.   Lambda/*Hin*dIII Sizing Standards.   The lambda/*Hin*dIII sizing standards are used on agarose gels when separating medium-sized pieces of DNA. Pieces containing fewer than 500 bp are not likely to be seen.

Lambda/*Hin*dIII Restriction Fragments (bp)
23,130
9,416
6,557
4,361
2,322
2,027
564
125

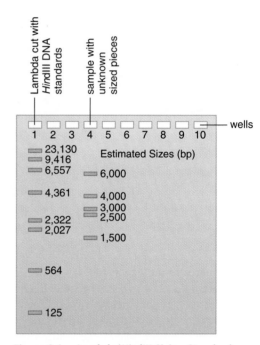

Figure 8.1.   Lambda/*Hin*dIII Sizing Standards on Gel.   The lambda/*Hin*dIII standards are used to estimate the sizes of other bands on the gel. Sizing standards are also called markers.

Purpose

Do the restriction fragments produced during a lambda DNA/*Hin*dIII digestion match the bands present in the commercially available lambda DNA + *Hin*dIII standard markers?

What are the number and lengths of restriction fragments produced during a lambda DNA/*Eco*RI digestion?

Given the bands in each digestion, evaluate each for use, as a possible sizing standard, to determine the lengths of other DNA fragments. Is one better suited as a sizing standard than the other? If so, why?

Materials (per team)

Tube rack for 1.7 mL tubes	*Eco*RI enzyme, 5000 U	Lambda/*Hin*dIII, 50 µg/µL +
Reaction tubes, 1.7 mL	*Hin*dIII enzyme, 5000 U	dye
Permanent lab marker pens	Sterile deionized water	Power supply
Ice bucket	Microcentrifuge	Ethidium bromide, 0.5 µg/mL
Micropipet, P-10	Water bath, 37°C	Gel photo imaging system
Micropipet tips for P-10	Agarose, 0.8%	Paper, thermal
Micropipet, P-100	TAE buffer, 1×	Printer, thermal
Micropipet tips for P-100	Gel box, horizontal, for	Gloves, large
Lambda DNA	agarose gels	Glasses, safety, plastic
Reaction buffer, 10×	Power supply	Weigh boat, 5.5"×5.5"

Environmental Health
and Safety Officer

Safety Precautions

- EtBr is a hazardous chemical.
- EtBr is to be used by the supervisor only.
- Wear goggles and gloves while in an area where EtBr is used.

Procedure

- **Keep reagents on ice.** The reagents and enzymes are temperature sensitive.
- **Use sterile technique.** DNA is easily destroyed by contaminant enzymes. Contaminants might also inhibit restriction-enzyme performance.
- **Pipet slowly and carefully.** You are using tiny volumes of reagents. These are easily measured incorrectly.

Part I: Preparing Digests

1. Label four **sterile** 1.7-mL reaction tubes as specified on the reaction matrix. The restriction digests will take place in these tubes. Keep tubes on ice unless otherwise directed.
2. Add reagents to each reaction tube as shown in Table 8.2. Pipet each reagent directly into the solution that is already in the tube. Make sure to watch the end of the pipet tip to ensure that all of each reagent is added. Change tips for each delivery. Buffer goes into the tube before enzyme. **Always add enzyme last.** Make sure you use the restriction buffer matched specifically to a particular restriction enzyme.

Table 8.2.   **Lambda Restriction Digestion Reaction Matrix**

Labeled Tubes	λ DNA	10X Restriction Buffer	Enzyme	Sterile H$_2$O	Total Reaction Volume
H	10 µL	2 µL	2 µL *Hind*III	6 µL	20 µL
E	10 µL	2 µL	2 µL *Eco*RI	6 µL	20 µL
+C	10 µL	2 µL	—	8 µL	20 µL
–C	—	2 µL	2 µL *Hind*III	16 µL	20 µL

37°C   4°C

3. Tightly close the caps on the tubes. Give a 1- to 2-second pulse in the microfuge to mix and pool the reactants. (Be sure the tubes are in a balanced arrangement on the rotor!)
4. Incubate the restriction digests at 37°C for a few hours.
5. Store the digests at 4°C until they are used in gel electrophoresis.

Part II: Analyzing the Digests

6. Pour a 0.8% agarose gel with the six-toothed comb set into the end slots.
7. Place 300 mL of 1X TAE electrophoresis buffer in your gel box.
8. Place the agarose gel in the gel box in the correct orientation.
9. Get an empty reaction tube for preparing the sizing standards. Label it "Std."
10. Into tube "Std," place the following and mix:

    5 µL of lambda DNA + *Hin*dIII (standard marker pieces of known size)
    2 µL of 10X restriction buffer
    13 µL of sterile distilled water

11. Line up tubes, in a rack, in the order they will be loaded.
12. Add 3 µL of DNA loading dye to each tube. Change tips each time.
13. Give the tubes a 1- to 2-second pulse in the microfuge to mix and pool reactants.
14. Load all 23 µL of each tube into a well of your gel. Load Tube H into Well 1, Tube E into Well 2, and continue in the order the tubes were prepared. Change tips each time.
15. Run the gel at 110 V for approximately 45 minutes, or until the loading dye travels at least halfway on the gel.
16. After the gel has run, stain it with EtBr (No. 17) or methylene blue solution (see the instructor). Or, if time is short, move the gel into a weigh boat and zipper-type plastic bag, and store it in a tiny bit of buffer overnight until there is time to stain and photograph it.

Environmental Health
and Safety Officer

17. Place the gel in an EtBr solution (for staining) for a minimum of 15 minutes. **Remember the safety precautions. Only the instructor should use EtBr. Wear goggles and gloves when in the presence of EtBr.**

18. The instructor will pour off the EtBr and fill the staining tray with deionized water. Let sit for 2 minutes; then pour off the water.

19. Photograph your gel for a permanent record. Place the photo in the data section of your notebook. Identify and label the known lambda/*Hin*dIII standard sizing fragments (Std tube). The size of these known standard fragments, in base pairs, follows:

| 23130 | 9416 | 6557 | 4361 | 2322 | 2027 | (564, 125—difficult to see) |

20. Label the well of each lane and identify what was loaded into each well.

21. Estimate the size of the unknown bands by comparing them to the known lambda fragments. Record these values in a data table in your notebook, and label them on the photograph, on the bottom of each of their lanes.

Data Analysis/Conclusion

Study the bands in the "H" lane. These are the bands produced by your *Hin*dIII digestion of the λ DNA. The bands in this lane should match the bands in the "Std" lane. Do they? Why or why not? If so, how were they produced? If not, list three reasons that the banding pattern might not be the same in these lanes.

Study the bands in the "E" lane. These are the bands produced by your *Eco*RI digestion of the λ DNA. If you determine the size of all the bands in the *Eco*RI lane, what amount should their total equal? Should any of the bands in the *Eco*RI lane match the bands in the "Std" or "H" lanes? Do they? Why or why not? If so, how were they produced? If not, explain why not.

Do all groups in the class have similar banding pattern data? Why or why not? Discuss the possible errors that could lead to varying results, for the same digestions, from one team to another.

Evaluate the usefulness of each of the digests (the lambda/*Hin*dIII digest and the lambda/*Eco*RI digest) in producing bands that allow accurate sizing of other unknown DNA fragment samples. Explain in depth what makes for a good sizing standard and why one of these digests is better than the other for this purpose.

Thinking Like a Biotechnician

1. What is the purpose of the +C and -C tubes? Did they give expected results? Should there have been any other "C" tubes? If so, what would be in them?

2. A technician runs the samples of the restriction digestion, and, in one lane, there are almost twice the number of bands expected. Give a possible reason for the extra bands.

3. A technician needs smaller sizing standards than the ones produced from a lambda/*Hin*dIII digestion. She wants to create a smaller sizing standard. There is another restriction enzyme, *Hae*III, in the −20°C freezer. It cuts DNA more often than *Hin*dIII (since it has a shorter, more common recognition site). A lambda/*Hae*III digestion is performed, and the samples are run on a gel. Smaller bands are seen. How might the technician estimate the size of these pieces?

Laboratory 8b   Restriction Digestion Used to Verify the pAmylase Plasmid

This lab was developed with the assistance of Pat Seawell, Gene Connection, and Diane Sweeney, Crystal Springs/Uplands School.

Background

Amylase is an enzyme that speeds the breakdown of starch to sugar. If genetic engineers see a need for large-scale production of the amylase enzyme to supply to several industrial customers, they can produce it in the lab.

One approach is to find naturally occurring bacteria (eg, *Bacillus subtilis*) or fungi that make amylase. They could grow these "wild" bacteria or fungi and then extract the amylase protein from them. Often, though, the naturally occurring bacteria or fungi grow too slowly, or their production of amylase is too low for commercial use. Also, there is the possibility that a native amylase-producing bacterium could be dangerous or pathogenic.

Scientists already have, in culture, bacteria and fungi that they know how to grow safely in large quantities. These "model" organisms can be coaxed to produce proteins in large amounts. The bacterium grown by most genetic engineering companies is *E. coli*. One of the fungi is *Aspergillus*. If these model organisms can be given the foreign DNA that codes for amylase production, they might produce large amounts of amylase. They could be transformed into amylase producers. The amylase these genetically engineered cells make could then be isolated, purified, and sold for a profit.

To engineer cells to make amylase, one needs to construct a vector that can carry the amylase gene into the cells. To make a recombinant plasmid coding for amylase production, the amylase gene (just over 2000 bp) is excised from a native source and pasted into an existing plasmid (pUC18). The new plasmid might be called pAmylase, pAmy for short, since it contains the amylase gene (see Figure 8.2). Along with the amylase gene, pAmylase would contain an ampicillin-resistance (Amp^R) gene since that was already present in the precursor

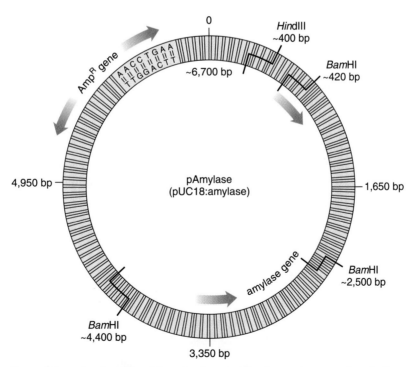

Figure 8.2.   pAmylase Plasmid.   pAmylase contains the amylase gene. In cells, the amylase gene is transcribed and amylase is produced. Starch clearing occurs on Luria Bertani (LB) starch agar plates around colonies that are transformed with pAmylase. An Amp^R gene is also part of pAmylase. The Amp^R gene allows a second way to detect that the plasmid got into cells, since only *E. coli* cells transformed with the Amp^R gene will grow on ampicillin agar.

plasmid vector, pUC. If a bacteria cell, such as *E. coli,* receives this plasmid, it will gain two new phenotypes, amylase production, and ampicillin resistance.

Before we transform *E. coli* cells with pAmylase DNA, we want to confirm that the DNA we are using has the characteristics of pAmylase. This can be done by restriction digestion. The pAmylase plasmid has a size of approximately 6700 bp. It contains a single restriction site for the *Hind*III restriction enzyme. It contains three sites, at specific locations, for the *Bam*HI restriction enzyme. The products of the restriction digestion by these enzymes can be seen on an agarose gel.

Purpose

When a suspected sample of pAmylase is cut by restriction enzymes, do the resulting DNA fragments indicate that the sample has the characteristics of pAmylase?

Materials

Tube rack for 1.7 mL tubes	*Bam*HI enzyme, 2500 U	Lambda/*Hind*III, 50 µg/µL +
Reaction tubes, 1.7 mL	Mixture of *Hind*III/*Bam*HI	dye
Permanent lab marker pens	enzymes	Power supply
Ice bucket	Sterile deionized water	Ethidium bromide, 0.5 µg/mL
Micropipet, P-10	Microcentrifuge	Gel photo imaging system
Micropipet tips for P-10	Water bath, 37°C	Paper, thermal
Micropipet, P-100	Agarose, 0.8%	Printer, thermal
Micropipet tips for P-100	TAE buffer, 1×	Gloves, large
pAmylase plasmid, 0.2 µg/µL	Gel box, horizontal, for	Glasses, safety, plastic
Reaction buffer, 10×	agarose gels	Weigh boat, 5.5"×5.5"
*Hind*III enzyme, 5000 U	Power supply	

Environmental Health and Safety Officer

Safety Precautions

- Wear goggles and gloves while in an area where EtBr is used.
- EtBr is a hazardous chemical.
- EtBr is to be used only by the supervisor.

Procedure

- **Keep reagents on ice.** The reagents and enzymes are temperature sensitive.
- **Make sure the restriction buffer is at the correct concentration.** If necessary, change the volumes accordingly.
- **Use sterile technique.** DNA is easily destroyed by contaminant enzymes. Contaminants might also inhibit restriction enzyme performance.
- **Pipet slowly and carefully.** You are using tiny volumes of reagents. These are easily measured incorrectly. Small pipeting errors can have a significant impact on the results.

Part I: Preparing Digests

1. Label five sterile 1.7-mL reaction tubes, A through E. The restriction digests will take place in these tubes. Keep the tubes on ice.
2. Add reagents to each reaction tube as shown in Table 8.3. Pipet each reagent directly into the solution that is already in the tube. Make sure to watch the end of the pipet tip to

Table 8.3. pAmylase Restriction Digestion Reaction Matrix

Tubes	pAmylase	10X Restriction Buffer	Enzyme	Sterile H$_2$0	Total Reaction Volume
A	4 µL	2 µL	2 µL *Hind*III	12 µL	20 µL
B	4 µL	2 µL	2 µL *Bam*HI	12 µL	20 µL
C	4 µL	2 µL	2 µL mixture	12 µL	20 µL
D	—	2 µL	2 µL mixture	16 µL	20 µL
E	4 µL	2 µL	—	14 µL	20 µL

37°C

4°C

ensure that all of each reagent is added. Change tips for each delivery. Buffer goes into the tube before the enzyme. **Always add enzyme last.**

3. Tightly close the caps on Tubes A through E. Give each tube a 1- to 2-second pulse in the microfuge to mix and pool reactants. (Be sure the tubes are in a balanced arrangement on the rotor!)

4. Incubate the restriction digests at 37°C for a few hours.

5. Store the digests at 4°C until they are used in the electrophoresis.

Part II: Analyzing the Digests

6. Pour a 0.8% agarose gel with the six-toothed comb set in the end slots.

7. Place 300 mL of 1X TAE electrophoresis buffer in your gel box.

8. Place the agarose gel in the gel box in the correct orientation.

9. Label an empty reaction tube "F."

10. Into Tube F, place the following:

> 5 μL of lambda DNA + *Hin*dIII (standard marker pieces of cut DNA of known size)
> 15 μL of deionized water

11. Line up Tubes A through F in a rack.

12. Add 3 μL of DNA loading dye to each tube. Change tips each time.

13. Give the tubes a 1- to 2-second pulse in the microfuge to mix and pool reactants.

14. Load all 23 μL of each tube into a well of your gel. Load Tube A into Well 1, B into Well 2, etc. Change tips each time.

15. Run the gel at 110 V for approximately 1 hour until the loading dye goes at least halfway on the gel. While you wait, draw a diagram in your notebook showing the sample that was loaded into each lane, and the concentration and voltage of the gel run.

16. After the gel has run, stain it with EtBr (No. 17) or move the gel into a weigh boat and store it in a tiny bit of buffer overnight. Methylene blue staining is an alternative. **Remember to follow the safety precautions.**

17. Place the gel in an EtBr solution (for staining) for a minimum of 15 minutes. **Remember to follow the safety precautions. Only the instructor should use EtBr. Wear goggles and gloves when in the presence of EtBr.**

18. The supervisor will pour off the EtBr and fill the staining tray with water. Let it sit for 2 minutes, then pour off the water.

CleanUp Kit

Environmental Health and Safety Officer

19. Photograph your gel for a permanent record. Glue the photo in the data section of your notebook. Identify and label the lambda standard fragments. The size of the DNA lambda standard fragments, in base pairs, follows. Estimate the size of the unknowns by comparing them to the known lambda fragments.

23130   9416   6557   4361   2322   2027   (564, 125—difficult to see)

- You can roughly estimate the lengths of the unknown bands by "eyeballing" the position of the unknown bands versus the known standard bands. Make a better estimate (more quantitative) by plotting the data on semilog graph paper with the standard fragment sizes along the y-axis and the distance they travel from the well along the x-axis. Draw a best-fit straight line through these data to produce a standard curve. To estimate the sizes of the unknowns, look at the intersection of the distance the unknowns traveled.

- You can make an even better estimate by letting Microsoft® Excel® create the standard curve for you. To do this, open a Microsoft® Excel® spreadsheet. Make a 2-column data table with the standard fragment sizes in the first column and the distance the fragments traveled in the second column. Using the Chart Wizard option in Excel®, plot the data on an XY scatter line graph. Click on the x-axis, and choose "options." Click on "logarithmic scale." This plots the x-axis logarithmically so that the line straightens out. Next, click on the line and choose, "Add a Trendline" from the Chart Menu. Select, "Logarithmic," then choose "Options," and click on "Show Equation." Now you should have a best-fit, straight line, standard curve, plus the equation of the line on the graph. To calculate a size for an unknown fragment, measure the distance traveled on the gel "y," and solve for ln (x). When you get ln (x), using f_x, determine "exp (x)"for the ln (x) value, and it will give the size of the unknown fragment. See the example below.

If an unknown fragment travels 1.8 cm, then y = 1.8.

1.8 = -0.5393 ln (x) + 6.2701

ln (x) = 8.2887

exp (8.2887)

x = 3979 bp

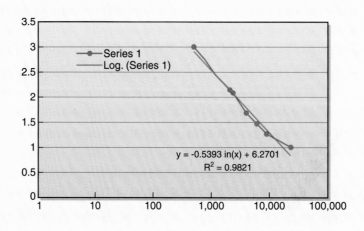

20. Place a label at the well of each lane, identifying the sample that was loaded into the well.
21. In a data table in your notebook, record the size of all of the DNA bands. On the photographs, label the length of each DNA fragment on the bottom of each of their lanes.

Data Analysis/Conclusion

Are the observed bands in the gel what was expected after restriction digestion? Do the digestion fragments indicate that the plasmid sample studied here has the characteristics of the pAmylase plasmid? Give evidence for your statement. Do all groups in the class have similar data? Why or why not? Discuss the possible errors that could lead to varying results from one team to another. If the digestion confirms that the sample is pAmylase, why is that information valuable?

Thinking Like a Biotechnician

The pAmylase used in this experiment is added to the tubes at 0.2 µg/µL. After the other reagents for the digestion are added, the final volume is 10 µL.

1. What is the actual concentration of plasmid DNA in Tube H?
2. What mass of plasmid DNA is in Tube H?
3. A restriction map can be drawn showing the relative positions of the *Bam*HI restriction sites to the *Hin*dIII site. To do this, determine the size of the fragments cut by each enzyme; then try to "fit" the pieces together like a jigsaw puzzle. In the past, restriction digestion mapping helped scientists determine the A, T, C, G sequence on a piece of DNA. Can you explain why?

Laboratory 8c   Transformation of *E. coli* with pAmylase

This lab was originally developed by Diane Sweeney, Crystal Springs/Uplands School. It was modified by Gene Connection and Ellyn Daugherty.

Background

In the 1970s, scientists wanted to develop an economical method of producing large quantities of amylase. *E. coli* is a bacterium with an excellent transformation "track record." Although it does not make amylase in nature, *E. coli* can be transformed in the laboratory to produce amylase.

Transforming *E. coli* takes several steps. First, the gene of interest (in this case, the amylase gene) must be inserted into a plasmid that contains an additional selection gene. In this activity, a pAmylase plasmid (pAmy) is used. pAmylase contains both the amylase production gene (from *Bacillus subtilis*) and the ampicillin resistance gene (Amp^R) from pUC18. The Amp^R gene produces an enzyme that destroys ampicillin in the media on which the bacteria grow. Ampicillin would normally delay the growth of *E. coli* cells, but if the cells acquire the Amp^R gene, they can survive in its presence.

To transform *E. coli* cells, researchers first grow them in broth culture and then treat them with CaCl$_2$, which makes them competent, or more likely to take up pieces of foreign DNA. Scientists are not sure what happens when cells are made competent, but it is thought that the CaCl$_2$ enlarges channels in the cells' membranes, making it easier for the plasmid to get into the cells (see Figure 8.3).

The competent cells are mixed with the recombinant pAmylase plasmid. A heat shock, followed by a cold shock, is given to the mixture, and plasmids are drawn in and trapped inside the cells. Next, the cells are grown in recovery broth, which gives them time to repair their damaged membranes and begin to express their new genes. The culture, containing a mix of transformed and nontransformed cells, is plated on selection media containing ampicillin and starch. Only the cells that are transformed will be able to grow on the ampicillin-containing, starch-agar selection media.

Under the best circumstances, transformation efficiency occurs in only about one in 10,000 cells. The transformed cells are deposited on the selection media, where they grow into colonies. Each cell in the colony is a clone of the original cell deposited in that location. All the cells in the clone contain the new DNA (a new genotype), and they will express the new characteristics (new phenotypes), in this case, ampicillin resistance and amylase production. If the transformation is successful, a colony of cells can be grown in broth and scaled up into larger volumes for manufacturing purposes.

Purpose

To transform *E. coli* with a "recombinant" pAmy plasmid, which contains a gene for ampicillin resistance and a gene for amylase production.

To demonstrate that the transformation was successful and that the newly inserted genes are being expressed by the transformed *E. coli* cells.

50 mM CaCl$_2$

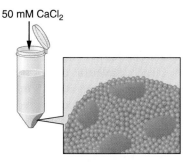

To make compentent cells, calcium chloride is added.

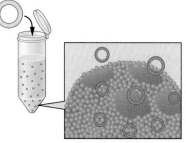

The calcium chloride is thought to make the cell's membrane proteins move apart slightly, widening the pores and allowing easier entry of plasmids.

Figure 8.3.   Making Competent Cells.   When cells are treated with CaCl$_2$, more plasmids enter into cells, increasing transformation efficiency (the number of cells transformed).

Environmental Health and Safety Officer

Materials

Poured LB agar plates	Lab gas lighter	Micropipet tips for P-100
Poured LB/amp agar plates	Inoculating loop, Ni/Cr wire	Micropipet, P-10
Poured LB/amp/2% starch	Water bath, 37°C, shaking	Micropipet tips for P-10
plates	Tubes, 15 mL capped	pAmylase plasmid, 0.005
Permanent lab marker pens	Tube racks for 15 mL tubes	µg/µL
Aluminum foil	Centrifuge for 15 mL tubes	Sterile deionized water
Laminar flow hood	Plastic beaker, 1L	Water bath, 42°C
Lysol® disinfectant	Bleach, 10%	Water bath, 37°C
Tubes, 50 mL, sterile	50 mM CaCl$_2$, cold	Sterile LB broth
Tube racks for 50 mL tubes	Ice bucket	Pipets, 1 mL, sterile
Pipets, 10 mL, sterile	Micropipet, P-1000	Pipet pump, blue
Pipet pump, green	Micropipet tips for P-1000	Glass spreaders
E. coli JM109, stock plate	Tube rack for 1.7 mL tubes	Incubator oven, 37°C
Glasses, safety, plastic	Reaction tubes, 1.7 mL	
Bunsen burner	Micropipet, P-100	

Environmental Health and Safety Officer

Procedure

- The plates must "dry out" for at least 24 hours before use. Prepare them in advance. They remain usable for up to 1 week if stored in the dark. Cover them in aluminum foil to make sure they stay dark.
- All tips, tubes, and pipets must be sterile.
- Use sterile technique throughout the procedure. Use a laminar flow hood, if available.
- Keep cells on ice unless otherwise directed.
- Dispose of all biohazards appropriately.

Part I: Preparing Competent Cells

37°C

1. Place 10 mL of sterile LB broth in a sterile 50-mL capped, conical centrifuge tube.
2. Inoculate the broth with a small amount of bacteria from one colony of JM109 AMY-bacteria. Cap the tube and finger-flick the broth to distribute the cells. Be sure the bacteria are well suspended.
3. Incubate the cultures at 37°C for 24 hours in a shaking hot water bath.
4. Transfer all 10 mL of overnight culture to a sterile 15-mL centrifuge tube. Spin the broth culture in a tabletop centrifuge at moderate speed for 10 minutes. The cells will pellet at the bottom. Carefully pour off and discard the supernatant into a trash container containing 10% bleach. **Save the cell pellet.**
5. Using a sterile pipet, add 0.5 mL of **cold** 50-mM CaCl$_2$ to the cell pellet. Resuspend the cells by repeatedly pipeting them up and down. **Be gentle.** These cells are stressed.
6. Tightly cap the tube and keep on ice for at least 20 minutes, or store overnight in the refrigerator.

Part II: Transforming the Competent Bacteria

4°C

7. Obtain two sterile 1.7-mL microtest tubes. Label one "C" (for control, no DNA added) and the other "D" (for DNA). Do not touch the inside of the tube or cap.
8. Check to make sure that the competent cell mixture is very cloudy with bacteria. Gently finger-flick the tube to ensure that no bacteria are lying on the bottom of the tube. Be gentle with these cells, they are fragile and can burst and die easily. Using sterile tips, add 150 µL of competent *E. coli* cells to each tube.
9. Place both tubes on ice and keep very cold until Step 13.
10. Add 10 µL of sterile distilled water to Tube C. Mix by finger-flicking. Wrist-flick the sample to pool the reagents. Return Tube C to ice.
11. Add 10 µL of pAmylase to Tube D. Pipet the plasmid **directly** into the cell suspension. Mix by finger-flicking. Wrist-flick the sample to pool the reagents. Return Tube D to ice.
12. Leave the cells on ice for a minimum of 15 minutes.

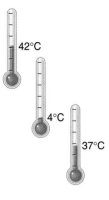

13. After 15 minutes, move your ice bath containing Tubes C and D next to the hot water bath. As quickly as possible, transfer both tubes from the ice to the hot water bath (42°C for JM109) for a "heat shock" of **exactly** 90 sec. **Move the tubes as quickly as possible since the more distinct the heat shock, the greater the transformation efficiency.**

14. After 90 seconds, quickly return the tubes to the ice bath for 3 minutes. Move the tubes as quickly as possible from the heat to the cold. **The more distinct the cold shock, the greater the transformation efficiency.**

15. Using a sterile 1-mL pipet, add 250 µL of sterile LB broth to each tube. Mix by finger flicking. Wrist-flick the sample to pool the reagents.

16. Incubate the tubes at 37°C for 10 to 15 minutes before plating.
    Note: You may stop at this point and store the tubes in the refrigerator overnight.

Part III: Plating the Bacteria on Selection Media

17. Disinfect the countertop by cleaning with disinfectant. Disinfect hands by thorough washing with hand soap or by using a hand disinfectant/sanitizer. Use a laminar flow hood, if available.

18. Obtain one plate each of 2% starch LB agar/ampicillin (selection plates), amp/LB agar (control), and LB agar (control). Draw a line down the center of each plate. Label one side "C" and one side "D." Also, add your initials and the date to each plate.

19. Finger-flick Tube C to resuspend the cells. Transfer 50 µL of the cell suspension to the center of each of the C sections on the three plates.

20. Finger-flick Tube D to resuspend the cells. Transfer 50 µL of the cell suspension to the center of each of the D sections on the three plates.

21. Spread cells over the surfaces of each section as follows:

Spreading Cells

Environmental Health and Safety Officer

- Practice sterile technique for spreading cells. Wash hands. Wear safety goggles. Tie hair back. Roll up sleeves. Remove all flammable materials
- Dip the spreading rod into a beaker of methyl alcohol. Do not let alcohol roll down the rod onto your hand! Pass through a flame to ignite the alcohol. Do not hold the rod in the flame! Let the flame burn out.
- Cool the spreading rod by touching it to the agar in an area off to the side.
- Use the rod to evenly spread the cell suspension over the section of the plate. Keep spreading for about 30 seconds, or until the rod begins to stick slightly to the agar.
- Spread the cells in each section by repeating the steps above. Dip the rod in alcohol and flame between sections.

22. Leave the plates on the countertop, undisturbed, flat, and right side up for 15 minutes so the suspension will be absorbed by the agar.

23. Invert the plates, stack them together, and place them **upside-down,** in a 37°C incubator for 48 hours.

24. Disinfect countertop, and wash your hands.

25. In your notebook, record your predictions about where colonies should grow on your plates. Consider which samples were spread on what type of agar. Think about and record the numbers of colonies you expect to see.

Part IV: Observing and Recording Your Transformation Results

26. Retrieve the Petri plates from the incubator. Look very closely for bacterial growth. Hold your plates up to the light or against a dark background to help visualize the transformed colonies. Look for "halos," areas of clearing around colonies. Halos result when transformed bacteria produce amylase, because the amylase diffuses out and breaks down the starch in the agar around the colony. By placing the Petri plates in the refrigerator overnight, the halos become much more visible (see Figure 8.4). Also, if the cells will not be used after transformation, a diluted iodine solution (1:10 Lugol's solution) may be added

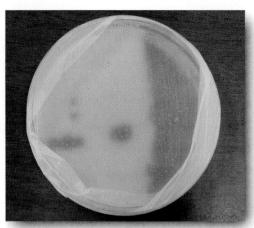

Figure 8.4. **These starch/amp LB agar plates show starch digestion, in halos, around pAmylase-transformed colonies. The ampicillin delays the growth of nontransformed cells.** Photo by author.

to the agar surface. The iodine will stain starch-containing surfaces black while leaving halos golden-brown. Iodine staining makes halos very visible.

27. Observe, draw, and label the plates showing **all** colonies and any halos. Make measurements so that your data drawing is 100% accurate.

28. Count the number of colonies (or do sampling and then multiply) on each plate. In your notebook, record these data in a table.

Data Analysis/Conclusion

Was the transformation protocol successful in creating amylase-producing, ampicillin-resistant *E. coli* cells? Give evidence and explanations about what happened on each selection plate. Compare your plates with others in the class. What does your transformation efficiency look like compared with that of other groups? Identify three techniques that could have resulted in poor transformation efficiency. If any plate produced any colonies of transformed cells, describe what should be done next with those cells.

Thinking Like a Biotechnician

1. Explain how a D plate could have absolutely nothing growing on it.
2. Sometimes, nontransformed satellite colonies are seen around a main transformed colony. Are there any satellite colonies on your plates? Observe and record the satellite colonies' morphology (size, shape, and color) compared with the transformed colonies. Give reasons why the satellite company may be present and exhibit a different growth rate than the transformed cells.
3. Not all the cells in the original culture are transformed. What evidence do you have to support this statement? Determine the transformation efficiency of your protocol. Cells from the transformed broth culture can be plated out as a 1:10, 1:100, 1:1000, or 1:10,000 serial dilutions on starch/amp LB agar. The number of colonies per unit volume in the original transformed culture can be calculated by multiplying the number of colonies counted in one of the dilutions by the dilution factor. This will give the number of cells/volume plated. Divide this number into the number of transformed colonies on your D LB/amp/starch plate and multiply by 100. This gives the transformation efficiency. A ratio of 1:10,000 transformed cells (0.01%) is considered a good result.

Laboratory 8d Growing and Monitoring Bacterial Cultures

Background

After cells have been transformed, they must be grown in ever-increasing volumes. During this scale-up process, the clones must be monitored. The culture's growth rate is of critical importance. Cells must be healthy, growing and multiplying to produce as much product as possible. The goal is to have the cell numbers doubling every 20 minutes, which is called "exponential growth." It is called the "stationary phase" when a culture slows its growth rate because of a lack of nutrients or space, or because there are too many waste products.

To ensure the maximum growth rate, there must be sufficient food nutrients, space, and oxygen. Also, the temperature and pH must be optimal. Technicians regularly take samples and measurements to ensure that the cell cultures are growing and producing product at the maximum rate.

Purpose

To start, maintain, and monitor broth and plate cultures of nontransformed cells.
To document whether or not the culture exhibits exponential growth.

Materials

Balance, tabletop milligram	Laminar flow hood	Water bath, 37°C, shaking
Weigh boat, 3.5"×3.5"	Lysol® disinfectant	Pipets, 5 mL, sterile
Lab scoops	Glasses, safety, plastic	Pipet pump, green
LB agar base	Bunsen burner	Tubes, glass, 13×100 mm
Beakers, 250 mL	Lab gas lighter	Peg racks for 10–13 mm tubes
Glass rods	Petri dishes, 100×15 mm, sterile	pH paper, wide-range pH 0–14
Magnetic stir bars		
Hot plate stirrer	*E. coli* JM109, overnight plate culture	pH paper, narrow-range pH 0–6
Hot hands protector		
Media bottle, 250 mL	Inoculating loop, Ni/Cr wire	pH paper, narrow-range pH 5–10
LB broth base	Incubator oven, 37°C	
Media bottle, 125 mL	Tubes, 50 mL, sterile	Spectrophotometer, Spectronic 20 D+
Sterilizer/autoclave	Tube racks for 50 mL tubes	

Procedure

- Review sterile technique, media prep, plating, and safe handling of bacteria.
- Work in pairs to prepare the media. Each pair of students should make their own batch of agar, start their own plate cultures, and make their own broth and broth cultures.

Part I: Preparing Media

1. Prepare 125 mL of LB agar in a 250-mL beaker. Do not forget to add the dH_2O slowly, mixing the media into a paste. In your notebook, set up a ratio to determine the amount of agar media to mix for the volume you desire, based on the recipe on the media bottle.

$$\frac{\text{mass of media (g) on the bottle}}{1000 \text{ mL of } dH_2O} = \frac{\text{mass of media (g) for the volume to be made}}{\text{volume of the media to be made (mL)}}$$

Remember to heat the media, while stirring, to just below boiling to suspend the media. Using "hot hands" to hold the hot beaker, transfer the media to a 250-mL media bottle. **Loosely attach the cap.** Label the bottle. Autoclave at 15 to 20 psi for 15 to 20 minutes.

2. Prepare enough media for three batches of 50 mL of LB broth. That will be 150 mL in a 250-mL beaker. Do not forget to add the dH_2O slowly, mixing the media into a paste. In your notebook, set up a ratio to determine the amount of broth media to mix for the volume you desire, based on the recipe on the media bottle.

$$\frac{\text{mass of the media (g) on the bottle}}{1000 \text{ mL of } dH_2O} = \frac{\text{mass of the media (g) for the volume to be made}}{\text{volume of the media to be made (mL)}}$$

Remember to heat the media, while stirring, to just below boiling to dissolve the media. Transfer approximately 50 mL of the broth to three 125-mL media bottles. **Loosely attach the caps.** Label the bottles. Autoclave at 15 to 20 psi for 15 to 20 minutes. Cool before using.

65°C

3. After the agar media has been sterilized and cooled to 65°C, pour the agar into labeled (on the bottom edge), sterile, Petri plates (in a sterile laminar flow hood, if available). Pour the plates about 1/2 full (approximately 20 mL). If a flow hood is not available, clean and disinfect a lab bench in an area of the lab with very little air circulation. Allow the plates to cool undisturbed for 24 hours before using. There should be enough agar for approximately six plates.
   Note: The agar and broth media made in steps 1 through 3 will be used during the next few lab sessions.

Part II: Starting the Cultures

37°C
4. Streak two plates with stock *E. coli* JM109. Use sterile technique and the "triple-Z " streaking method (see Lab 4g).
5. Place the plates, upside down, in the incubation oven, at 37°C, for 24 to 48 hours.
6. After the incubation period, photograph each plate culture. Count the number of isolated colonies in the second "Z" and third "Z" on each plate. Report this value in your notebook.
7. From an isolated colony, start a 50-mL broth culture in a sterile laminar flow hood. This is Broth Culture 1.
8. Pick an isolated colony, and circle it on the bottom of the Petri plate.
9. Use a sterile inoculating loop to sample the colony on the plate, and transfer it to one of the media bottles. Label the culture tube, and include the culture start time. Place the broth culture in a shaking hot water bath.
10. After 24 hours, the broth culture should be cloudy with suspended bacteria cells.

Part III: Monitoring the Cell Cultures
Note: Start this 4 hours before class begins.

37°C
11. In a sterile laminar flow hood, seed a fresh batch of 50 mL of LB broth with 2 mL of Broth Culture 1. Swirl to thoroughly suspend the cells throughout the new media. Place the culture in a 37°C shaking hot water bath for 4 hours.
12. **After** the initial 4-hour growth period, using your best sterile technique take a 4-mL sample and place it in a 13×100-mm glass tube or cuvette. Using pH paper, measure its pH. Using the VIS spectrophotometer, read both its absorbance and transmittance at a wavelength of 600 nm. Use the sterile LB broth from the third media bottle as a blank solution. Make sure to withdraw all samples from the culture, under sterile conditions, in the laminar flow hood. Do this every hour for the next 5 hours of class.

Data Collection
13. In your notebook, make a data table and graph showing the change in the broth culture's pH over time.
14. In your notebook, make a data table, and record the culture's absorbance and the transmittance data over the same time period.

Data Analysis

Produce a growth-curve line graph of the absorbance data The graph reflects the change in cell concentration over time. Label the three growth phases, on the graph, as follows: the initial, slow growth period as the "lag phase," the period of rapid cell multiplication as "exponential growth," and the period when cell multiplication slows, as the culture becomes crowded, as "stationary phase."

Conclusion

Describe the changes in the pH, absorbance, and transmittance in the broth culture over time, and explain the reason(s) for the changes. Does it appear that the culture exhibited exponential growth? Explain. Does it appear that the culture exhibited the stationary phase? Explain. Give reasons why the culture may not have grown as expected. Describe what would happen to the culture next if it were, or were not, growing properly.

Thinking Like a Biotechnician

1. How can a technician be confident that a culture is not contaminated with unwanted bacteria?
2. How can you tell when a culture has reached the stationary phase?
3. How can you tell if a culture has sufficient aeration?

Laboratory 8e   Scaling-Up *E. coli* Cultures for Amylase Production

Background

When pAmylase-transformed bacteria produce starch-cleared halos on starch/ampicillin agar, it demonstrates amylase production. Although this is quite an accomplishment, growing transformed cells on Petri plates does not produce enough amylase for the marketplace. For manufacturing, bacteria must be grown, in liquid media, in increasingly larger volumes. This is called "scale-up."

During "scale-up," a colony of interest is inoculated into broth media. The broth is placed in a shaker and aerated at a particular temperature. Under optimum conditions, the cells of bacteria divide rapidly, using up the nutrients in the broth and producing new molecules, including amylase. The culture is assayed periodically to check for amylase production and activity.

As the cells grow and divide, nutrients in the broth decrease, waste products increase, cells become crowded, and culture growth slows. At this point, the cells must be transferred to larger volumes of broth in larger containers: the culture is scaled-up to the next volume. When the volume and concentration of amylase in the culture are sufficient, the culture is "harvested." During harvesting, the cells are separated from the broth by filtration or centrifugation. Then, depending on where the protein is found, the amylase is purified from either the broth or from the cells. Purification of proteins from broth culture is presented in later lab activities.

Purpose

What are the characteristics of a transformed *E. coli* broth culture during "scale-up"?
Is there evidence of amylase activity from the transformed cells in the broth culture?
At what time should a 100-mL culture be "scaled-up"?

Materials

Environmental Health
and Safety Officer

Balance, tabletop milligram	Sterilizer/autoclave	Petri dishes, 100×15 mm,
Weigh boat and lab scoops	Laminar flow hood	sterile
LB broth base	Lysol® disinfectant	Inoculating loop, Ni/Cr wire
Starch, soluble	Glasses, safety, plastic	Water bath, 37°C, shaking
Beakers, 250 mL	Bunsen burner and gas lighter	Pipets, 5 mL, sterile
Glass rods	Ampicillin, 4 mg/mL, sterile	Pipet pump, green
Magnetic stir bars	Pipets, 1 mL, sterile	Tubes, glass, 13×100 mm
Hot plate stirrer	Pipet pump, blue	Peg racks for 10–13 mm
Hot hands protector	Transformed *E. coli* JM109	tubes
Media bottle, 250 mL	(plate culture from Lab 8c)	

Procedure

37°C

1. Prepare and sterilize 100 mL of 1% soluble starch/LB broth (or purchase premixed LB broth) in a 250-mL media bottle. Record the calculations you used to plan the recipes.
2. After the media has cooled to room temperature, under sterile conditions, add 1 mL of ampicillin solution to each bottle.
3. Select a transformed colony with a large halo.
4. Using sterile technique, inoculate the 100 mL of broth with the colony from the selection plate that shows both the fastest growth and the greatest amylase production.
5. Place the inoculated broth in a rapidly shaking water bath at 37°C for 4 hours.
6. Hourly, after the first 4 hours, begin taking sterile 4-mL samples of the broth culture. Put the samples into 13×100-mm cuvette tubes.
7. Using 300 µL, test all samples of the broth culture for amylase activity using the assays developed in Lab 6c. Measure the amount of starch breakdown compared with a control and measure the amount of sugar production.
8. Also, as in Lab 8d, use the spectrophotometer to determine the absorbance (and, indirectly, the concentration) of the broth every hour. Use sterile, uninoculated broth as a blank.
9. In a data table in your notebook, record the absorbance of the culture for the time periods (5 hours) studied.

Data Analysis

Graph the absorbance of the cell culture for the time period studied. This represents the growth curve for the culture. Look for "exponential growth" of the culture, the phase in which the number of cells is doubling with every cell cycle, or, for these data, the time period in which the absorbance is doubling.

Conclusion

What is the apparent growth rate of this culture compared with the growth rate of the nontransformed cells in the last activity? Did this culture reach stationary phase during the time period it was monitored? Is there evidence of amylase activity from these transformed cells? Determine and report the time at which the culture should be "scaled-up" to the next volume.

Thinking Like a Biotechnician

1. What was done in this cell culture to decrease the chance of nontransformed cells growing or contaminating the culture?
2. Propose methods to increase a culture's growth rate and determine the actual concentration of cells in a culture.
3. Propose methods to increase a culture's amylase production.

Laboratory 8f   Minipreparation of pAmylase using Lysozyme Digestion

Background

To confirm that the genetically engineered *E. coli* cells have been transformed with the correct DNA, technicians use a miniprep procedure to extract the plasmids and analyze them through restriction digestion. In this miniprep procedure, the extraction of the plasmid from the cells occurs when the cells are treated with lysozyme solution. The enzyme, lysozyme, degrades the bacterial cell walls, causing the cells to explode. A series of alcohol washes isolates the plasmid from other cell constituents.

Purpose

How well is pAmylase extracted from transformed *E. coli* JM109 cells using the lysozyme digestion method?

Materials

Note: Recipes for making the buffer solutions appear at the end of the Procedures section.

Environmental Health and Safety Officer

50 mL transformed *E. coli* JM109	Micropipet, P-1000	Ice bucket
(LB/amp/2% starch in 250 mL bottle)	Micropipet tips for P-1000	Reaction tubes, 0.5 mL
	STE buffer (see recipe)	Isopropanol
Tube rack for 1.7 mL tubes	Micropipet, P-100	Ethanol, 70%
Reaction tubes, 1.7 mL	Micropipet tips for P-100	Dry block heater/heat block,
Permanent lab marker pens	Lysozyme, 10 mg/mL (see recipe)	65°C
Pipet, 2 mL		TE buffer (see recipe)
Pipet pump, blue	Dry block heater/heat block, 37°C	RNase, 10 mg/mL
Microcentrifuge, high-speed, 16K×g	Dry block heater/heat block, 100°C	UV/Vis spectrophotometer
Plastic beaker, 1L	Lid locks for 1.7 mL tubes	UV-cuvettes
Bleach, 10%		Pasteur pipets, 9"
		Pasteur pipet bulbs

Procedure

Read all of the procedures before starting. Determine which solutions need to be prepared. Prepare all the solutions before starting. Store all solutions at 4°C, except STE buffer. Store STE buffer at room temperature.

Environmental Health
and Safety Officer

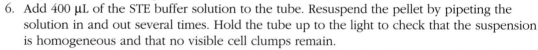

1. Obtain 50 mL of *E. coli*/pAmylase overnight culture (in a 250 mL media bottle) in LB/2% starch/amp broth.
2. Shake the culture tube to resuspend the *E. coli* cells before taking a sample.
3. Label a sterile 1.7-mL tube with your initials. Transfer 1.5 mL of the overnight suspension of transformed cell culture (*E. coli*/pAMP) to the tube.
4. Close the cap, and place the tube in a **balanced** configuration in a microcentrifuge. Spin for 3 minutes at maximum speed to pellet the cells.
5. Pour off the supernatant (broth) from the tube, into either the waste beaker containing 10% bleach or another sterile tube for later amylase purification. **Be careful not to disturb the cell pellet.** Invert the tube, and tap it gently on the surface of a clean paper towel to thoroughly drain off the supernatant.
6. Add 400 µL of the STE buffer solution to the tube. Resuspend the pellet by pipeting the solution in and out several times. Hold the tube up to the light to check that the suspension is homogeneous and that no visible cell clumps remain.
7. Add 35 µL of the 10-mg/mL lysozyme solution to the tube. Close the cap, and mix the solutions by rapidly inverting the tube five times.
8. Place the tube in a 37°C heat block for 5 minutes.
9. Add a "locking cap" and boil the tube in a 100°C heat block for 50 seconds.
10. Stand the tube on ice for 5 minutes.
11. Using a sterile, 2-mL pipet, transfer all of the cell suspension to a sterile 0.5-mL tube. Let the tube stand on ice for 5 minutes.
12. Put a tiny bit of crushed ice in a 1.7-mL tube. Place the 0.5-mL tube in the 1.7-mL tube. Find a partner that has the same double-tube configuration. Make sure the mass of his or her tubes equals the mass of your tubes. Place the microcentrifuge tubes in a **balanced** configuration in a centrifuge, and spin the tubes at maximum speed for 15 minutes to pellet a precipitate along the side of tube.
13. Transfer approximately 500 µL of supernatant (plasmid DNA in solution) from the 0.5-mL tube into another sterile 1.7-mL tube. **Avoid pipeting the precipitate,** and wipe off any precipitate clinging to outside of the tip prior to expelling the supernatant.
14. Add 500 µL of isopropanol to each tube of supernatant. Close the caps, and mix vigorously by rapidly inverting the tubes five times. Let the tubes stand on ice for 15 minutes.
15. Place the tubes in a **balanced** configuration in a high-speed microcentrifuge, and spin them for 5 minutes at maximum speed to pellet the nucleic acids. Align the tubes in the rotor so that the cap hinges point outward. The nucleic acid residue, visible or not, will collect under the hinge during centrifugation.
16. Pour off the supernatant from the tube. **Be careful not to disturb nucleic acid pellets** containing the plasmid. Invert the tube, and tap it gently on the surface of clean paper towel to thoroughly drain off the supernatant.
17. Add 500 µL of 70% ethanol to the tube, and close the cap tightly. Flick the tube several times to wash the pellet. Wrist-flick the sample to pool the plasmid and ethanol on the bottom of the tube.
    Stop Point: Store the plasmid DNA in ethanol at −20°C until ready to continue.

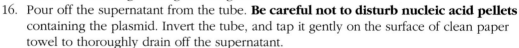

18. Place the tube in a **balanced** configuration in a microcentrifuge, and spin it at maximum speed for 5 minutes.
19. Pour off the supernatant from the tube. **Be careful not to disturb the nucleic acid pellet.** Invert the tube, and tap it gently on the surface of a clean paper towel to thoroughly drain off the supernatant.

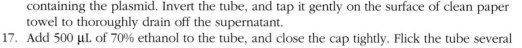

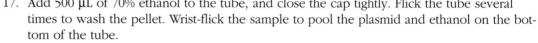

20. Dry the nucleic acid pellets by placing the tubes, with their caps open, in a 65°C heat block for about 5 minutes.
21. At the end of the drying period, hold each tube up to check that no ethanol droplets remain. If ethanol is still evaporating, an alcohol odor can be detected by sniffing the top of

the tube. All of the ethanol must be evaporated before proceeding to Step 22. Repeat Step 19, if necessary.

22. Add 100 µL of TE buffer containing RNase at 20 µg/mL to each tube. Resuspend the pellets by smashing them with the pipet tip, and vigorously pipeting in and out. Rinse down the side of the tube several times, concentrating on the area where the pellet should have formed during centrifugation (beneath the cap hinge). Make sure that all of the DNA has dissolved, and that no particles remain in the pipet tip or on the side of tube.

23. Freeze the sample at –20°C until ready to use. Thaw before use.

24. Use the UV spec, set at 260 nm, to determine the concentration of plasmid DNA, as explained in the text. To calculate the concentration of DNA in a sample, use a simple ratio. It is known that 50 µg/mL of pure, double-stranded DNA absorbs approximately 1 au of light at 260 nm. One can determine the concentration of an unknown DNA sample using the following equation:

$$\frac{50\ \mu g/mL}{1\ au\ at\ 260\ nm} = \frac{X\ \mu g/mL}{the\ absorbance\ of\ sample\ at\ 260\ nm}$$

Pool the samples, if the concentration is less than 0.02 µg/mL, or if the volume is less than 50 µL.

25. Conduct a restriction digestion to confirm that the plasmid is, indeed, pAmylase. Use the procedures in the restriction digestion run earlier in this chapter. Run gels on a 10% TBE vertical gel, if available, or a 1% agarose gel. Stain the gel with EtBr and photograph it. **Remember to follow the safety precautions. Only the instructor should use EtBr. Wear goggles and gloves when in the presence of EtBr.**

Environmental Health and Safety Officer

Good Manufacturing Practices

- Centrifuge the tubes with the hinge on the "up" side so that the pellets will always be on the "hinge" side. This is helpful if the pellets are hard to see.
- Good pipeting is critical for the correct change in pH.
- Do not be concerned if the pellet at Step 15 is small or invisible. Pure DNA in solution is clear.
- Large pellets often indicate contamination.

Recipes for Plasmid MiniPrep

Salt/TRIS/EDTA (STE) Buffer. Make 100 mL.
Store at 4°C or at room temperature.
Mix together the following:

 2 mL of 5 *M* NaCl
 1 mL of 1 *M* TRIS (pH 8.0)
 0.2 mL of 0.5 *M* EDTA
 91.8 mL of deionized water
 5 mL TRITON X-100, 10%

Lysozyme Buffer. Make 50 mL.
Store at 4°C.
Mix together the following:

 10 g of sucrose
 1.25 mL of 1 *M* TRIS (pH 7.4)
 1 mL of 0.5 *M* EDTA

in deionized water to a total final volume of 50 mL.

TRIS/EDTA (TE) Buffer. Make 100 mL.
Store at 4°C
Mix together the following:

1 mL of 1 M TRIS (pH 8.0)
200 µL of 0.5 M EDTA
99 mL of deionized water

Data Analysis/Conclusion

Do the UV spectrophotometer data support that there is DNA in the samples? Give evidence. Do the digestion fragments indicate that the plasmid extracted during the miniprep has the characteristics of the pAmylase plasmid? Do the observed bands in the gel, after restriction digestion, show what was expected? Give evidence for your statement. Do all groups in the class have similar data? Why or why not? Discuss the possible errors that could lead to varying results from one team to another. If the digestion confirms that the sample is pAmylase, why is that information valuable?

Thinking Like a Biotechnician

1. If no whole or digested plasmid bands are present on the gel, does that mean that no plasmid was extracted or no transformation occurred?
2. What other technique could be used to determine whether the miniprep samples actually do contain DNA?
3. A concentration of 0.005 µg/µL is usually required for a transformation. Did your miniprep yield enough (at least 10 µL) of a sufficient concentration (0.005 µg/µL) of plasmid for another transformation?

Laboratory 8g   Alkaline Cell Lysis Minipreparation of pAmylase

Background

To confirm that the genetically engineered *E. coli* JM109 cells have been transformed with the "correct" DNA, we will attempt to extract the plasmids and analyze them through restriction digestion. In this miniprep procedure, the extraction of the plasmid occurs when the cells are treated with sodium dodecyl sulfate (SDS) and sodium hydroxide (NaOH) at a high pH. The SDS dissolves the cell membrane and precipitates proteins. The NaOH destroys the cell wall and also precipitates proteins. A series of alcohol washes isolates the plasmid from other cell constituents. This method is a little more complicated than the lysozyme miniprep, but it may give better yields.

Purpose

How well is pAmylase extracted from transformed *E. coli* JM109 cells using the alkaline-cell-lysis method?

Materials

Note: Recipes for preparing the STE, lysozyme, and TE buffer solutions appear at the end of the Procedure section.

Environmental Health and Safety Officer

50 mL transformed *E. coli* JM109 (LB/amp/2% starch in 250 mL bottle)	Micropipet, P-100	Pipet pump, blue
	Micropipet tips for P-100	Isopropanol
	GTE buffer (see recipe)	Ethanol, 95%
Tubes, 15 mL and racks	Micropipet, P-1000	Dry block heater/heat block, 65°C
Centrifuge for 15 mL tubes	Micropipet tips for P-1000	
Permanent lab marker pens	SDS/NaOH solution (see recipe)	TE buffer (see recipe)
Pipet, 10 mL, sterile		UV/Vis spectrophotometer
Pipet pump, green	Potassium acetate/acetic acid solution (see recipe)	UV-cuvettes
Centrifuge for 15 mL tubes	Tube rack for 1.7 mL tubes	Pasteur pipets, 9"
Plastic beaker, 1L	Reaction tubes, 1.7 mL	Pasteur pipet bulbs
Bleach, 10%	Pipet, 2 mL, sterile	

Procedure

Read all of the steps before starting. Determine which solutions need to be prepared, and prepare them before starting. Store all the solutions at 4°C.

1. Obtain 50 mL of *E. coli*/pAmylase overnight culture (in a 250 mL bottle) in LB/2% starch/amp broth.
2. Shake the culture tube to resuspend the *E. coli* cells before taking a sample.
3. Label a sterile 15-mL tube with your initials. Use a sterile 10-mL pipet to transfer 1.5 mL of *E. coli*/pAMP overnight suspension to the tube.
4. Close the cap, and place the tube in a **balanced** configuration in a tabletop centrifuge. Spin for 7 minutes to pellet the cells.
5. Pour off the supernatant (broth) from the tube, into either a waste beaker with 10% bleach solution, or another sterile tube for later amylase purification. **Be careful not to disturb the cell pellets.** Invert the tube, and gently tap on the surface of a clean paper towel to thoroughly drain the supernatant.
6. Add 100 μL (0.1 mL) of the GTE buffer solution to the tube. Resuspend the pellet by pipeting the solution in and out several times. Hold the tube up to the light to check that the suspension is homogeneous and that no visible cell clumps remain.
7. Add 200 μL (0.2 mL) of the SDS/NaOH solution to the tube. Close the cap, and mix the solutions by rapidly inverting the tube five times.
8. Place the tube on ice for 5 minutes. The suspension will become relatively clear.
9. Add 150 μL (0.15 mL) of ice-cold potassium acetate/acetic acid solution to the tube. Close the cap, and mix the solution by rapidly inverting the tube five times. A white precipitate will immediately appear.
10. Place the tube on ice for 5 minutes.
11. Using a sterile 2-mL pipet, transfer all of the cell suspension to a sterile 1.7-mL tube. Let the tube stand on ice for 5 minutes.

Environmental Health and Safety Officer

12. Place the microcentrifuge tube in a **balanced** configuration in a centrifuge, and spin for 5 minutes to pellet the precipitate along the side of tube.
13. Transfer 400 μL of supernatant (plasmid DNA in solution) from the 1.7-mL tube into another sterile 1.7-mL tube. **Avoid pipeting the precipitate,** and wipe off any precipitate clinging to the outside of the tip prior to expelling the supernatant.
14. Add 400 μL of isopropanol to each tube of supernatant. Close the cap, and mix vigorously by rapidly inverting the tube five times. Let the tube stand at room temperature for **only** 2 minutes. (Isopropanol preferentially precipitates nucleic acids rapidly; however, proteins remaining in solutions also begin to precipitate with time.)
15. Place the tubes in a **balanced** configuration in a high-speed microcentrifuge, and spin for 5 minutes at the highest speed to pellet the nucleic acids. Align the tubes in the rotor so that

cap hinges point outward. The nucleic acid residue, visible or not, will collect under the hinge during centrifugation.

16. Pour off the supernatant from the tube. **Be careful not to disturb the nucleic acid pellets** containing the plasmid. Invert the tube and tap gently on the surface of a clean paper towel to thoroughly drain.

17. Add 200 µL of 95% ethanol to the tube, and close the cap tightly. Flick the tube several times to wash the pellet. Wrist-flick the sample to pool the plasmid and ethanol on the bottom of the tube.

Stop Point: Store the plasmid DNA in ethanol at –20°C until ready to continue.

18. Place the tube in a **balanced** configuration in a microcentrifuge, and spin for 3 minutes.

19. Pour off the supernatant from the tube. **Be careful not to disturb the nucleic acid pellet.** Invert the tube, and tap gently on surface of a clean paper towel to drain thoroughly.

20. Dry the nucleic acid pellets by placing the tubes, with the cap open, in a 65°C heat block for about 5 minutes.

21. At the end of the drying period, hold each tube up to check that no ethanol droplets remain. If ethanol is still evaporating, an alcohol odor can be detected by sniffing the mouth of tube. All of the ethanol must evaporate before proceeding to Step 22. Repeat Step 19, if necessary.

22. Add 25 µL of TE buffer to each tube. Resuspend the pellets by smashing them with the pipet tip, and vigorously pipeting in and out. Rinse down the side of tube several times, concentrating on the area where the pellet should have formed during centrifugation (beneath the cap hinge). Ensure that all of the DNA has dissolved and that no particles remain in the pipet tip or on the side of tube.

23. Pool all the DNA/TE solutions prepared into one tube. Freeze at –20°C until ready to use. Thaw before use.

24. Use the UV spec, set at 260 nm, to determine the concentration of plasmid DNA, as explained in the text. To calculate the concentration of DNA in a sample, use a simple ratio. It is known that 50 µg/mL of pure, double-stranded DNA absorbs approximately 1 au of light at 260 nm. One can determine the concentration of an unknown DNA sample using the following equation:

$$\frac{50\ \mu g/mL}{1\ au\ at\ 260\ nm} = \frac{X\ \mu g/mL}{the\ absorbance\ of\ sample\ at\ 260\ nm}$$

Pool the samples, if the concentration is less than 0.02 µg/mL, or if the volume is less than 50 µL.

25. Conduct a restriction digestion to confirm that the plasmid is indeed pAmylase. Use the procedures in the restriction digestion run earlier in this chapter. Run gels on a 10% TBE vertical gel, if available, or a 1% agarose gel. Stain the gel with EtBr, and photograph it. **Remember to follow the safety precautions. Only the instructor should use EtBr. Wear goggles and gloves when in the presence of EtBr.**

Good Manufacturing Practices

- Use centrifuge tubes with the hinge on the "up" side so that the pellets will always be on the "hinge" side. This is helpful if pellets are hard to see (as in step 13).
- Good pipeting is critical for the correct change in pH.
- Do step 12 quickly, and make sure that the centrifuge is immediately available for Step 13.
- Do not be concerned if the pellet at step 13 is small or "invisible." Pure DNA in solution is clear.
- Large pellets often indicate contamination.

-20°C

65°C

-20°C

Environmental Health and Safety Officer

Recipes for Plasmid Miniprep

GTE + RNase. Make 100 mL.
Store at 4°C or room temperature.
Mix together the following:

>   0.9 g of glucose
>   2.5 mL of 1 *M* TRIS, pH 8.0
>   2 mL of 0.5 *M* EDTA
>   94.5 mL of deionized water plus 10 mg RNase A/100 mL

SDS/NaOH Cell Lysis Solution. Make 100 mL.
Store at room temperature.
Mix together the following:

>   0.8 g of NaOH pellets into 80 mL of deionized water

Environmental Health
and Safety Officer

Gently, mix in 10 mL of 10% SDS
Add deionized water until a total volume of 100 mL is reached.

TE Buffer. Make 100 mL.
Store at 4°C
Mix together the following:

>   1 mL of 1 *M* TRIS, pH 8.0
>   200 µL of 0.5 *M* EDTA
>   99 mL of deionized water

6 *M* Potassium Acetate/Acetic Acid Neutralization Solution, pH 5.5. Make 100 mL.
Store at 4°C or room temperature.
29.4 g of potassium acetate in 50 mL of H_2O, pH to 5.5 with acetic acid (approximately 11 mL), bring to a final volume of 100 mL with deionized water

Data Analysis/ Conclusion

Do the UV spectrophotometer data support that the samples contain DNA? Give evidence. Do the digestion fragments indicate that the plasmid extracted during the miniprep has the characteristics of the pAmylase plasmid? Do the observed bands in the gel, after restriction digestion, show what was expected? Give evidence for your statement. Do all groups in the class have similar data? Why or why not? Discuss the possible errors that could lead to varying results from one team to another. If the digestion confirms that the sample is pAmylase, why is that information valuable?

 *Thinking Like a Biotechnician*

1. In biotechnology, "time is money." If one procedure works as well as another, and costs less, that is the procedure which will be used. Which of the miniprep procedures (lysozyme or alkaline lysis) appeared to take longer to conduct? Explain.
2. A concentration of 0.005 µg/µL is usually required for a transformation. Did your miniprep yield enough (at least 10 µL) of a sufficient concentration (0.005 µg/µL) of plasmid for another transformation?
3. Which miniprep procedure, lysozyme (last lab) or alkaline lysis (this lab), worked better to produce the largest yield of a relatively pure plasmid? Give evidence.

Chapter 9

Protein Product Purification and Analysis

Before large fermentation tanks of cell culture are started, transformed cells are grown in flasks of progressively larger volumes. Here, cultures started from colonies grown on Petri plates are grown in a few hundred milliliters of broth. If cells are healthy, producing high concentrations of protein, and growing at the maximum rate, they will be transferred to about 10 times the volume of broth in the next scale-up.
Photo by author.

During the manufacturing process, techniques developed in research and development (R&D) are applied to large volumes (large scale) of broth, with the goal of producing large amounts of pure protein to sell. Manufacturing includes growing and monitoring transformed cells in progressively larger volumes of broth. At each step, dozens of assays confirm the health and productivity of each culture.

To harvest large volumes of protein from the cell cultures that produced them, the cells are spun down and separated from the broth media. The protein of interest is purified (separated) from the other proteins in the sample using filtration and column chromatography.

In the following lab activities, you will learn how to scale-up cultures and harvest the protein of interest from the culture. The skills on which to focus include the following:

- spinning down cells in a centrifuge and removing them from a culture
- using dialysis to move the proteins in a broth sample into a new or more appropriate buffered solution
- separating and documenting proteins using ion-exchange column chromatography
- verifying the presence and activity of a protein of interest using assays and polyacrylamide gel electrophoresis (PAGE)

The goal of manufacturing is to produce a product in large enough volumes to generate revenue for the company. If a company cannot develop a product for manufacturing in 10 to 15 years, it will probably not survive. As of May 2005, only a few dozen companies had marketed recombinant protein products, although hundreds of other companies were entering into manufacturing of such products. It is within these companies that employment opportunities mushroom.

Laboratory 9a Harvesting Amylase from Bacterial Cultures

Background

As transformed bacteria cells grow in culture, they produce the protein of interest along with other proteins and molecules of all kinds. When the culture has a sufficient volume and concentration of cells, it is "harvested" by separating and purifying the protein of interest from the cells and other molecules in the broth.

Harvesting begins by centrifuging or filtering the broth. These processes separate the cells from the broth that contains the protein of interest. When amylase isolation is the goal, the cells are discarded, and the scale-up broth, containing a large number of proteins secreted by the cells, is run over chromatographic columns. These columns separate proteins from the mixture, based on their size, shape, and charge.

During the separation and purification process, assays are performed, and gels are run to ensure the presence, concentration, and activity of the protein.

Purpose

To determine whether broth that contains amylase can be separated from bacterial cultures.

Materials

Environmental Health and Safety Officer

Poured LB/amp/2% starch plates	Bunsen burner	Water bath, 37°C, shaking
Laminar flow hood	Lab gas lighter	Pipet, 10 mL, sterile
Lysol® disinfectant	Inoculating loop, Ni/Cr wire	Pipet pump, green
Transformed *E. coli* JM109 (plate culture from Lab 8c)	Incubator oven, 37°C	Tubes, 15 mL, capped
	LB/amp/2% starch broth, 50 mL, sterile, in 250 mL media bottle	Tube racks for 15 mL tubes
Glasses, safety, plastic		Centrifuge for 15 mL tubes

Procedure

37°C

1. Using sterile technique, streak transformed cells onto LB/2% starch/amp agar plates. Let the cells grow for 24 hours, upside down, in a 37°C incubation oven. Look for halos around the colonies to confirm the presence and activity of amylase in the colonies on the selection plates.

2. Obtain 50 mL of sterile LB/2% starch/amp broth. Using sterile technique, inoculate the broth with a colony of transformed cells and allow them to grow overnight in a shaking, 37°C water bath.

3. Using sterile technique, transfer 10 mL of the broth culture into 15-mL sterile, capped, centrifuge tubes.

4. Spin in a labtop centrifuge for 10 minutes. A pellet of cells should form at the bottom of the tube.

5. Pour the supernatant (the broth) into another sterile centrifuge tube. Label all tubes with the culture name, your initials, and the date. Discard the pellet of cells or use for a plasmid preparation (see Chapter 8 lab activities).

6. Using several samples of the broth, conduct amylase activity assays using the procedures outlined in early lab activities (see Chapter 6 lab activities).

7. Create a data table in your notebook, and record the results of the assay(s) in a quantitative fashion. Determine the average results.

8. Refrigerate the remainder of the broth in the sample tube until ready to use. If the sample is to be stored for more than a few days, filter-sterilize it to prevent degradation.

9. If the proteins in the broth are to be purified using column chromatography, conduct a buffer-exchange dialysis to get the proteins into the appropriate chromatographic buffer (see Lab 9b).

Data Analysis/Conclusion

Use the bacterial and human amylase assays from earlier lab activities as standards for comparison. What amount of amylase activity appears to be present in the broth? Give evidence for your statement. Explain why the broth shows more or less activity than the standards. Describe the next steps in the use of the broth. Describe what would happen next in an amylase purification process.

 *Thinking Like a Biotechnician*

1. If the assays for amylase activity do not show much activity, does that mean there is no amylase in the broth? What may be done to remedy the problem?
2. Without using an activity assay, how could a technician confirm that amylase, and not some other carbohydrate-interacting enzyme, is in the broth?
3. What key ingredient would be needed to design an ELISA to recognize and measure the amylase in the broth?

Laboratory 9b   Dialysis of Proteins into Different Buffers

Background

Often, protein molecules, such as in the Chapter 6 seafood-muscle-tissue protein study, are extracted from animal cells in a sample preparation buffer containing sodium dodecyl sulfate (SDS). Although this buffer works well for extraction and PAGE, the SDS interferes with most column chromatography. Therefore, a dialysis of the sample into a new buffer must be conducted.

The new buffer must be one suited for the given chromatography. In an ion-exchange chromatography, such as the one in the following lab activity, the chromatography buffer might be a 50-mM sodium monophosphate buffer. The sample extraction buffer must be exchanged out of the sample solution and replaced with the chromatography buffer without losing the molecule of interest.

A dialysis is done by placing the sample in dialysis tubing and tying off the ends to produce a dialysis bag. The dialysis bag is placed in a beaker of buffer for many hours to allow molecules small enough to move in and out of the pores of the dialysis tubing to reach equilibrium. There should be a minimum of 10 volumes of the new buffer to sample volume in a buffer exchange (see Figure 9.1).

Figure 9.1.   Dialysis should take place at 4°C to decrease protein degradation. If a stir plate is available, add a stir bar, and set the stir plate to the lowest speed.
Photo by author.

Purpose

To exchange the buffer in a protein solution for a different buffer that is suitable for chromatography.

Materials

$50 mM$ NaH_2PO_4 monohydrate, pH 7.2	Plastic beaker, 1L	Glucose test strips
Beaker, 2L	Tubes, 15 mL, capped and rack	Reaction tubes, 1.7 mL and rack
Dialysis tubing, 1", 18 kD MW cut-off	24-well microtiter plate, 50/CS	Lid locks for 1.7 mL tubes
Scissors	Micropipet, P-1000 and tips	Benedict's solution
Pipet, 5 mL, sterile	Micropipet, P-100 and tips	Dry block heater/heat block, 100°C
Pipet pump, green	Lugol's iodine solution	
	Glass rods	

Procedure

Note: Prepare the 2 L of 50-mM sodium monophosphate buffer, pH 7.2, prior to starting the activity.

1. Cut a piece of 18,000-D dialysis tubing. The tubing must be at least 3 times as long as the length necessary to hold the volume of sample to be dialyzed. The volume to be dialyzed will be determined by the supervisor or instructor.
2. Soak the tubing in deionized water until it is thoroughly wetted.
3. Gently, rub the end of the tube with your thumb and finger until it opens.
4. Tie a snug knot in one end of the tube. Be careful to not rip or tear the dialysis tubing.
5. Using a pipet, transfer the entire sample to be dialyzed to the inside of the bag (see Figure 9.2). It should fill the bottom third of the bag. Be careful to not spill any of the sample.
6. Press any remaining air out of the bag.
7. Tie the other end of the bag, about 2 cm from the end, with a snug knot. Be careful to not tear the tubing.
8. Rinse the outside of the bag.
9. Place the bag in dialysis buffer (50 mM sodium monophosphate buffer, pH 7.2). The minimum volume required is 10 times the volume inside the dialysis bag. Place the dialysis set-up in the refrigerator and leave it for 10 to 24 hours.
10. Discard the outer buffer. Refill with an equal volume of fresh 50-mM sodium monophosphate buffer, pH 7.2.
11. Repeat step 10.
12. Remove the bag from the dialysis bucket. Pat dry. Carefully cut open the bag (place it in a clean beaker, in case it spills), and pipet the contents into a sterile storage tube.
13. Conduct an amylase activity assay (see Lab 6c) on the dialyzed sample. Report the data in a data table. If the concentration of amylase has decreased substantially from the activity in the broth before dialysis (which also can be inferred from an increase in volume), concentrate the sample using a 10-kD centrifuge filter (see Figure 9.3). Report how much was concentrated as well as the results of any additional amylase assays.

Figure 9.2. **Over a large, clean beaker, transfer sample to a prepared dialysis tube. This way, if any of the sample spills, it can be retrieved.**
Photo by author.

Data Analysis/Conclusion

Describe the appearance of the bag before and after the dialysis period. Describe what has happened during the dialysis procedure to the solutes and solvents that were inside or outside of the bag at the start of the dialysis process. Draw a diagram that illustrates the movement of substances during the dialysis. Does the dialyzed sample show amylase activity? Explain. Whether the sample shows activity or not, propose what should be done next with the dialyzed sample.

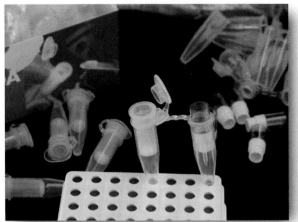

Figure 9.3. These are two types of 10-kD microtest tube centrifuge filters. They may be used to concentrate a protein sample or to replace one protein buffer with another. Add sample to be concentrated to the top chamber. Spin for a few minutes in a centrifuge. Buffer will be pulled down, but the proteins that are larger than 10 kD remain in the top chamber and are concentrated. The longer the spinning time, the more concentrated the sample becomes. If a replacement buffer is desired, it can be added to the concentrated protein sample. Check the technical manual that comes with the filters for recommended spinning times and conditions.
Photo by author.

Thinking Like a Biotechnician

1. How can you be certain that amylase has not diffused or leaked out of the dialysis bag during dialysis?
2. Before dialysis, on inspection of the broth, cloudy areas are visible. What is the most likely cause of the cloudiness and what, if anything, should be done about it?

Laboratory 9c   Using Ion-Exchange Chromatography to Separate Proteins

This lab was developed by with the assistance of David Peers, Genentech, Inc, South San Francisco, CA.

Background

In ion-exchange chromatography, resin beads of a certain charge (positive [+] or negative [-] are used in the column. A mixture of proteins is added to the column, and if the pH and column capacity are correct, everything passes through the column except the protein of interest. This is because the column resin and pH are chosen to produce the "most opposite charge" of the protein of interest on the beads. If the charge on a bead is positive, it will bind to negatively charged molecules. This technique is called anion exchange. If the beads are negatively charged, they bind to positively charged molecules (cation exchange). A scientist picks a resin to use based on the properties of the protein of interest. Under ideal conditions, during ion-exchange chromatography, the protein binds to the oppositely charged beads. Buffers are used to flush contaminant proteins out of the column. Finally, some buffer containing an ion with a greater attraction to the bead than the protein of interest knocks (elutes) the protein off the bead (this is the ion exchange). Often, a high-salt buffer is used to elute the desired protein from the column (see Figure 9.4).

Purpose

Using ion-exchange chromatography, how well can lysozyme (positive [+] charge at pH 7.2) be separated from albumin (negative [-] charge at pH 7.2)?

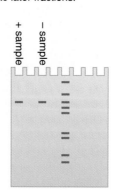

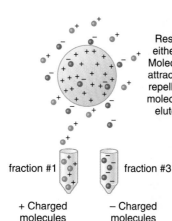

Resin beads are charged either positive or negative. Molecules in the mixture are attracted to the beads or are repelled into fractions. Stuck molecules are knocked off or eluted into later fractions.

fraction #1   fraction #3

+ Charged molecules are collected in early fractions.

− Charged molecules are eluted into later fractions.

Figure 9.4. **Ion Exchange Resin.** Resins are manufactured with ions attached. The ions present a certain degree of positive or negative charge, depending on the buffer pH.

Materials

Equilibration buffer (50 mM NaH_2PO_4 monhydrate, pH 7.2)

Elution buffer (50 mM NaH_2PO_4 monohydrate, 0.5 M NaCl, pH 7.2)

Bovine serum albumin (BSA), 2 mg/mL in NaH_2PO_4 buffer

Lysozyme, 2 mg/mL in NaH_2PO_4 buffer

Tubes, 15 mL, capped and racks

Chromatography columns with frit, 5 mL, tops and bottoms

DEAE Sepharose™ resin

Pipets, 10 mL, 5 mL, and 2 mL and pumps

Tubes, glass, 13×100 mm, caps, and peg racks

Micropipet, P-1000 and tips

Bradford reagent

Spectrophotometer, Spectronic 20 D+

Figure 9.5. **This small polyprep column is used early in R&D to determine whether a particular molecule can be separated from others by one method or another. A small amount (ie, 2 mL) of an ion-exchange resin is added to the column. If you look closely, you can see the white resin in the bottom one-third of the column. Molecules either bind to or are repelled by the charges on the resin beads.**

Photo by author.

Procedure

- Prepare the equilibration (100 mL) and elution (50 mL) buffers prior to starting the activity.
- Each group will run one of the protein samples (albumin alone, lysozyme alone, or the mixture) and share results.

1. Using a pipet, add 2 mL of suspended DEAE Sepharose™ (anion) resin to a chromatographic column (see Figure 9.5). Let it settle by gravity until you see a much defined, settled top.
2. Take off the stopper, and let the buffer drip through until there remains only a tiny bit on top of the column. Replace the stopper on the bottom of the column.
3. Add 10 mL of equilibration buffer (to wash out the preservative) and let it pass through the column.
4. Number a set of 13×100-mm test tubes 1 through 6.
5. Move the column to over collection test tube No. 1. Gently add (the "load") 0.2 mL of the appropriate sample (without disturbing the top of the bed): lysozyme, albumin, **or** lysozyme + albumin (add 0.4 mL if you are in the mixture group) to the top of the appropriate column. Remove the column stopper, and allow the sample to "load" into the

column. Collect the flow-through in test tube No. 1. Plug the column at the instant the sample loads into the resin bed (to avoid drying out the resin bed).

6. Move the column to over collection test tube No. 2. Add 2 mL of equilibration buffer and let it pass through the column. Collect the flow-through in test tube No. 2.

7. Repeat step 6, three more times, collecting fractions into test tubes No. 3 through 5. Each time, stopper the column just before the column runs dry.

8. When the fourth wash (into test tube No. 5) is complete, move the column over test tube No. 6. Add 2 mL of elution (high-salt) buffer to the top of the column. Collect the flow-through into test tube No. 6.

9. Add 5 mL of equilibration buffer to the columns and let it pass through to clean it.

10. Test each fraction in "your" run with Bradford reagent to determine the presence of protein. Follow the directions below:

- Turn on the Spec 20 D and let it warm up for at least 15 minutes.
- Add 3.0 mL of Bradford reagent to each of the test tubes No. 2 through 6.
- Cover each of the tubes with a 13×100-mm tube cap.
- Invert each tube three times to mix. Be gentle. Do not allow the solution to foam up. Do not mix up the test tube covers. Look at the colors of the solutions in the tubes. Are they the colors you expected? Yes or no? Why or why not? Record your observations in your notebook.
- Make up a blank with 2.0 mL of equilibration buffer and 3.0 mL of Bradford reagent. Mix.
- Set the Spec to 595 nm. Do you know why a wavelength of 595 nm is used? Zero the transmittance (left-hand knob) with **nothing** in the sample holder. Wipe off the blank. Insert it into the sample holder. Set the transmittance to 100% (using the right-hand knob) with the blank in the sample holder.
- Wipe the outside of each tube, and read the absorbance of each sample.

11. In your notebook, create a data table similar to Table 9.1 to record the absorbance of all the fractions. Collect data from two other groups so that you have absorbance data for albumin alone through the column, lysozyme alone through the column, and the mixture of lysozyme and albumin through the column,

Table 9.1. **Absorbance of Ion-Exchange Fractions at 595 nm.**

Sample	Fraction No. 1	Fraction No. 2	Fraction No. 3	Fraction No. 4	Fraction No. 5	Fraction No. 6
lysozyme						
albumin						
both						

Data Analysis

Examine the absorbance data. Considering that the minimum absorbance reading on a Spec 20 D is 0.02 au, and the maximum is 2.0 au, do the numbers make sense for what was expected? Explain. Plot your data on a three-line, line graph. Let each line represent the absorbance of ion-exchange fractions from one of the three protein samples.

Conclusion

Do your data show that the column actually separated lysozyme from albumin? Yes or no? Consider the peaks and valleys of each line. Explain why the shape of each line looks the way it does. If the results are not what you expected, discuss errors that might lead to fallacious data. Explain how the ability to separate molecules, such as albumin and lysozyme, on a column is utilized at a biotechnology company. If the separation of albumin and lysozyme was not complete on the column, propose a modification of the protocol that might improve the separation.

Thinking Like a Biotechnician

1. A technician checks the column bed volume on a column that is supposed to be 2 mL. If the bed volume is not 2 mL, is this a problem? Why or why not?
2. The column drips very slowly. Suggest a method to increase the rate of flow through the column. How can you check to ensure that this method does not compromise the separation?
3. A scientist would like to know the charge of a certain protein at pH 7.2. How could this column be used to help determine the overall charge of the protein at pH 7.2? What problems might occur using the proposed approach and how might they be addressed?

Laboratory 9d Using Ion Exchange Chromatography to Purify Amylase from Scale-up Broth

Background

Running an ion-exchange column can reveal information about the characteristics of a molecule. For example, a sample containing a protein of interest may be run on a negatively charged column. If the protein sticks to the column, then the technician may deduce that the protein has a positive charge at the pH of the column. On the other hand, if the protein flows through the column without sticking, it is either very weakly charged or has an overall negative charge.

When the overall charge of a protein at a particular pH is known, a technician can begin to develop a purification protocol for that protein when it is in a mixture.

Purpose

What is the net overall charge of amylase at pH 7.2?
Can amylase be separated from other proteins in a dialyzed, scale-up broth sample by ion-exchange chromatography?

Materials

Equilibration buffer (50 mM TRIS, pH 7.2)	Tubes, 15 mL, capped and racks	Micropipet, P-1000 and tips
Elution buffer (50 mM TRIS, 0.5 M NaCl, pH 7.2)	Chromatography columns with frit, 5 mL, tops and	Bradford reagent
Pipets, 10 mL, 5 mL, and 2 mL and pumps	bottoms	Spectrophotometer, Spectronic 20 D+
Amylase, 10 mg/mL in TRIS buffer	DEAE Sepharose™ resin	
	Tubes, glass, 13×100 mm, caps, and peg racks	

Procedure

- Prepare the equilibration (100 mL) and elution (50 mL) buffers prior to starting the activity.
- Each group will run either the 10 mg/mL amylase stock solution, a dilution of the stock amylase solution, or the scale-up broth that has been dialyzed into the buffer of 50 mM TRIS buffer, pH 7.2. Groups will share their results.

1. Using a pipet, add 2 mL of suspended DEAE Sepharose™ (anion) resin to a chromatographic column. Let it settle by gravity until you see a defined, settled top.
2. Remove the stopper, and let the storage buffer drip through until there remains only a tiny bit on top of the column. Replace the stopper on the bottom of the column.

3. Add 10 mL of equilibration buffer (to wash out the preservative) and let it pass through the column. Discard the flow-through.
4. Label a set of test tubes No. 1 through 6.
5. Samples: Most groups will run dialyzed broth samples in their column. Two groups should each run a stock 10 mg/mL amylase standard or a dilution of the standard, as follows:

   - If your group is running a dilution of the 10-mg/mL stock solution, prepare the diluted sample at this time. Dilute the stock with the equilibration buffer.
   - Diluted samples = 5 mg/mL amylase and 2.5 mg/mL amylase
   - Record in your notebook which load sample your group used.

6. Move the column to over collection test tube No. 1. Gently add 0.2 mL of your assigned sample (either your group's amylase solution or the scaled-up broth sample) to the top of the appropriate column. Try not to disturb the top of the column bed. Remove the column stopper, and allow the sample to "load" into the column. Collect the flow-through in test tube No. 1. This fraction is called the "load."
7. Move the column to over collection test tube No. 2. Add 5 mL of equilibration buffer and let it pass through each column. Collect the flow-through in test tube No. 2. This fraction is called "wash No. 1."
8. Repeat step 7, three more times, collecting fractions into test tubes No. 3 through 5. Stopper the column just before the column runs dry. These are washes No. 2 through 4.
9. While the column is "running," conduct a Bradford assay on the collected fractions. Before adding Bradford reagent to each tube, take a subsample of 250 μL and put it into a labeled, 1.7-mL, sterile microtube. The subsamples will be used for running PAGE gels at a later date. Store the subsamples at 4°C.
10. When the fourth wash (into test tube No. 5) is complete, move the column to over test tube No. 6. Add 2 mL of elution (high-salt) buffer to the top of the column. Collect the flow-through into test tube No. 6. This fraction is called the "elution."
11. Add 5 mL of equilibration buffer to the columns and let it pass through to clean them.
12. Determine the absorbance of each Bradford-reagent-treated fraction at 595 nm.

    If there is no protein in a fraction, the absorbance should be zero. Do not forget to zero the spec with a blank before you determine the absorbance of the fractions. Do you know what should be in the blank?
13. In your notebook, create a data table to record the data for your ion-exchange column. Include one column for each of the other samples.

    If you do not have a spectrophotometer or enough time, the color change of the Bradford reagent is striking enough to see that protein is present. Create a numerical key (5 → 0) to represent the amount of color in the samples.

Data Analysis

Plot the absorbance of the fractions for each column on a multiple-line, line graph. Do the lines look the way you expected? Consider where the peaks and valleys on the lines should be. Why might the results look different than you expected?

Conclusion

Does it appear that amylase molecules were bound to the column, and then released by the elution buffer? If so, what does that say about their charge? If not, what does that tell you about the charge on the amylase molecules? Did molecules in the broth behave similarly to molecules in the amylase standards? If so, what does that mean in terms of the ability to use this technique to purify amylase from broth cultures? If not, what does this mean? Explain the value of a biotechnology company running broth samples on an ion-exchange column and what product is expected.

Thinking Like a Biotechnician ━━━━━━━━

1. The load for each column was 0.2 mL of sample. How much amylase, in milligrams, was loaded onto each of the standard columns?
2. What is the value of running a 1:2 serial dilution of the amylase standards on columns?
3. If the amylase does not appear to bind in any of the columns, what might the technician try next?

Laboratory 9e — Identifying Amylase after Column Chromatography—Using SDS-PAGE

Background

The recombinant amylase produced in the transformation lab (Lab 8c) has a molecular weight of approximately 61,000 D (61 kD). Using this information, you can visualize the suspected amylase sample collected in the elution fraction of the ion-exchange purification on an SDS-PAGE gel (see Figure 9.6). If the amylase is present in sufficient concentration, it will appear as a band at a specific location. Its size can be estimated by comparing the location of the band with the proteins of known molecular weights (standards) run at the same time. Using PAGE, a technician can determine whether amylase was indeed separated from other proteins found in the transformed cell-culture broth.

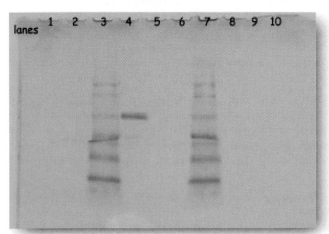

Figure 9.6. This PAGE gel has protein molecular weight sizing standards in lanes 3 and 7. A band, suspected to be amylase, is seen in lane 4.

Photo by author.

Purpose

Using an SDS-PAGE gel, can amylase be detected in the fractions from the ion-exchange chromatography? To what degree did the ion-exchange chromatography purify amylase from the broth sample?

Materials

Samples of dialyzed broth (Lab 9b)	Dry block heater/heat block, 80°C	Petri dishes, 150×15mm
Ion exchange fractions (Lab 9d)	Gel box, vertical, for PAGE	Coomassie® Blue R-250 stain
Amylase, 5 mg/mL in TRIS buffer	PAGE gel, 10% TG, 10 well	Coomassie® Blue R-250 Destain
Micropipet, P-100	Transfer pipets, 3 mL	Lab rotator, 12×12
Micropipet tips for P-100	PAGE gel loading dye (see Lab 5f)	White light imaging system
Reaction tubes, 1.7 mL	PAGE gel loading tips	Paper, thermal
Tube rack for 1.7 mL tubes	Protein sizing markers, 15-150 kD	Printer, thermal
Microcentrifuge	Power supply	Gloves, large
		Glasses, safety, plastic

Procedure

- Prepare all gel running buffers, stains, and destains prior to starting the activity. Recipes for these are found in Lab 5f.
- Each group runs the fractions from their own group's column chromatography.

80°C

1. Place 20 µL of each sample (preload sample, load, four washes, and elution) into five microtest tubes.
2. Place 20 µL of the amylase stock solution into a microtest tube.
3. Add 5 µL of PAGE loading dye into each tube. Gently mix.
4. Set up the gel box with a labeled, 10-well gel. Fill chambers with PAGE-SDS electrophoresis running buffer.
5. Heat the samples to 80°C for 5 minutes. While the samples are heating, rinse the wells of the gel with buffer.
6. Load 25 µL of each sample. Load 5 µL of preheated molecular-weight protein standards into Lane 5. In your notebook, record exactly what you loaded into each lane.
7. Run the gel for 1-1/2 hours at 35 mA or until the loading dye is about 0.5 cm from the end of the gel.
8. Stain with Coomassie® Blue stain for 3 to 12 hours.
9. Destain the gel using the microwave destain method (Lab 5g).
10. Photograph the gel, and glue the photo into your notebook. Label the contents of each well, the sizes of the standard bands, and the sizes of the sample bands. If your instructor wants the gel saved, dry the gel on a drying rack for 2 weeks.

Data Analysis/Conclusion

Observe the bands in the sample lanes. Is a 61-kD band (amylase) visible in any of the lanes? If so, in which lanes is it found? Do the number and the darkness of the bands make sense to you? If not, why? Is there evidence that the ion-exchange column has purified the sample? Explain. How do the results of this gel impact the fate of any purified amylase in the column fractions? If these results were achieved in a manufacturing facility after harvesting and purifying a fermentation batch, what would happen to the fractions containing amylase?

Thinking Like a Biotechnician

1. A technician runs a gel from an ion-exchange chromatography. He or she sees six bands in the wash samples and three bands in the elution, including a band at 61 kD. Has amylase been purified from other proteins in the broth? Explain.
2. What should the technician in question 1 do next?
3. A PAGE gel with ion-exchange fractions is run. If the only bands visible on the gel are the standards, what might be done to the column fraction samples to try to see any protein present in them?

Chapter

10 Plant Breeding

Here, a plant biotechnician collects seeds from an *Arabidopsis* plant breeding experiment. Seeds represent the next generation of plants. When planted, the seedlings will be studied in an attempt to identify plants that exhibit some desired characteristic.
Photo by author.

Plant biotechnology is a vast field that includes the long-standing practices of plant breeding, asexual plant propagation, and the isolation and manufacturing of plant compounds. It also includes the newly developed techniques of plant tissue culture, plant genetic engineering, and modification of plant compounds for medical and industrial purposes. Plant biotechnologists have many exciting opportunities to work in R&D and manufacturing positions in agricultural, pharmaceutical, and industrial settings within companies, government agencies, and educational institutions.

In this chapter's lab activities, you will learn about growing and observing plants as well as conducting plant breeding experiments. The skills you will develop include:

- identifying plants parts and using them in breeding experiments
- measuring plant growth including seed germination, shoot growth, and floral development
- setting up and monitoring a dihybrid, heterozygous plant breeding experiment
- analyzing the results of a breeding experiment using statistical tests

Plant breeding can result in variations in offspring, for example, the great range of types of roses. To produce offspring that are identical to the parents, such as thousands of identical orchid plants, researchers use asexual propagation methods. Asexual plant propagation and other plant biotechnology advances are presented in future chapters.

Laboratory 10a   Flower Morphology/Dissection

Background

Although plant breeding is one of the oldest forms of biotechnology, it remains one of the most common methods of improving plant products, including crops, ornamental plants, and plants for industrial purposes. Breeding involves sexual reproduction and, for most commercial plants, that means crossing flowering plants.

The function of a flower is to produce the next generation of seeds. Plant breeders must be able to recognize and manipulate flowers and their parts to produce new varieties. Breeders select pollen from plants with specific characteristics and transfer their pollen to other plants with specific characteristics, with the goal of generating offspring with particular characteristics.

Most flowers contain both male and female parts; these are called complete flowers (see Figure 10.1). The male portion of a flower is the stamen. The stamen produces pollen grains that house the sperm nuclei. The female portion of the flower is the pistil, which contains ovules that hold one or more egg cells. When fertilized, the ovules develop into the seeds. Surrounding the reproductive structures of the flower are the petal and sepals, respectively. The petals and sepals protect the developing flower bud and aid in pollinator attraction. Some flowers lack one or more of these structures and, therefore, are called "incomplete."

Pollination occurs when pollen is transferred from a stamen to a pistil. Some flowers are self-pollinators, while others are cross-pollinated (with other flowers) by wind, insects, or animals. Once pollination occurs, eggs are fertilized by the sperm nuclei of the pollen grains. Fertilized eggs develop into seeds of the next generation.

Purpose

What is the variation that can be seen in the structure of different flowers?
What inferences can be made as to the function of different flowers?

Materials

Magnifying hand lens, 2×
Forceps, fine-tipped
Scalpel handles, #4 and blades, #22
flowers (lily, iris, kalanchoe, fuchsia, pea, azalea, jasmine, or campanula, etc)

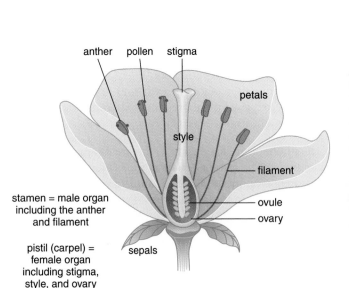

Photo by Timothy Wong.

Figure 10.1.   Parts of a Flower.   Knowledge of flower parts (left) is helpful in classifying plants and understanding a plant species' genetics and evolution. Wisconsin Fast Plants, or *Brassica rapa*, (right) have "perfect flowers" with all four flower parts (sepals, petals, stamen, and pistil). At 15 days, the flowers are open and the pistil is visible in the center with the stamen surrounding it.

Procedure

1. Obtain a lily flower and examine its parts. In most lily flowers, the sepals and the petals are the same color. You can tell them apart by where they are attached to the floral stem. Sepals are to the outside of the petals.
2. Dissect the lily flower parts from the flower slowly, from the outside to the inside of the flower. In your notebook, make a data table to record the number, color, and location of the floral parts, and other observed characteristics of the lily (see Table 10.1).
3. Repeat your dissection and observations of four other flowers.
4. Propose hypotheses for the type of pollination that occurs in each flower. Use the Internet to find examples of plants pollinated by the wind, insects, animals, or self-pollination. Record the information in a different data table in your notebook (see Table 10.2). Cite the Web sites you used.

Table 10.1. **Anatomical Differences in Flowers**

Flower	Sepal Number and Color	Petal Number and Color	Stamen Number and Color	Pistil Number and Color	Position of Ovary to Petals	Other Characteristics

Table 10.2. **Modes of Flower Pollination**

Flower	Predicted Mode of Pollination and Why (Hypothesis)	Actual Mode of Pollination (Referenced)

Data Analysis/Conclusion

Using the information you have gathered, consider how the shape of each flower may affect its function. Check your predictions by finding referenced information on the Internet.

Thinking Like a Biotechnician

1. "Monocot" and "dicot" are two terms that describe the types of seeds, flower, and leaves of a flowering plant. Monocot plants are more closely related to each other than they are to dicots, and vice versa. Among other characteristics, most of the flower parts of monocots are in threes or multiples of threes, and their leaves have parallel veins. The flower parts of dicots are in fours or fives, or multiples of fours or fives, and their leaf veins are net-like. , Identify which of the flowers you have dissected and studied are probably monocots and which are probably dicots.

2. A flower is yellow and has long, dark lines running from the tip of a petal to the base, near the pistil attachment. What type of pollination might this plant use?
3. The petals of some flowers are fused into a long tube, with the pistil and stamen deep inside it. Suggest a reason that, over time, this type of flower has evolved.

Laboratory 10b Seed Morphology/Dissection

Background

Like all organisms, plants must reproduce, passing genetic information from parent to offspring. In flowering plants, seeds are the result of reproduction.

Every seed contains a tiny "baby" plant, called an embryo. The embryo has a root, called the radicle, on one end and the first set of true leaves on the other end (see Figure 10.2). Under the right conditions, the rest of the seed will protect and nourish the embryo until it is established as an independent seedling.

Anatomically, the seed is constructed for the purpose of ensuring that the embryo survives until it can grow aboveground and photosynthesize. The embryo has a section, the hypocotyl, that bends to push the epicotyl (the embryonic stem portion directly below the first set of true leaves) and true leaves out of the soil. Surrounding the embryo is a food source called the endosperm.

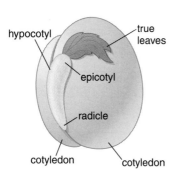

Figure 10.2. Structure of a Seed (left).   A seed protects and nourishes the next generation of a plant. The radicle, or embryonic root, is the first structure to emerge from a germinating seed. The two cotyledons, or seed leaves, are visible in this germinating seed.

The endosperm is packaged in a leaf-like structure called a cotyledon. When a peanut is split apart, the two pieces are each a cotyledon. Some seeds have one cotyledon, while other seeds have two cotyledons.

The endosperm in each cotyledon contains protein, sugar, starch, and fat molecules. This is the reason many other organisms eat seeds. The embryo produces enzymes that digest the endosperm. This produces food energy for the embryo until it is aboveground and able to photosynthesize.

Surrounding the endosperm is a seed coat. The seed coat protects the seed from mechanical damage and dehydration. Sometimes the seed coat is thick and woody, such as that of a Brazil nut, to give the seed additional protection. Since each plant grows in a unique environment, a seed's size, shape, and structure are a consequence of evolution. Plant species with seeds that function best in their environment survive until the reproductive age and pass the "good-seed genes" to the next generation. The large diversity of seed types is due to the "selection pressure" from each unique environment.

Purpose

What is the difference in the structure of different seeds?
What inferences can be made as to the function of different seed structures?

Materials

Magnifying hand lens, 2×	Ruler, metric, clear	Various seeds (peanut, corn,
Forceps, fine-tipped	Balance, tabletop milligram	pinto bean, pea, almond,
Scalpel handles, #4 and	Weigh paper, 7.6×7.6 cm	filbert nuts, Brazil nuts, or
blades, #22		grass, etc)

Procedure

1. Gather the seeds to be observed. Some seeds have been soaked, which makes them easier to dissect.
2. Dissect the peanut seed from the outside inward. Carefully separate the two cotyledons.
3. Observe the size, shape, color, and other characteristics of the seed and seed structures. In your notebook, construct a data table to record the seed data (see Table 10.3).
4. Repeat your dissection and observations for the other seeds.

Table 10.3. **Anatomical Differences in Seeds**

Seed	Seed Dimensions (mm)	Seed Mass (g)	Seed Coat Color/ Characteristics	Endosperm Color/ Characteristics	Embryo Dimensions (mm)	Other Characteristics

Data Analysis/ Conclusion

Summarize the similarities and differences you have observed in the seeds that you dissected. Suggest evolutionary reasons why a plant might produce seeds that exhibit their specific characteristics.

Thinking Like a Biotechnician

1. Discuss the advantages and disadvantages of larger seeds versus smaller seeds; more endosperm versus less endosperm; thick seed coats versus thinner seed coats; and any other differences you observe.
2. Go online and find four common methods of seed distribution or dissemination other than those dissected in this lab activity. Describe these in your notebook and record the Web site of each reference you used.
3. Dicots have two cotyledons (seed sections) and monocots have only one. Can you tell which of the seeds that you dissected are monocots and which are dicots? Does the venation (vein pattern) in the "true" leaves confirm this?

Laboratory 10c   Seed Germination: How Fast Is a Fast Plant?

Background

Seeds contain an embryo, the tiny plant that resulted from combining genetic information from the parents' sex cells. The embryo is the next generation of the plant. Germination, or seed sprouting, occurs when a seed's dormancy (resting state) is broken, and the embryo inside the seed starts to grow and becomes visible. An appropriate temperature, and an appropriate amount of water and oxygen trigger germination. Depending on the seed, germination can take a few days to several weeks.

When placed under favorable conditions, rapid-cycling *Brassica rapa* (*B. rapa*) seeds, also designated as Rbr seeds or Wisconsin Fast Plants (WFP), will germinate quickly (see Figure 10.3). They have been bred for rapid germination, growth, and seed production. They are ideal for genetic experiments because of these characteristics,

Figure 10.3. **Seed germination chambers allow seeds to be studied while they germinate.**
Photo by author.

in addition to their variety of interesting phenotypes. Many characteristics of WFPs can be manipulated and monitored through selective breeding experiments.

Purpose

What is the germination rate of *B. rapa* seeds compared with the germination of plant seeds?

Materials

Filter paper, 18.5 cm	F1 GgAa *Brassica rapa* seeds	Aged tap water, left out
Petri dishes, square, 100×15 mm	Seeds, carrot and cabbage	overnight
	Permanent lab marker pens	Forceps, fine-tipped
Reaction tubes, 1.7 mL	Cotton, absorbent	Transfer pipets, 3 mL
Tube rack for 1.7 mL tubes	Gauze squares, 6"×6"	Ruler, metric, clear
Bleach, 10%		

Procedure

Note: Sterilize instruments and materials prior to use.

1. Cut a piece of filter paper so that it is the same width as the Petri dish, but 10 cm longer. Draw a pencil line on the filter paper 1 cm down from the "top." This is where the seeds to be germinated will be placed.
2. Obtain a total of six (two *B. rapa*, two cabbage, and two carrot) seeds (see Figure 10.4).
3. Soak the seeds and the filter paper in 5% bleach solution for 5 minutes. Rinse with tap water.
4. Set up the Petri dish germination chamber as follows:

   a. Label the top edge of the Petri dish with your name and the date, using a permanent marker.
   b. Add absorbent cotton that has been soaked in aged tap water (squeeze out excess water) to the bottom of the dish.
   c. Add a gauze pad on top of the layer of absorbent cotton.
   d. Place the filter paper on the cotton so that the pencil line is at the top, and the bottom of the filter paper is folded down and around, underneath the wet, absorbent cotton.

5. Using sterile forceps, place the seeds on the filter paper, equally spaced on the pencil line (see Figure 10.5).
6. Using a transfer pipet, place 4 to 5 mL of water under the absorbent cotton, so that the filter-paper strip has plenty of water to absorb. Water will rise up the filter paper by capillary action and provide the seeds with the moisture they need to germinate.
7. Put the lid back on the dish. Keep the seeds in the dark until the first one germinates. Then, move the dish to a spot with indirect light. Do not let the chamber become too hot. Keep the filter paper moist, but not soaking wet, by adding water to the cotton reservoir when necessary. Keep the chamber vertical, so that the seeds will grow in response to gravity.
8. Every 12 hours, for 1 week, observe each seed. In a data table that you construct in your notebook, record the changes that occur to each seed over time. Look for seed swelling, color changes, and cracking, etc. Also, record the number of hours until each seed germinates. Create a bar graph that compares the germination time of each seed.
9. As the embryonic root (radicle) emerges, record the length of each seedling's root over time (growth rate) in a second data table. Consider the hour zero as the time the germination chamber is set up, and measure every 12 hours for 168 hours (7 days). Measure from the base of the cotyledons to the main root meristem, in millimeters (mm).

Figure 10.4. Cabbage and broccoli, like *Brassica rapa*, are members of the cabbage family (Brassicaceae) and are closely related to each other.
Photo by author.

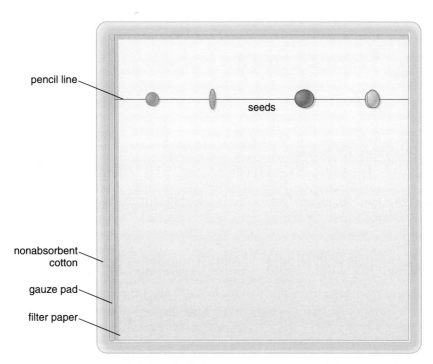

Figure 10.5. Germination Chamber Setup. Gently place the germination chamber in an almost upright position. This helps ensure that the roots will grow straight and downward for easy measuring.

10. Graph the length of *each* seed's root over time. The data for all four seeds should be shown on a four-color line graph. Determine the average growth rate in centimeters (cm) per day for each seedling. Report this value in your notebook, along with the calculations.

Data Analysis/Conclusion

Discuss the differences in germination rates in the different species. Do the observed germination rates support what was expected? Do the plants more closely related to *B. rapa* germinate any faster than the others? Did the fastest germinators also grow at the fastest rate once they had sprouted? Explain. List several possible errors in experimental technique that could affect the quality of data collected. Give an example of how a seed company might use an assay like the one conducted here.

Some seeds, such as those of *Arabidopsis thaliana,* are so tiny that they cannot be easily counted or planted. Here, Elizabeth Kohl, a Research Associate at Mendel Biotechnology, weighs a specific mass of seeds prior to planting for a hydroponic experiment. The seeds she is working with are transgenic, meaning that selected genes have been added to the plants that produced the seeds. In this case, genes have been added that are thought to help plants better tolerate certain environmental conditions, such as drought, high salt, or high or low mineral content.
Photo by author.

Thinking Like a Biotechnician

1. Of what value is a shorter germination time to a particular species and to a lab researcher studying plant genetics?
2. What other factors besides genetics may affect the expected germination rates? Explain how some of those factors might affect the germination rate.
3. What would happen if a tiny seed with only a small amount of endosperm were planted too deeply in the soil?

Laboratory 10d   Wisconsin Fast Plants: Model Organisms for Plant Breeding

Based on information from the *Wisconsin Fast Plants Manual,* published by Carolina Biological Supply Company © 1989 by Wisconsin Alumni Research Foundation.

Background

If you asked a scientist to name a specific type of bacterium, it is likely that *E. coli* would be the response. *E. coli* is well known as a genetic research organism because it is usually used in basic research. Scientists have conducted so many studies on this bacterium that they understand its life cycle as well as its environmental and nutritional requirements.

Like *E. coli, Drosophila melanogaster* (fruit flies), tobacco plants, *Arabidopsis thaliana* plants, mice, and the fungus, *Neurospora,* are often called "model" organisms. For research purposes, a model organism is a species that is used repeatedly and extensively for experimentation. Eventually, so much is known about the model organisms that scientists prefer to conduct experiments with them because they can more easily control these organisms.

A model organism often serves as a representative of other similar species. For example, scientists test mice and often apply the results to other mammals. To ensure safety and efficacy, tests are frequently conducted on chimpanzees before they are conducted on humans. The more closely related organisms are to each other, the better a model organism represents other organisms.

After more than 15 years of selective breeding, Dr. Paul H. Williams, of the University of Wisconsin at Madison, produced a variety of *B. rapa,* known as Wisconsin Fast Plants, with many characteristics desired in model organisms. These WFPs are excellent for research since they have the following characteristics:

- a short generation time (approximately 5 weeks from seeds to flowers to seeds)
- a relatively compact size, and they can be grown in a small space
- grow well in the laboratory (at room temperature, with continuous watering and fluorescent lighting)
- produce relatively large amounts of seeds that mature rapidly

Under optimum conditions, WFPs grow rapidly, producing flowers about 14 days after the seeds are planted (see Figure 10.6). Scientists selectively cross-pollinate WFPs using bee sticks. Fertilization occurs within a day of pollination. Seed pods develop and are visible 3 to 5 days after pollination. Twenty days after the final pollination, the plants are pulled and dried. Within a week, seeds can be harvested and a new generation planted.

In this activity, specific WFPs are cross-pollinated in a selective breeding experiment. Predictions of the possible offspring outcomes are made and analyzed.

Figure 10.6.   Wisconsin Fast Plants at approximately 14 days.
Photo by author.

To make predictions and evaluate the inheritance of specific traits, breeders use a chart called a Punnett Square. A Punnett Square analysis shows the possible gene (allele) combinations that could result when crossing specific genotypes. Preparing this analysis allows breeders to determine the probability of producing offspring with certain genotypes and phenotypes.

When considering the possible outcomes for the cross, follow the four steps shown below.

1. List the parents' genotypes. For example: TtGG   ×   ttgg
2. List the possible combinations of alleles in the gametes: TG or tG   tg
3. In a Punnett Square, show the possible combinations of genes that could occur in a random fertilization.

Punnett Square of the Cross

Genotypes of Male/Female Gametes	tg
TG	TtGg ← offspring possibility No. 1
tG	ttGg ← offspring possibility No. 2

4. Show expected genotypic results of the crossing of these gametes:

   1/2 of offspring are expected to be TtGg
   1/2 of offspring are expected to be ttGg

   Expected phenotype(s) of offspring:

   If T = tall and G = green, then
   1/2 of offspring are expected to be tall and green
   1/2 of offspring are expected to be short and green

In the following activity, you will set up a cross and analyze the results, taking into consideration what is expected to happen according to a Punnett Square.

Purpose

How closely do the data collected from an intended dihybrid, heterozygous cross of F1 green-leafed, anthocyanin-containing (purple) plants match what is expected?

Materials

WFP watering system, with reservoir, mat, wicks, and anti-algal squares
Liquid dishwashing soap
Planting quads (or pots or film tubes)
Bleach, 10%
Quad water wick strips
Plastic beaker, 1000 mL

Potting soil
Plastic beaker, 1L
Fertilizer pellets
F1 heterozygous non-purple stem, yellow-green leaf (GgAa) seeds
Forceps, fine-tipped
Pipets, transfer, 3 mL

Plant labels, sticks or tape
WFP light bank system
Plant support stakes
Dried bees
White glue
Toothpicks
Cups, Styrofoam
Petri dishes, 100×15 mm

Note: When the GGAA seeds grow into plants, they have green leaves and purple in their stems. The recessive mutants, "ggaa," have yellow-green leaves and no purple in the stems. The F1 seeds used in this cross were produced by crossing "GGAA" parent plants (green leaves, purple stems) with "ggaa" parent plants (yellow-green leaves, green stems).

Procedure

Part I: Planting WFP Seeds

1. In your notebook, show the entire problem, including the Punnett Square for the proposed cross. Calculate the expected percent of offspring from each phenotype resulting from crossing F1 parent plants, which are heterozygous for green leaf color, and for purple color, anthocyanin, in the stems.

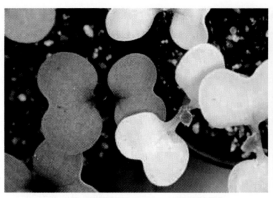

Green Leaf and Yellow-Green Mutant
© Wisconsin Fast Plants Program, University of Wisconsin-Madison.

Purple Wild Type and Nonpurple Mutant
© Wisconsin Fast Plants Program, University of Wisconsin-Madison.

2. Plant and grow the F1 (GgAa) seeds. See the planting instructions below. Start on a Monday or Tuesday to ensure daily watering until the seeds have germinated.

   a. Prepare the water reservoir (see Figure 10.7). Fill the reservoir 2/3 full with tap water. Add 3 mL of liquid detergent. Soak the mat in the soapy water for 1 minute. Squeeze the soapy water out of the mat. Repeat this process for a total of three times. After the last soaking, do not squeeze out the mat. Lay the soapy mat on the cover of the water reservoir so that the long mat tip will hang into the water reservoir. Make sure that the mat makes good contact with the cover and that no air bubbles are under the mat. If you are reusing a reservoir and mat, scrub it with soapy water, dunk it in 10% bleach for 15 minutes, and rinse it well with water before use.

   b. Fill the water reservoir with tap water.

   c. Place one copper sulfate square in the reservoir water.

   d. Place the reservoir cover, with the mat, on the reservoir so that the mat is in the water.

   e. Prepare the potting soil mixture by moistening it in a plastic beaker until it is slightly damp.

   f. Locate a Styrofoam quad (or a Styrofoam pot with a hole punched in the bottom) and label it with a label stick or labeling tape. Use a permanent marker. If you are reusing a quad, scrub it with soapy water, dunk it in 10% bleach for 15 minutes, and rinse it well with water before using.

   g. Obtain 4 wicks and push one wick into each cell until the wick tip extends 1 cm through the hole in the bottom of the quad. When a wet wick touches a wet mat, capillary action will draw the water into the quad (see Figure 10.8).

   h. Fill each cell of the quad or pot 1/2 full with moistened potting-soil mix (see Figure 10.9).

   i. Obtain 12 fertilizer pellets and add three to each cell/pot or quad.

   j. Fill each cell to the top with more potting mix. The soil should be loose, not packed down. Use a pencil to make a 4-mm depression in the soil surface of each cell.

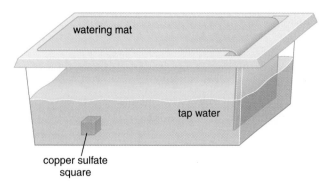

Figure 10.7. Setting Up the Water Reservoir. The water reservoir ensures a constant amount of water. It is critical that it is wetted thoroughly, and the air is squeezed out, so water will move via capillary action through the matting and up the wicks to the soil.

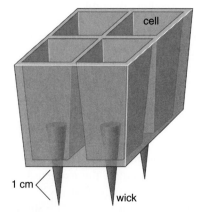

Figure 10.8. Setting Up the Quad. Each wick must be in contact with both the soil in the cell and the water on the mat.

k. Place two seeds into each depression.

l. Add just enough of the moistened potting soil to each cell to barely cover the seeds.

m. Using a pipet, water each quad thoroughly, but gently, until water drips out of the bottom of each cell. The soil and wick must be thoroughly wetted.

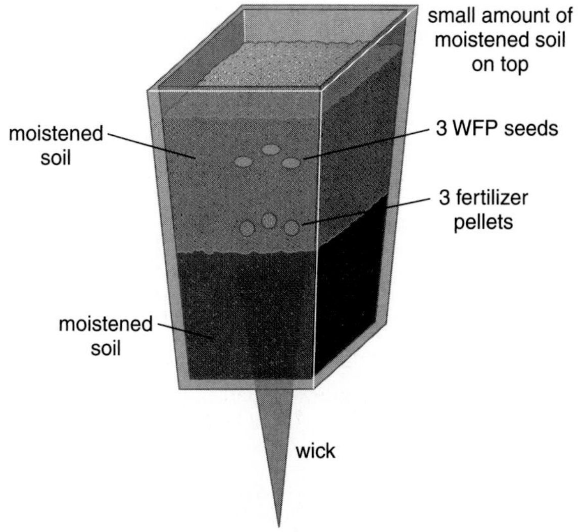

Part II: Growing Wisconsin Fast Plant Seeds and Plants

3. Place the quad on the water mat. Make sure that the wetted wick is in contact with the wetted mat. As other quads are added to the mat, make sure that all wicks are still in contact with the mat. Water each cell from the top before leaving the lab.

4. Place the water reservoir under the light bank. The top of the quad should always be 5 to 8 cm from the bulbs of the light bank. WFPs are very sensitive to insufficient light (six fluorescent light bulbs, in a light bank, are required). As the plants grow, raise the light bank to keep an average distance of about 6 cm between the bulbs and the plants (see Figure 10.10). Directions for a "homemade" light bank are on the Carolina Biological Supply Web site.

5. Once the WFP seedlings are showing the first set of true leaves, thin them out to maintain one plant per cell by pinching the unwanted plants off with your fingernails. Create a data table in your notebook to monitor stem growth over 2 weeks, measuring from the attachment of the first set of true leaves to the growing tip (see Figure 10.11).

6. If necessary, use small wooden stakes and plastic rings to support the plants as they grow. When flower buds appear, make bee sticks as directed below (see Figure 10.12).

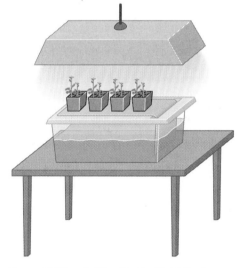

Figure 10.9. Planting WFP Seeds.   The seeds are planted close to the top to allow plenty of room for the roots to develop.

The equivalent of six flourescent bulbs should be kept at a distance of 6 cm from the growing plants at all times.

Figure 10.10.   Setting Up the Light Bank. Adjust the height of the light as often as necessary to keep it an average distance of approximately 6 cm above the plants.

Part III: Pollination of Plants and Harvesting F2 Seeds

7. Cross-pollinate F1 plants using the premade bee sticks (see Figure 10.12).

a. Make the bee sticks at least 24 hours in advance to allow the glue fumes to evaporate. Using white glue, glue a honeybee thorax (excised from a bee's body) onto a toothpick (see Figures 10.12 and 10.13).

b. Holding the toothpick end of the bee stick, rotate the bee-thorax end over the stamen of the flowers to pick up pollen.

c. Cross-pollinate other flowers by rotating the bee stick on other flower pistils. Continue to pollinate in this way for 2 to 3 days.

d. After 3 days of cross-pollination, remove all unopened flower buds. Record the date of the last cross-pollination in your notebook. Continue to remove all new flower buds, being careful not to disturb the developing seed pods.

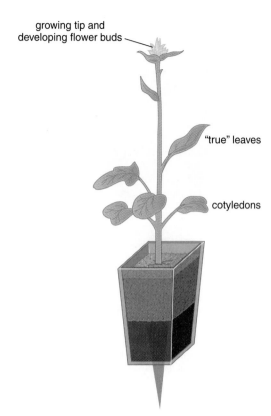

growing tip and
developing flower buds

"true" leaves

cotyledons

Figure 10.11. **The Growing Fast Plant.** As each plant grows, the cotyledons shrivel and may fall off. The soil level may compact with watering. Measuring should be done from the attachment of the first set of true leaves to the growing tip (left). Evaluate your plants' growth compared with other plants around the class. Plants that are growing more slowly than the others may need more light or an adjustment in watering. Since germination rates are approximately 80%, sprouted seedlings must be thinned to one plant per cell quad. The cotyledons are short-lived and present only until the true leaves are healthy. The cotyledons are round with smooth edges. The true leaves arise above them and are long and narrow with serrated edges.

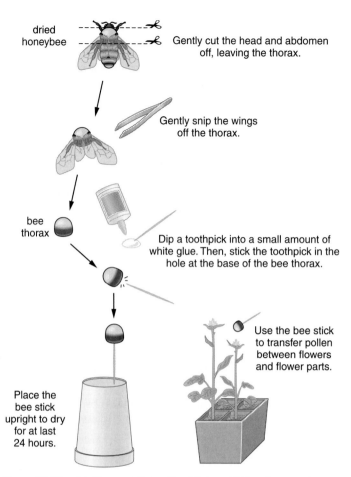

dried honeybee — Gently cut the head and abdomen off, leaving the thorax.

Gently snip the wings off the thorax.

bee thorax

Dip a toothpick into a small amount of white glue. Then, stick the toothpick in the hole at the base of the bee thorax.

Use the bee stick to transfer pollen between flowers and flower parts.

Place the bee stick upright to dry for at last 24 hours.

Figure 10.12. **Making and Using Bee Sticks.** White glue contains chemicals (fumes) that can sterilize bee pollen. Make the sticks early enough (at least 24 hours in advance) that the fumes diffuse before use.

Figure 10.13. **Do all work with WFP, including planting, making bee sticks, and harvesting seeds, over a lab mat. This work is messy, and cleanup is easier when lab mats are used.**

Photo by author.

8. Harvest the F2 seeds from their pods following the directions below:

   a. Remove the quads from the water reservoirs 20 days after the last pollination. Allow them to dry for at least 5 days.

   b. Using a Petri dish as a collection plate, harvest the seeds by gently rolling the dry seed pods between your hands. Seeds can be used immediately or stored in a cool, dry place for several months or more, if they are kept dry and in an airtight container.

Troubleshooting and Growing Hints (see Figure 10.14)

Dried plants: If the plants or soil in the quads dry out, water them from the top down and place them in a beaker of water for about 24 hours. Sometimes this will revive the plants.

Insect infestation: If insects or insect damage is apparent, try one of the two of the following methods:

- Pick the insects from your plants and squish them with your hand.
- Spray the plants with a solution of commercial insecticidal soap.
- Make sure to clean and, if necessary, spray the growing area before the next planting.

Bee sticks: Prepare the bee sticks by holding the bee and pinching off the abdomen, head, legs, and, finally, the wings. Dip a toothpick into a tiny amount of white glue. Stick the glue end of the toothpick into the hole of the thorax. Stick the bee sticks into the bottom of an inverted Styrofoam cup to dry.

9. Observe the results of the dihybrid, heterozygous cross by planting the F2 seeds (offspring of the F1 starting seeds). Grow them until the pigments in the stem and the cotyledons are visible and obvious (within the first 3 days of germination). Follow the same planting instructions used for the F1 generation, except that before the next planting, soak the water reservoirs, platforms, water mat, quads, and wicks in a 10% bleach solution for at least 15 minutes. Then, scrub the quads with a brush and rinse all materials thoroughly with water. Let all materials dry completely before reusing. Also, if there is a shortage of quads, plant five seeds per cell. The more seeds available to count give a larger sample size, which increases the validity of the results.

10. Once the F2 plants have sprouted enough for you to recognize their phenotypes (second or third day), count the number of plants in each of the four expected phenotypes: 1) green with anthocyanin; 2) green with no anthocyanin; 3) yellow-green with anthocyanin; and 4) yellow-green with no anthocyanin. Record these data (for the plants in your quad) in a data table in your notebook. If you are not sure of the phenotype of a certain plant, ask a colleague or two for their opinions.

11. Determine the expected number of offspring in each phenotype group and compare that number to the observed number of offspring in each phenotypic group. Remember that the percentage of each expected phenotypic group was calculated at the beginning of the procedures. Record this information in the data table. Determine whether the observed data are within 10% of the expected values. Add this information to the data table.

12. In your notebook, create a data table to show all the phenotypic data for the class. Record each group's observed and expected values, and the observed and expected totals for the class. Make a bar graph of the observed and expected values (totals) for the class.

Figure 10.14. A WFP Instruction Manual is available through Carolina Biological Supply Company at http://www.fast-plants.org/resources/manuals .html#FPMANUAL.

Photo by author.

Data Analysis/Conclusion

Analyze the data by determining whether the actual results are close enough to the expected results to support a valid dihybrid, heterozygous cross. Use the Chi Square analysis method to analyze the data (see the next activity). Give evidence for your statements. If your data do not come close to the expected values, give reasons for the poor results.

Thinking Like a Biotechnician

1. Use Microsoft® Excel® to determine the standard deviation (SD) for the average stem growth of your WFPs. If you do not know how to do this, access the Help feature from the Menu bar of Excel® and search for the topic.
2. For the F2 phenotypic counts, list at least three reasons why these counts might be inaccurate.

Laboratory 10e   How Can You Determine if the WFP Data Are Good Enough?

Background

In the WFP experiment, a known F_1 generation of WFP was grown. These F_1 plants were dihybrid, heterozygous for green leaves, and anthocyanin in the stems. Do you remember the genotypes of these plants?

When these F_1 plants flowered, they were cross-pollinated with other F_1 plants of the same genotype. Based on a large sample size and random breeding, the Punnett Square of this cross predicted a 9:3:3:1 ratio of offspring in each phenotypic group. Thus, in any population of F_2 offspring:

9/16 are expected to show the dominant/dominant traits of green with anthocyanin
3/16 are expected to show the dominant/recessive traits of green, with no anthocyanin
3/16 are expected to show the recessive/dominant traits of yellow, with anthocyanin
1/16 are expected to show the recessive/recessive traits of yellow, with no anthocyanin

We rarely get only 16 offspring, so it is more useful to consider the percentage of the offspring in each phenotypic group. Therefore, in any given population of offspring we expect the following:

56% (9/16) to show the dominant/dominant traits = green, with anthocyanin
19% (3/16) to show the dominant/recessive traits = green, with no anthocyanin
19% (3/16) to show the recessive/dominant traits = yellow, with anthocyanin
6% (1/16) to show the recessive/recessive traits = yellow, with no anthocyanin

Thus, in a population of 200 offspring, the following are expected:

112 are expected to be green, with anthocyanin (200 × .56)
38 are expected to be green, with no anthocyanin (200 × .19)
38 are expected be yellow, with anthocyanin (200 × .19)
12 are expected to be yellow, with no anthocyanin (200 × .06)

You may have more or fewer seeds as F_2 offspring in each phenotypic group from your F_1 plants. Through a Chi Square (χ^2) analysis of the phenotypic results of the F_2 offspring, the validity of the data collected can be evaluated.

How to Calculate the Chi Square Value (χ^2)

Use the equation below to calculate the χ^2 value for a set of data.

$$\chi^2 = \Sigma\,[(O\text{-}E)^2/E]$$

The terms represent the following:

   O = observed number for a phenotypic group
   E = expected number for a phenotypic group
   Σ = the Greek letter, Sigma, which represents the "sum of"

The χ^2 equation examines and compares each phenotypic group's observed data to the expected results. The difference is the deviation between the actual and the expected results. Then, Σ sums up all of the phenotypic group's deviations.

The final χ^2 value represents the sum of all of the deviations in the experiment. By looking on the Chi Square probability table (Table 10.4), one can see if the observed deviation from the expected results is small enough that it supports the experimental hypothesis. In this case, the hypothesis is that the data are similar enough to be considered a valid dihybrid, heterozygous cross (see Table 10.4). If the χ^2 value is too large (greater than the P = 0.05 value), the deviation from what is expected is so large that the data do not support a valid dihybrid, heterozygous cross.

Purpose

Does the χ^2 value for the WFP cross support the hypothesis that a dihybrid, heterozygous cross was conducted in the WFP breeding experiment?

Procedure

1. Determine the degrees of freedom (df) for the WFP dihybrid, heterozygous cross. The df is one less than the number of phenotypic groups.

Table 10.4. **Chi Square Probability Table.**   To use the table, find the χ^2 value for the degrees of freedom (phenotypic groups –1) in the experiment. If the χ^2 value falls to the left of the 0.05 column value, then the hypothesis is accepted (the data are good enough).

df*	0.95	0.90	0.70	0.50	0.30	0.20	0.10	0.05*	0.01	0.001 Probability
1	0.004	0.016	0.15	0.46	1.07	1.64	2.71	3.84	6.64	10.83
2	0.10	0.21	0.71	1.39	2.41	3.22	4.61	5.99	9.21	13.82
3	0.35	0.58	1.42	2.37	3.67	4.64	6.25	7.82	11.35	16.27
4	0.71	1.06	2.20	3.36	4.88	5.99	7.78	9.49	13.28	18.47
5	1.15	1.61	3.00	4.35	6.06	7.29	9.24	11.07	15.09	20.52
6	1.64	2.20	3.83	5.35	7.23	8.56	10.65	12.59	16.81	22.46
7	2.17	2.83	4.67	6.35	8.38	9.80	12.02	14.07	18.48	24.32
8	2.73	3.49	5.53	7.34	9.52	11.03	13.36	15.51	20.09	26.13
9	3.33	4.17	6.39	8.34	10.66	12.24	14.68	16.92	21.67	27.88
10	3.94	4.87	7.27	9.34	11.78	13.44	15.99	18.31	23.21	29.59

← Accept the experimental hypothesis | *Reject the experimental hypothesis →

*df = degree of freedom

Data are close enough to the expected results | Data are not close enough to the expected results

2. Using the data collected in the WFP cross, determine an χ^2 value for each of the following. Show all calculations for each χ^2 determination in your notebook.

- your own F_2 seeds from your own F_1 plants
- the F_2 seeds from the entire class' F_1 plants
- the F_2 seeds from multiple classes' F_1 plants

3. For each determination, report the spot where the χ^2 value falls on the Chi Square Probability Table.

Data Analysis/Conclusion

Describe the significance of each χ^2 value. How well does each set of data fit expectations for a dihybrid, heterozygous cross? Are any of the experimental results close enough to what was expected to occur during a dihybrid, heterozygous cross to show a valid experiment? Explain how results might not show a dihybrid, heterozygous cross even though all the seeds were GgAa. Did the χ^2 value improve as the sample size increased? Explain.

Thinking Like a Biotechnician

1. For each of the following cross pollinations for *B. rapa* plant characteristics, give the genotypes of the parents, gametes, and offspring, and the offsprings' phenotypes, as well as the expected results for a cross between parents that have 50 offspring.

   a. Cross a homozygous-dominant, green-leafed (G) plant with a homozygous-recessive, yellow/green-leafed plant.

   Parents' genotypes:
   Alleles possible in the gametes:
   Punnett Square of the cross:
   Genotypic results of crossing these gametes:
   Phenotype(s) of offspring:

   b. Cross a heterozygous, purple-stemmed plant with a homozygous-recessive one (pp).

   Parents' genotypes:
   Alleles possible in the gametes:
   Punnett Square of the cross:
   Genotypic results of crossing these gametes:
   Phenotype(s) of the offspring:

   c. Cross a plant, heterozygous for both green leaf color and purple stems, with a plant that is homozygous recessive for leaf color and heterozygous for stem color.

   Parents' genotypes:
   Alleles possible in the gametes:
   Punnett Square of the cross:
   Genotypic results of crossing these gametes:
   Phenotype(s) of the offspring:

2. For the cross in problem 1c, calculate the χ^2 value and explain its significance if the breeding experiment resulted in 20 green-leafed purple plants; 4 green-leafed, not purple plants; 18 yellow-leafed purple plants; and 8 yellow-leafed, not purple plants.

Chapter 11

Plant Cloning

A plant technician checks the growth of several sets of *Arabidopsis thaliana* (Arabidopsis) plants, some of which have received genes for drought tolerance (low water conditions). Arabidopsis plants are model laboratory plants and are often the plant of choice for indoor plant studies.
Photo by author.

Several areas of plant biotechnology are generating new products and significant amounts of interest. Many plant biotechnologists work in facilities focused on plant cloning using asexual plant propagation and integrating recombinant DNA technology with other propagation techniques.

As in all experiments, multiple replications of each experimental setup are conducted. For plant breeding or cloning experimental studies, that could mean many acres of crop plants or hundreds of flats or pots of plants in greenhouses or growth chambers. Good documentation skills are required to manage the typically large number of plant samples and related data.

In the following lab activities, you will learn how to clone and assess plants using some long-standing culture methods, as well as some of the more recent advances in plant biotechnology. You will develop and practice the following skills:

- starting and monitoring leaf and stem cuttings (clones)
- growing plants hydroponically
- testing the impact of plant hormones on plant growth and plant processes
- setting up and gauging the success of a plant tissue culture
- using molecular biology techniques such as DNA isolation and analysis to confirm a plant genetic engineering procedure

The ability to clone plants and to isolate and manipulate a plant's DNA code and protein production is opening up vast new areas for plant or plant-based product development.

Laboratory 11a Asexual Plant Propagation through Leaf and Stem Cuttings

Background

When plant growers want all the offspring of a particular plant to be identical to the parent plant, they do not want the plant to reproduce sexually. Instead, they want to make identical copies of the plant. These copies are called clones. Clones are made through asexual reproduction. One parent gives rise to several identical offspring. Clones can be produced by taking pieces of a plant (one cell, many cells, or even a whole plant organ), and growing them in the right environment.

Figure 11.1. **Coleus plants are commonly cloned through stem cuttings in water.**
Photo by author.

The oldest form of asexual plant propagation is the use of pieces of leaves or stems. These are called cuttings. Many plants grow well from cuttings (see Figure 11.1). Cuttings are grown in water or in sterile potting media. There are several types of media including perlite, vermiculite, soil, peat moss, and agar. Under suitable conditions, leaf cuttings may be induced to produce roots and stems, while stem cuttings may be induced to produce leaves and roots.

Purpose

How successfully can two species be "cloned" from leaf and stem cuttings?
How does rooting medium affect root production in these cuttings?

Materials

Environmental Health and Safety Officer

Plastic beaker, 1 L	Bleach, 5%	Scalpel blades, #22, for #4
Potting soil	Several large *Fucshia* plants	handles
Vermiculite	Several large *Kalanchoe*	Liquid detergent
Sand	plants	Pipets, transfer, 3 mL
Cups, Styrofoam, 6 oz	Scalpel handles, #4	Lab scoops
Permanent lab marker pens		Beakers, 250 mL

Procedure

- The instructor will assign an experimental treatment to the lab team.
- Each student is responsible for one experimental setup with three replications.
- All media should be sterilized before use.
- A setup is a pot containing some medium and three cuttings. The setup variations are listed in Table 11.1.

1. In a 1 L container, moisten the medium with water until it is thoroughly wetted.
2. Punch four holes in the bottom of a Styrofoam cup. Use a permanent marker to label the outside with your name and the treatment.
3. Fill the cup loosely with the selected moistened medium. Tap the soil down gently to 0.5 cm from the top.

Table 11.1.   **The Number of Roots in Cuttings in Different Media**

Plant	Medium	Cutting	Average Number of Roots
Fuchsia	potting soil mix	stem	
Fuchsia	vermiculite	stem	
Fuchsia	sand	stem	
Fuchsia	potting soil mix and vermiculite	stem	
Fuchsia	sand and vermiculite	stem	
Fuchsia	sand and potting soil mix	stem	
Fuchsia	potting soil mix	leaf	
Fuchsia	vermiculite	leaf	
Fuchsia	sand	leaf	
Fuchsia	potting soil mix and vermiculite	leaf	
Fuchsia	sand and vermiculite	leaf	
Fuchsia	sand and potting soil mix	leaf	
Kalanchoe	potting soil mix	stem	
Kalanchoe	vermiculite	stem	
Kalanchoe	sand	stem	
Kalanchoe	potting soil mix and vermiculite	stem	
Kalanchoe	sand and vermiculite	stem	
Kalanchoe	sand and potting soil mix	stem	
Kalanchoe	potting soil mix	leaf	
Kalanchoe	vermiculite	leaf	
Kalanchoe	sand	leaf	
Kalanchoe	potting soil mix and vermiculite	leaf	
Kalanchoe	sand and vermiculite	leaf	
Kalanchoe	sand and potting soil mix	leaf	

4. Sterilize the work area with 5% bleach solution before making any cuttings.
5. For leaf cuttings, use a sterile scalpel to remove some young leaves from one of the parent plants. Use a small- to medium-size leaf (3 to 5 cm^2). To sterilize the leaves, immerse them in a 5% commercial bleach/liquid detergent (1 drop detergent:1 L bleach) solution for 10 seconds, then dunk them three times in sterile distilled water. Use sterile forceps to move them.
6. Use a sterile scalpel to cut the leaf petiole (leaf stem) to 0.5 cm from the leaf base. Cut the leaf petiole at a 45° angle to increase the amount of exposed meristematic tissue. Use a pencil wiped with 5% bleach to make an indentation in the medium, wide and deep enough to insert your cutting. Place the leaf cutting in the medium so that its base is submerged at least 2 cm or 1/3 of the way. Gently pat the medium around the cutting.
7. For stem cuttings, take a stem or stem piece that has at least three nodes (nodes are where leaves attach). Remove the leaves from at least the two bottom nodes. Trim off large leaves, leaving one or two small leaves at the top. To sterilize the stem cutting, immerse it in a 5% commercial bleach/liquid detergent solution for 10 seconds, and then dunk it three times in sterile distilled water. Use sterile forceps to move it.
8. Use a sterile scalpel to cut the stem base back to 0.5 cm from the bottom node. Cut the stem at a 45° angle to increase the amount of exposed meristematic tissue. Use a pencil to make a hole in the medium, deep enough to insert your cutting. Place the stem cutting in the medium so that at least one node, or possibly two, is submerged. Gently pat down the medium around the cutting.
9. Use a large transfer pipet to water the cutting medium with aged tap water from the top down until water drips from the bottom holes.

10. Place the labeled pots in a spot with indirect light (classroom light) for 3 to 4 days before moving the pots to the plant light stand.

11. Check daily to make sure that the medium is damp but not soaked. Add water as necessary. Do not over-water. The day the cuttings were started is "Day 0."

12. Look for evidence of new growth. Record changes in each cutting (color, wilting/turgidity, number of leaves, etc) over time in three separate data tables. The title of the data tables should be as follows:

    a. Changes in color in _____ cuttings over 28 days
    b. Changes in turgidity in _____ cuttings over 28 days
    c. Changes in number of leaves in _____ cuttings over 28 days

    Design data tables to record daily observations even if there are no observations on some days. Make the data as quantitative as possible, attempting to convert qualitative data to numerical data, as in a 5 → 1 system. For example, for color, 5 = green to 1 = white. For turgidity, 5 = firm and completely turgid, and 1 = limp and not turgid at all. Remember that there are three replications. Remember to include averages, comments, and the number of roots/cuttings.

13. After 28 days, gently scoop up each cutting from the medium. Gently remove the medium from the roots by carefully dunking in a beaker of water and rinsing with a transfer pipet. Be careful not to rinse soil down the sinks! Be careful not to break any roots.

14. Count the number of roots present on each cutting. Create a new data table for these data.

15. Average each set of results for your variation of the experiment. Share your averaged data with other lab teams in the class.

16. Create a data table to compare the average root data from the class groups (see Table 11.1).

Data Analysis

Using class averages, graph the average number of roots produced by each type of plant cutting in each medium. Does it appear, overall, that one group of leaf or stem cuttings rooted better than others? Explain. Does it appear, overall, that the *Fuchsia* rooted better than *Kalanchoe*, or vice versa? Explain.

Conclusion

Discuss the results of the class' cuttings experiment. How successfully were the plants cloned? Give your answers as percentages of the total number of cuttings attempted, and explain any findings that seem to indicate that the rooting medium affected root production. Discuss possible reasons for the results obtained. Propose variations in the experiment to improve the results.

 *Thinking Like a Biotechnician*

1. The procedures suggest smaller leaf sizes for leaf cuttings. What is a possible disadvantage of a large leaf cutting?

2. The media in this experiment was sterilized. Discuss the advantages and disadvantages of sterilizing the media before using it in this experiment.

3. Suggest a method of encouraging more root development in cuttings that are slow to root or that do not root.

Laboratory 11b   Asexual Plant Propagation through Runners

Background

Clones may be started from runners. Runners grow as long side branches off a plant, and they produce tiny replicates of the parent plant at the end of the runner. These tiny replicates can be placed in media until they develop roots (see Figure 11.2). The runners can then be cut from the parent plant and are able to live independently (see Figure 11.3). Strawberry plants and spider plants *(Chlorophytum comosum)* are well known for propagation through runners.

Purpose

What is the difference in the rate of plantlet growth when attached or unattached to the parent plant?

Materials

Spider plants *(Chlorophytum comosum),* purchased/grown for at least 6 months earlier to allow
    for spider formation
Cups, Styrofoam, 6 oz
Soil, potting
Scissors, stainless steel
Permanent lab marker pens
Lab scoops
Beakers, 250 mL

Procedure

Note: Students will start plantlets either attached to or not attached to the parent plant.

1. Find a developing plantlet at the end of a spider plant *(Chlorophytum comosum)* runner.
2. Embed the plantlet in a Styrofoam pot of prepared potting soil so that the base of the plantlet is covered with moistened potting soil mix.
3. Depending on which trial that you are assigned, either leave the runner attached to the parent plant or cut the runner (near the plantlet) to separate the plantlet from the parent plant.
4. Remove any dead or dying leaves from each plantlet. Count and record the number of leaves on the plantlet (consider this Day 0).
5. Place the plants in a location with indirect light.
6. Check every day to make sure that the medium is damp, but not soaked.

Figure 11.2. **When strawberry plants grow, they send out lateral stems (runners) along the soil surface. New stems and leaves grow from the runners into new plants at regular intervals.**
© Patrick Johns/Corbis.

Figure 11.3. **Young strawberry plants are started by placing the runners barely embedded in soil, letting them root, and cutting them from the parent plant.**
Photo by author.

7. Look for evidence of new growth. Record changes in the runner plantlets (color, wilting/turgidity, and number of leaves, etc) over time in three separate data tables. The title of the data tables should be as follows:

    a. Changes in color in _____ plantlets over ___ days
    b. Changes in turgidity in _____ plantlets over ___ days
    c. Changes in number of leaves in _____ plantlets over ___ days

    Design data tables to record daily observations, even if there are no observations on some days. Make the data as quantitative as possible, attempting to convert qualitative data to numerical data as in a 5 → 1 system. For example, for color, 5 = green and 1 = white. For turgidity, 5 = firm and completely turgid and 1 = limp and not turgid at all.

8. Grow the plant and plantlets until the plantlets have at least two new sets of leaves. Record the number of days until the appearance of the second new leaf. Gather data on "the number of days to two leaves" for each plantlet in the class. Put those data on a histogram that shows the frequency of plants growing two leaves by a certain number of days (eg, day 15, day 16, day 17, or day 18, etc).

9. When the instructor decides to end the experiment (after "two new set of leaves" data), gently scoop up the plantlet from the medium. Gently dunk the plantlet's rooting area in a beaker of water; then use a transfer pipet to gently wash the remaining medium from the roots. Be careful not to rinse soil down the sinks! Be careful not to break any roots. Count the number of roots present on the plantlet.

10. Share your data for the number of roots on the plantlet with other groups in the class. Collect enough data to have three samples that were attached to the parent plant and three samples that were not. Create a new data table for these data. Create a bar graph to show the average number of roots on unattached and attached runner plantlets after ___ days.

Conclusion

Discuss any evidence that plantlets attached to parent plants have an advantage over plantlets severed from the parent before rooting. In the discussion, include any explanations for the observed results and any concerns you have about the experimental design.

Thinking Like a Biotechnician

1. What benefits might the runner plantlets gain by remaining attached to the parent plant?
2. What disadvantage might the runner plantlets have by being attached to the parent?
3. Why might the size and/or age of a runner plantlet skew the results of this experiment?

Laboratory 11c   The Effect of Hormone Concentration on Plant Propagation

Background

When applied at the "right" concentration, a plant hormone, or plant growth regulator, can speed root and/or shoot development in cuttings. Powdered commercial rooting hormones, available for home use, contain a synthetic auxin, present at some concentration. The instructions do not specify use at a particular concentration. The user dips the cutting into the powdered hormone, and a variable amount sticks to the plant tissue.

For use in industry, hormone concentration must be optimized to ensure the maximum amount of root growth in the shortest amount of time. It is challenging to determine the optimum concentration of one hormone versus another. In this activity, the effect of varying the concentration of one hormone on *Fuchsia* rooting is determined.

Purpose

What is the optimum concentration of 1-naphthale-neacetamide, the auxin in rooting compound, for stimulation of rooting in *Fuchsia* stem cuttings?

Materials

Balance, weigh boat, lab scoops
Commercial plant rooting compound
Beakers, 250 mL
Plastic funnels, short-stemmed
Filter paper, 12.5 cm
Graduated cylinder, 25 mL
Bottle, media, 250 mL
Scalpel handles, #4
Scalpel blades, #22 for #4 handles
Tubes, 50 mL and racks
Parafilm®
Cotton, nonabsorbent
Aluminum foil
Pipet, 10 mL and pump

Environmental Health and Safety Officer

Figure 11.4.   **This is one brand of rooting hormone available at local nurseries.**
Photo by author.

Procedure

1. The auxin, 1-naphthaleneacetamide, is found as 0.20% of the mass of the rooting compound. Prepare 200 mL of a rooting compound solution where the 1-naphthaleneacetamide is represented as 10 mg/mL in the solution. To do this, add 2 g of rooting compound to 200 mL of dH$_2$O. This is the stock solution.

    The math is as follows: 0.20% = 0.2 g/100 g = 200 mg/100 g = 200 mg/100 mL = 2 mg/mL, which is 5 times less than the desired 10 mg/mL. So, multiply the 0.2 g per 100 g by 5, which equals 1 g/100 mL, and add 2 g into the 200 mL of water.

    Note: The rooting compound contains inert materials that are not plant hormones, and they do not dissolve. To ensure a clear solution, filter the stock solution through a Whatman filter paper funnel. The clear filtrate is the 10 mg/mL stock solution used below.

2. Prepare a serial dilution of the 10 mg/mL stock solution to end up with four solutions of decreasing concentration. Save all extra stock solution for refilling tubes later in the experiment. Label all vessels completely.

    100 mL of 5 mg/mL 1-naphthaleneacetamide
    100 mL of 2.5 mg/mL 1-naphthaleneacetamide
    100 mL of 1.25 mg/mL 1-naphthaleneacetamide
    100 mL of 0.625 mg/mL 1-naphthaleneacetamide

3. Using a sterile scalpel, remove five *Fushsia* branches of about the same size and nodal arrangement. Remove the leaves from the two bottom nodes of each *Fuchsia* cutting. Trim off large leaves. Cut the stem base to 1 cm from the bottom node. Cut the stem at a 45° angle to increase the amount of meristematic tissue exposed.

4. Fill five 50-mL sterile, conical centrifuge tubes with 45 mL of one of each of the four 1-naphthaleneacetamide solutions. To the fifth tube, add some plain sterile, aged water as a negative control. **The solution volume must remain at 45 mL throughout the experiment.**

5. Seal the top of each tube with Parafilm®. Punch a hole in each. Place one of the *Fuchsia* cuttings to the desired depth, through the Parafilm®, into each tube. Wrap some nonabsorbent cotton around each cutting to keep it upright in the tube. Make sure the cotton does not get wet (see Figure 11.5). Wrap the outside of the tube in aluminum foil to keep the rooting area dark. Place a tape label on the outside of each setup.

6. Check the tube regularly (every other day) to make sure that there is still 45 mL of solution in each tube. If the volume is less than 45 mL, add enough of the appropriate solution to bring it back up to 45 mL.

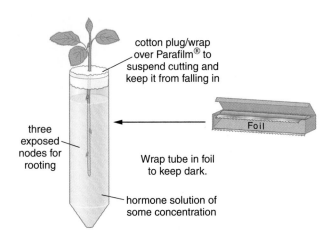

cotton plug/wrap over Parafilm® to suspend cutting and keep it from falling in

three exposed nodes for rooting

Wrap tube in foil to keep dark.

Foil

hormone solution of some concentration

Figure 11.5. **If Parafilm® is available, it can be pulled over the tube opening. Then, a small hole can be punched in the Parafilm®, and the cutting, resting on cotton, can be inserted through the hole. This provides additional support so that the cutting and cotton do not fall into the solution.**

7. Record the date (number of days) when the first root appears on each cutting. Create a data table to record the "days to first root" data. Rewrap the tube in foil to exclude light.
8. At the end of each week, for 4 weeks, count the number of roots present on each cutting. Make a data table to record the data.

Data Analysis

Using your lab group's data, graph the number of roots that each hormone concentration produced by Day 28 of the experiment. On a different graph, show the number of days until the first root appeared in each concentration.

Collect class data (make a class data table) so that there are at least eight replications of the experiment to examine (average). When possible, use averaged data rather than individual trials. Averaged data are usually more valid than individual values. Prepare graphs showing all of the class data.

Conclusion

In a conclusion statement, discuss the results of your experiment. Does it appear that the hormone concentration affected the rooting of *Fuchsia* cuttings? How so or how not? Do other results in the class support your lab group's results? Do any data seem odd or fallacious? Why so or why not? Propose applications of these results, as well as further experiments.

Thinking Like a Biotechnician

1. Does it appear that there is a limit to the amount of hormone that will affect the rooting process? If so, above what concentration is there no additional effect? Sketch a graph showing how such results would look.
2. How can you tell if the concentration of hormones is too high in all of the treatments?
3. On the graph, how would a line appear if there were no relationship between the rooting hormone concentration and rooting?

Laboratory 11d   Cloning African Violets

This lab was inspired by a lab written by Doug Lundberg that appeared in *The Science Teacher* in April 1987. It can be found at http://academy.d20.co.edu/kadets/lundberg/violets.html.

Background

Although African violets (*Saintpaulia ionantha*) are native to subtropical areas, they are very popular houseplants throughout the world. One reason that African violets are so popular is because of their showy flowers. Another reason is that they are easy to asexually propagate indoors, in the home or in greenhouses. This is fortunate, since African violets cannot easily be propagated outdoors or by seeds.

Like many herbaceous plants, African violets can be cloned through plant tissue culture (PTC). Leaf tissue may be taken, sterilized, and grown into a complete plantlet in the "right" type of plant tissue culture (PTC) medium (see Figure 11.6). The PTC medium contains all the nutrients and hormones needed, at the proper concentration, to promote callus (undifferentiated cell division) and cell differentiation. On PTC medium, plantlets can grow and develop until they are able to photosynthesize and can be transplanted into a soil or soil-like medium.

A PTC produces genetically identical offspring in a relatively short time. Growers of ferns, lilies, raspberries, and many other plants also use PTC methods similar to those conducted here on African violet tissue.

Figure 11.6. Under the right conditions, African violets are asexually propagated through leaf cuttings and plant tissue culture.
Photo by author.

Purpose

What different stages in the cloning of African violets are observed by the time explants reach transplantable size?
What percentage of tissue cultures result in viable plantlets?
What is the yield of offspring from a single PTC explant?
What is the average yield of offspring from all the explants in the class?

Materials

Environmental Health and Safety Officer

Bleach, 10%	Weigh boat, 3.5"×3.5"	Tubes, 50 mL, sterile
Ethanol, 70%	Lab scoops	Tube racks for 50 mL tubes
Scalpel handles, #4	pH Meter and electrode	Petri dishes, 60×15 mm, sterile
Scalpel blades, #22 for	pH Buffer, pH 7.0	Pipets, 2 mL and pump
#4 handles	Hydrochloric acid, 1 M	Parafilm®
Scissors, stainless steel	Potassium hydroxide, 1 M	Murashige-Skoog
Forceps, fine-tipped	Plant tissue culture agar	Pretransplant Medium,
Sterilizer/autoclave	Beaker, 2 L	for African violets
Murashige-Skoog	Hot plate stirrer	Tape, Labeling
Multiplication Medium,	Beakers, 250 mL	Cups, Styrofoam, 6 oz
for African violets	Tissue culture tubes and caps	Plastic beaker, 1 L
Sucrose	Laminar flow hood	Soil, potting
Balance, tabletop milligram	African violet plants	Plastic vegetable bags

Procedure

Part I: Preparing Reagents/Medium

1. Prepare the ethanol and bleach solutions required in the materials list. Sterilize deionized water, forceps, scissors, scalpels, and any other items in an autoclave for 15 to 20 minutes at 15 to 20 psi.

2. Prepare the multiplication medium (for between 50 and 100 tubes) by combining the pre-mixed Murashige-Skoog multiplication medium packet with 800 mL of distilled water and 30 g of sucrose. Bring the pH to 5.7 with 1 M HCl or 1 M KOH. Pour the mixture slowly into a 2-L beaker containing 8 g of plant tissue agar, mixing the agar into the solution while pouring. Bring the final volume to 1 L with deionized water. Heat until *just before* boiling. DO NOT LET IT BOIL.

3. Pour the mixture into test tubes, about 7 to 10 mL into each for small tubes, and 15 to 20 mL each for large tubes. The agar should fill approximately 1/2 of the tube.

4. Cover test tubes with PTC tube caps. The caps allow for gas exchange, but they will still maintain sterility after autoclaving.

Figure 11.7. **Tissue cultures can be set up in almost any kind of vessel that can be autoclaved and kept sterile. Here, flasks plugged with gauze and covered loosely with aluminum foil are used instead of fancy tissue culture tubes.**
Photo by author.

5. Autoclave the medium-filled tubes at 15 to 20 psi for 20 minutes (see Figure 11.7). Do not "overautoclave" since some of the hormones are heat-sensitive and could break down, which could affect the hormone concentration.

Part II: Preparing the Explants

- African violet tissue culturing is challenging because the leaves are covered with tiny hairs (trichomes). Because the trichomes trap tiny particles, including bacteria and fungi, it is critical to properly wash the leaves to remove any particles without damaging the plant tissue.
- Do all of your work in a sterile laminar flow hood that has been disinfected using 10% bleach and 70% ethanol.
- Unless directed otherwise, wash and rinse in small volumes of solutions in sterile Petri dishes. Setting up a series on washing plates ahead of time works well. Make sure leaf disks do not go into a solution that contains another explant.

6. Remove a medium-size leaf from a healthy African violet or other test plant. For about 1 minute, gently rinse both sides of the leaf under tap water to remove any large pieces of debris.
7. To disinfect the surface of the leaf and remove any remaining particles, shake it vigorously three times in three consecutive capped, sterile, 50-mL, conical centrifuge tubes containing sterile distilled water.
8. To sterilize the leaf, use sterile forceps to dunk it in 70% ethanol three times.
9. In a sterile Petri plate, use a sterile scalpel to cut a leaf disk approximately 1 cm by 1 cm square from the middle of the leaf near the base. Include some of the center vein (containing meristematic tissue) in the leaf disk.
10. To sterilize the leaf disk, immerse it in a 10% commercial bleach solution for 3 minutes.
11. Rinse the leaves by dunking them in three separate washes of fresh, sterile distilled water.
12. Place the sterilized leaf disk, bottom side up, on the surface of the multiplication medium in the PTC tubes (see Figure 11.8). The leaf section edges should just break the surface of the medium, but the "bottom" side should still be exposed to air. **Be extremely careful not to introduce contamination into these culture tubes. Use sterile pipets to position the disks.**
13. Cap and label the multiplication-medium culture tube. Use a small piece of Parafilm® to secure the tube top, but allow a tiny slit for air exchange. Place the cultures, in a rack, in "room light." Avoid bright light for the first three days. Then place the cultures under plant grow lights for the remainder of the experiment.
14. Set up a data table to record observations of the changes in the African violet tissue culture over time. Include observations of changes in color, swelling, fuzziness, or contamination, etc. Use numerical data wherever possible. Make observations once per week. Include the number of plantlets developing on the explant.

Part III: Maintenance of Clones

- The clones usually need to be transferred to pretransplant medium, but not always. It depends on the number of plantlets (and whether they are to be subdivided), and the amount of shoots and roots on each plantlet. If an explant has only one plantlet, and if it has a well-developed shoot and root, skip the pretransplant steps. For most cultures, though, continue at step 15.
- Two days before it is needed, make a batch of pretransplant medium, which stimulates root production. Use the same procedures used for the multiplication medium, substituting Murashige-Skoog Pretransplant Medium base for Murashige-Skoog Multiplication Medium base.

15. After 5 to 6 weeks in multiplication medium, the explants should be covered with small plantlets (shoots with no roots).
16. Use sterile technique and sterile forceps to place the leaf pieces inside a sterile Petri dish. Use a sterile scalpel to cut the small plantlets away from each other.

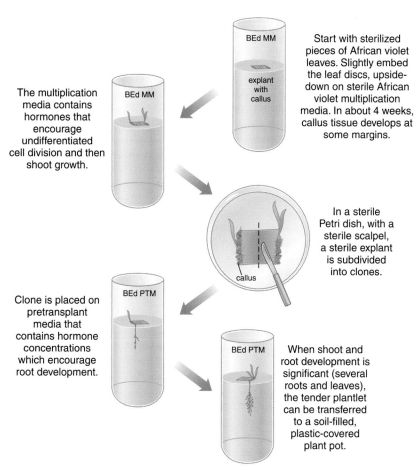

The multiplication media contains hormones that encourage undifferentiated cell division and then shoot growth.

BEd MM

BEd MM

explant with callus

Start with sterilized pieces of African violet leaves. Slightly embed the leaf discs, upside-down on sterile African violet multiplication media. In about 4 weeks, callus tissue develops at some margins.

callus

In a sterile Petri dish, with a sterile scalpel, a sterile explant is subdivided into clones.

Clone is placed on pretransplant media that contains hormone concentrations which encourage root development.

BEd PTM

BEd PTM

When shoot and root development is significant (several roots and leaves), the tender plantlet can be transferred to a soil-filled, plastic-covered plant pot.

Figure 11.8. African violet tissue culture.

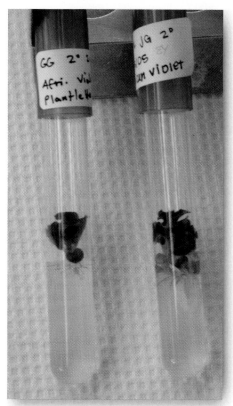

Photo by author.

17. Move the plantlets to individual culture tubes of pretransplant medium. Record the number of plantlets transferred. Make sure the explants are in contact with the media with no air gaps. Cap the culture tubes and put them in "room light" for 4 to 6 weeks.

18. When many roots are visible in the culture tube, set up a labeled Styrofoam pot with four holes punched in the bottom for water drainage. Add moistened potting soil to within a centimeter of the top. Make a depression for the roots of the plantlet.

19. Gently, move the plantlets from the pretransplant medium to the soil. Very gently, wash all of the medium from the plantlets' leaves and roots with room-temperature, aged tap water before planting. Place the plantlet in the soil until only the root is submerged in soil and the explant is at the soil surface. Gently, pat it into place. Record the number of plantlets moved to soil.

20. Maintain humidity by putting the small pots in a larger container, which has 1 to 2 cm of water in the bottom. Cover both containers with cellophane wrap or a vegetable bag to produce a tiny greenhouse environment.

21. After 1 week, fold back the bag a little every day for another 1 to 2 weeks, until it is all the way off. This is called "hardening off," and gives the transplant a chance to repair damaged roots and get used to the new humidity. Record the number of plantlets still appearing healthy and viable after 2 weeks.

Data Collection/Analysis

Record the number of successful tissue cultures in the class. Determine what percentage of each tissue culture produced offspring that were still alive after each transfer. Determine the average number of plantlets per explant that survived until the "greenhouse" stage. Make graphs to show these results. Discuss the expected yield versus the actual yield. Make suggestions for improving the number of successful clones.

Thinking Like a Biotechnician

1. Discuss the texture of the PTC media compared with that of LB agar. Propose a reason for any difference.
2. If the explant shows no signs of swelling or callus after 6 weeks, what may be the reason?
3. Suggest a few other herbaceous plants that might be successfully cultured using the same media and protocol.

Laboratory 11e   Using Hydroponics to Develop Fertilizers

How does a company know the "best" concentration for each ingredient in a fertilizer? Propose an experimental procedure to determine the optimum concentration of one fertilizer ingredient (calcium nitrate) on hydroponically grown tomato plants. Use 12 plants (four groups of three). Keep the budget for plants and chemicals below $100. Be sure to include all recipes for any nutrient solutions, as well as all measurements, units, replications, and conditions, etc.

Purpose

What are the effects of adding calcium nitrate solutions of various concentrations on the growth and appearance of tomato or green bean plants?
How might changing calcium nitrate concentrations in fertilizers improve plant growth?

Materials

Lab scoops	Calcium nitrate, 4-hydrate	Tomato or green bean plants
Plastic bucket	Aluminum foil	(at least two sets of leaves)
Plastic beaker, 1 L	Parafilm®	Funnel, plastic
Balance, weigh boat, lab scoops	Silent air pump, air stone, tubing	Tape, labeling
Chemical Set, Plant Nutrition, Sargent Welch #WL9195E	Plant light system	Permanent lab marker pens

General Procedure for Creating an Experimental Plan

- Plan out an experiment including step-by-step procedures of how to set up and monitor the hydroponics experiment on either tomato or green bean plants.
- Determine what solutions you will need for your proposed experiment and how to prepare them.
- Write up your proposal, including all recipes and protocols for solution preparation and data collection. Include references and sources for purchasing reagents, including the source, amount, and price.
- Submit this to the supervisor for evaluation and approval.
- If your experimental plan is selected as most promising, the class will proceed with the procedures.

Procedure

1. Grow tomato or green bean plants in flats until the second set of true leaves is just visible, or purchase them from a nursery.
2. Prepare solutions as described in the approved experimental plan.

3. Gently, scoop up each plant and plunge it into a bucket of water to wash the soil off the roots.

4. Set up hydroponic tanks to hold a total of three plants each, following the directions below:

Hydroponic Tank Design

a. Use 1-L, clear, plastic tri-pour beakers.

b. Fill each to 800 mL with the appropriate solution.

c. Cover each tightly with Parafilm®, which will supply the major support for the plants. Wrap the outside with aluminum foil. Leave a small slit in the foil, on the side, to observe the solution level.

d. Punch five holes in the Parafilm® (one in the middle and four surrounding it).

e. Into three of the holes, gently place three plants (approximately the same size), supported by nonabsorbent cotton.

f. Into a fourth hole, place the tube from an aquarium pump. Secure it so that it will bubble continuous air into the tank.

g. Into the fifth hole, place a 20-cm length of plastic tubing that connects to a funnel (on the other end, for adding more solution) without disturbing the rest of the tank.

h. Secure everything so that it will not fall over during the experiment (4 weeks). Add more aluminum foil to the outside, as necessary, to block light from the roots.

5. On a data table, record the initial appearance of each plant. Number each plant in each tank so that you can keep track of them. Record the number of leaves/plant, the "average" amount of green color/leaf, and a column for other observations, such as spotting, leaf curling, or insect damage.

6. Check the solution level in the tanks once a week. Using the funnel apparatus, fill the "tank" back up to 800 mL with the appropriate solution.

7. Once a week, record data on plant health as described in step 5.

8. If substantial differences in the experimental groups are apparent at 4 weeks, stop the experiment. If differences are not apparent, continue the experiment for a total of 8 weeks.

9. At the end of the experiment, remove the plants from their tanks (keep track of which is which by putting a 3-cm tape label around each stem).

10. Allow the plants and roots to dry overnight. Weigh each plant. Record the final plant weight data in a data table.

Thinking Like a Biotechnician

Prepare graphs that best demonstrate the effects of varying the concentration of added calcium nitrate solutions to hydroponically grown tomatoes. Write a formal conclusion with the results of the experiment, presenting evidence and explanations for the results. Discuss possible errors in the experimental design that could lead to misleading results. Propose or make recommendations about adding calcium nitrate to fertilizers to improve plant growth.

Laboratory 11f Developing an Optimal Extraction of Spoolable DNA from Plant Cells

Background

To study or modify the genetic information of a plant, one must be able to extract and manipulate the plant's cellular (genomic) DNA. The procedure is similar to the extraction of DNA from bacterial or mammalian cells. The cells must be burst open, and the rest of the cell's molecules must be separated from the cell's DNA.

Using a blender or a mortar and pestle, plant cells are burst open by grinding the cells in an *extraction solution*. Typical extraction solutions contain deionized water, plus a buffer, detergents, and/or enzymes.

As the cells dump their contents into the extraction solution, cell debris and unwanted molecules settle to the bottom. Centrifuging can facilitate this separation. The supernatant (top layer), containing the DNA, can be poured off. Using a glass rod, the DNA is extracted out of solution by gently folding ethanol into the DNA extraction mixture. DNA molecules are not soluble in ethanol, and they move away from it and stick onto the glass rod. Given the right conditions, relatively pure DNA can be extracted.

An extraction solution requires some kind of detergent to dissolve the plant cell's membrane and burst the cells open. The detergent also precipitates proteins, removing them from solution. Some protocols use 5 mL of either Dawn (Procter and Gamble, Inc) dishwashing detergent or 10% sodium dodecyl sulfate (SDS) in volumes of 0.5 to 1 mL per 100 mL.

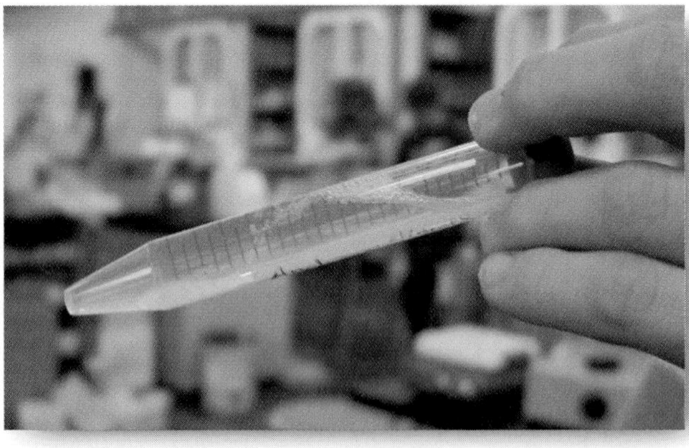

Salt is often used in an extraction solution. The NaCl precipitates proteins and covers the DNA molecules' negative charge, which results in better DNA isolation. It is common to use 2 or 5 M NaCl in volumes of 1 to 5 mL of NaCl per 100 mL of extraction solution.

Protocols for extraction vary depending on the type of cells used as the source of DNA. Process development of the extraction procedures will produce the best conditions for maximum DNA yield.

To ascertain the presence of DNA, an ethidium bromide (EtBr) dot test can be conducted or an agarose gel can be run. Using a UV spectrophotometer, an absorbance reading can determine the concentration of DNA in a sample.

Figure 11.9. DNA strands wrap around each other and may trap air bubbles. This makes it easier to see globs of DNA in solution.
Photo by author.

Purpose

What are the best procedures for the extraction of measurable, spoolable amounts of genomic, chromosomal DNA (gDNA) from a target plant sample (eg, spinach)?

Can the yield of DNA extraction be improved with procedural modifications (process development)?

Materials

Environmental Health and Safety Officer

Spinach leaves
Balance, weigh boats, lab scoops
Pipets and pumps
Glass rods, 200 mm
Sodium dodecyl sulfate (SDS), 10%
Water bath, 60°C
Beakers, 50 mL
Ethanol, 95%
TE buffer

Tubes, 15 mL, sterile and racks
Gel box, horizontal, and power supply
0.8 agarose in 1× TAE (see Lab 4h)
Electrophoresis buffer, 1X TAE
Reaction tubes, 1.7 mL and rack
Gel loading dye, DNA
Micropipets and tips

Lambda/*Hind*III, DNA standards
Ethidium bromide, 0.5 μg/mL
Gloves and safety goggles
Gel photo imaging system
UV/Vis spectrophotometer/ cuvettes
UV spectrophotometer cuvettes
Pasteur pipets, 9"
Pasteur pipet bulbs

Safety Precautions
- Gloves and goggles are required when using EtBr.
- Only the instructor should use EtBr.

Procedure

1. Spoolable amounts of spinach plant DNA will be the target of the extraction process development. Plan to use 5 g of plant tissue for each extraction. Plan to repeat each trial three times, and then average the results.

2. Consider a typical DNA extraction (ie, from *E. coli* cells, from protocols found on the Internet, and from discussions in the Background section of this text). Plan how you might conduct a DNA extraction from your plant samples. Limit your group to 1 hour of research time on the Internet, and 1 hour of planning and writing your procedures. Record all bibliographical references.

   Include all of the following in your procedures:

   What ingredients could be in the extraction solution(s) or buffer(s)?
   How many steps are there to the procedure? What are the steps? What equipment should be used?
   What volumes of solutions? At what concentrations? With heat? On ice?
   How will you get rid of contaminants (eg, centrifuging or filtering)?
   How will you spool the DNA?
   How will you access your retrieved DNA volume?

3. Outline the general procedures for the extraction, separation, and spooling using Microsoft® Word® on the computer. Record all steps and procedures. Plan to do three replications of the procedure, simultaneously, so that you have results to average. Print copies of these procedures for all members of your group. Save them on the computer for further editing. Title them. Call them the "1st Run_Your Intitials.doc."

4. Prepare the extraction solution, and any other solutions or reagents that you plan to use. Label and store them properly.

5. Conduct the extractions and prepare for the DNA spooling. USE ONLY 2 mL of SAMPLE PER SPOOLING.

6. After the spooling, shake off the excess ethanol and scrape the spooled DNA into a sterile, 15-mL, conical centrifuge tube containing 2 mL of TE buffer. For each variation of the process, determine the volume of DNA that was extracted by calculating the amount of displacement of TE buffer by the spooled DNA. Add these data to a data table with all other observations.

7. Store all samples, in clearly labeled tubes, in your own rack at 4°C until the DNA has dissolved into the TE solution (2 to 4 days).

8. Test samples using EtBr Dot Testing (Lab 4d), Gel Electrophoresis (Lab 11H), or UV Spectrophotometry (Lab 11i) (see Figure 11.10).

9. Construct data tables and graphs to report quantitative data for each extraction and spooling.

10. Suggest a variation of your experiment to your supervisor. Repeat steps 3 through 13, but alter just one variable from the first run.

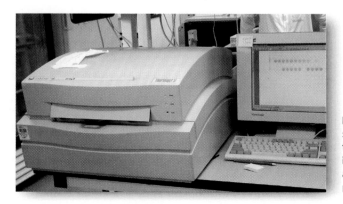

Figure 11.10. **A fluorometer is a type of spectrophotometer that reads the concentration of DNA in 96 wells (seen on monitor) in picogram amounts (considerably smaller amounts than those isolated in this activity).**
Photo by author.

Thinking Like a Biotechnician

Write a formal conclusion of the results of the two versions of your experiment. Present evidence and explanations as to the amount of DNA extracted and spooled in your samples versus other groups, as well as data from your first run versus your second run. Discuss possible errors in the experimental design that could lead to misleading results. Propose or make recommendations about further DNA extractions.

Laboratory 11g   Using Commercial Kits for DNA Extractions from Cells

Background

Spooling DNA is fun, but scientists rarely need the amounts of DNA that spooling provides. However, it is mainly the gDNA that is spooled. So, when scientists want plasmid DNA (pDNA), or samples with lower volumes, they can use commercially available kits to extract relatively pure samples of gDNA or pDNA from a variety of prokaryotic and eukaryotic cells.

There are several reasons to use commercial kits. One is that the buffers used in the extractions are often challenging to prepare. Many are at a very high concentration or require significant amounts of pH adjustment. Sometimes, it is worth the cost to save the technician's buffer prep time.

Another reason to use a kit is that they are relatively cheap. Since they can be used for several extractions, the cost per extraction may be only a few dollars.

Using commercially available kits is especially advantageous when attempting to extract DNA from plant cells. Since plant cells have a large amount of carbohydrates in their cell walls, plant DNA extraction is a bit more challenging than DNA extraction from animal or bacteria cells.

Purpose

To compare the effectiveness (measuring the concentration and purity) of two commercial kits in extracting spinach gDNA.

Materials

Spinach leaves
Micropipets and tips
PureGene® Cell and Tissue Kit, No. D-5500A, Gentra Systems, Inc

DNeasy® Plant Mini Kit, Qiagen, Inc
UV/Vis spectrophotometer/ cuvettes
Pasteur pipets, 9"

Pasteur pipet bulbs

Procedure

1. Get copies of the protocols from each kit for extracting plant DNA
2. Follow the directions to produce three 50-µL samples of gDNA. Use the 1.7-mL tube top to punch the leaf, and use the leaf tissue that results.
3. Determine the amount and purity of DNA in each sample through UV spectrophotometry (Lab 11i). Record all the data in your notebook. Compare the yield of each extraction.
4. Prepare a form (or use your facility's version of a "Purchase Order/Requisition") to order each of the kits above. Include all the necessary information, as if you were ordering it to be delivered to your laboratory/department.
5. Find one other DNA extraction kit online that would provide approximately the same kind and quantity of DNA as the kits tested above. List the ordering information and explain how this kit differs in reagents, procedures, and products.

Thinking Like a Biotechnician

1. Write a statement that reviews, for your supervisor, the pros and cons of using each kit. Include an assessment of the price, time, equipment, ease of use, and product yield.
2. Suggest a gel electrophoresis method for assessing the type and quality of DNA in each extraction.
3. Explain why using DNA extractions contaminated with proteins could lead to future experimental problems.

Laboratory 11h   Determining the Presence of DNA in Plant Extractions

Background

DNA is colorless in solution, so its presence in a sample must be determined either indirectly, using an indicator, or with an instrument, such as a spectrophotometer. The most common indicator/stain used to colorize DNA molecules is ethidium bromide (EtBr). EtBr intercalates itself between DNA bases, affecting the light-absorbing properties of the molecule. When mixed together, the DNA/EtBr glows orange under UV light. The higher the DNA concentration, the more the EtBr intercalates, so the glowing is brighter. In gel electrophoresis, EtBr is usually used to "stain" DNA gels. When exposed to UV light, the EtBr-stained DNA molecules show as bands of glowing orange on the gel.

Purpose

To examine spinach DNA extraction samples for the presence of DNA, using vertical gel electrophoresis.

Materials

Environmental Health and Safety Officer

TBE buffer concentrate, 1X
TBE gel, 1.0 mm, 10%
Gel box, vertical (PAGE)
Power supply
Pipets, transfer, 3 mL
Micropipets and tips
DNA, salmon testes, in TE (2 mg/mL)
Spinach DNA samples (Labs 11f, 11g)

Reaction tubes, 1.7 mL and rack
Permanent lab marker pens
Lambda/HindIII, DNA standards
Gel loading dye, DNA
Loading tips, PAGE gel
Weigh boat, 5.5" × 5.5"
Ethidium bromide, 0.5 µg/mL
Glasses, safety, plastic

Gloves, large
Gel photo imaging system
Paper, thermal
Printer, thermal
UV/Vis spectrophotometer
UV spectrophotometer cuvettes
Pasteur pipets, 9"
Pasteur pipet bulbs

Safety Precautions
- Gloves and goggles are required when using EtBr.
- Only the instructor should use EtBr.

Procedure

1. Prepare 300 mL of 1X TBE buffer from 5X TBE. Set up a 10% TBE gel in a vertical gel box.
2. Prepare up to nine samples to load on the gel from the spinach DNA extractions. **Label all tubes.**

   - Place 20 µL of 2 mg/mL of salmon sperm DNA solution (positive control, known) in a 1.7-mL tube and add 3 µL of DNA loading dye. Mix thoroughly, but gently.
   - Place 20 µL of each extraction sample (unknowns of your choosing) to be tested in a 1.7-mL tube and add 3 µL of DNA loading dye. Mix thoroughly, but gently.

- Place 20 µL of deionized water (negative control) in a 1.7-mL tube and add 3 µL of DNA loading dye. Mix thoroughly, but gently.

3. Draw a diagram to show which well will contain each sample. Include a well for loading 5 µL of the DNA sizing standards (lambda DNA/*Hin*dIII mixed with loading dye).
4. Load 23 µL of each sample into its assigned well. Change tips for each sample. Load the standards into Well 5.
5. Run the gel at 100 V for 30 to 40 minutes, until the loading dye is about halfway down the gel.
6. Transfer the gel to a weigh boat for staining. Add EtBr staining solution until the gel is just covered. **Note: Gloves and goggles are required when using EtBr. The instructor will add the EtBr for you.**
7. Stain for 15-20 minutes, and then rinse with deionized water. Place the gel on a transilluminator light box. Look for the amount of pink-orange glow compared with the positive and negative controls to ascertain whether or not your sample contains DNA. Photograph the gel for a permanent record.
8. Glue the photo in the middle of the record sheet. Label all the sample wells, standard fragments, and sample bands on the gel photograph.
9. Assign a numerical value to the amount of glowing of your sample compared with the standards. Assume that "5" represents the positive standard, and "0" represents the negative standard. Record these values in a data table.

Environmental Health
and Safety Officer

Conclusion

Determine which method resulted in the largest amount of the purest DNA. Write a formal conclusion discussing the "results with evidence and explanation" (REE), "possible errors" (PE), and "practical applications" (PA) of the experiment.

 *Thinking Like a Biotechnician* ▬▬▬▬▬▬▬

1. If samples float out of wells and do not sink when loading, what may be the cause?
2. The salmon sperm DNA is used as a positive standard. Are you able to use it to estimate the concentration of your spinach DNA samples? Explain why or why not.
3. Why are contaminant proteins not visible on these DNA gels?

Laboratory 11i   Determining the Purity and Concentration of DNA Samples

Background

A UV spectrophotometer (or a fluorometer) can be used to study the concentration and purity of DNA samples in solution. These instruments measure DNA concentration and purity in solution by measuring a sample's absorbance of UV light (the optical density, or OD), at specific wavelengths. Spectrophotometers can detect to microgram per milliliter (µg/mL) units, and a fluorometer can measure to nanogram per milliliter (ng/mL) units.

To determine the concentration of a DNA solution, the OD (absorbance) is measured in absorbance units (au) at 260 nm. Since 50 µg/mL of DNA in solution gives an absorbance of 1 au, using the following formula (DNA Concentration Equation) will give an approximate concentration in µg/mL:

DNA Concentration Equation

$$\frac{50\ \mu g/mL}{1\ OD} = \frac{X\ \mu g/mL}{OD\ at\ 260\ nm}$$

For example, a 1-mL sample is placed in a calibrated UV spectrophotometer. The absorbance is read at 260 nm and is determined to be 0.365 au. What is the approximate concentration of DNA in the sample?

$$\frac{50\ \mu g/mL}{1\ au} = \frac{X\ \mu g/mL}{0.365\ au} = 0.365 \times 50\ \mu g/mL = 18.25\ \mu g/mL\ \text{of DNA in the sample}$$

A simple test can determine DNA purity in a sample. The test determines the ratio of absorbance at 260 nm (the wavelength of DNA absorbance) compared with the absorbance at 280 nm (the wavelength of protein absorbance). This is called an A260/A280 reading.

DNA Purity Equation

$$\frac{OD\ (260\ nm)}{OD\ (280\ nm)}$$

If the 260/280 ratio is approximately 1.8, the DNA sample contains a significant amount of DNA, and it is considered fairly clean or pure. The closer the 260/280 ratio is to 2.00, the more RNA contamination is suspected. More protein contamination is suspected as the ratio approaches 1.50 or less.

For example, a 1-mL sample is placed in a calibrated UV spectrophotometer. The absorbance at 260 nm and is determined to be 0.365 au. The absorbance is also read at 280 nm and is determined to be 0.233 au. To what degree is the sample contaminated?

$$\frac{OD\ (260\ nm)}{OD\ (280\ nm)} = \frac{0.365\ au}{0.203\ au} = 1.798$$

Thus, the sample is relatively pure, with little RNA or protein contamination. Determining an A60/A280 valve is so common that on some spectrophotometers there is an A260/A280 button.

When determining the purity of a sample, the A260/A280 reading will not be accurate if the concentration of DNA is too low. A technician must consider this when making inferences about the samples.

Purpose

What is the approximate concentration and relative purity of DNA in the spinach DNA samples?

Materials

Reaction tubes, 1.7 mL and rack	TE buffer	Pasteur pipets, 9"
Permanent lab marker pens	Plant DNA Samples	Pasteur pipet bulbs
Pipets and pumps	(previous labs)	Methanol
Balance, weigh boats,	UV/Vis spectrophotometer/	
lab scoops	cuvettes	
Beakers, 100 mL	UV cuvette, 50 μL and adapter	

Procedure

Note: Some UV spectrophotometers have preprogrammed A260/A280 readings. If the spec you are using has this feature, all readings can be taken at one time.

Part I: Concentration Determinations

1. Prepare 0.5 mL of each plant DNA extraction sample in 1.7-mL reaction tubes. If possible, avoid diluting the samples, but the cuvettes must hold 0.5 mL or more of the sample to obtain an accurate reading.

If necessary, perform a dilution (1:2, 1:3, or 1:4) of the sample using TE buffer to ensure a 0.5-mL sample. Keep track of the sample's dilution so that the concentration of the undiluted sample can be determined following the analysis of the diluted samples.

2. Calibrate the UV spectrophotometer at 260 nm by using a TE buffer blank. If using a quartz cuvette, rinse the cuvette with methanol (for cleaning) and deionized water, as directed by the instructor (see Figure 11.11). Then, add 1 mL of TE buffer for blanking.

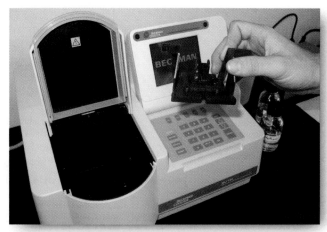

Figure 11.11. **Spectrophotometer with a 50-µL adaptor and cuvette.**
Photo by author.

3. Now, add 0.5 mL of a sample solution. If the sample's volume is low, consider using a 50-µL adaptor and cuvette. Read the OD and record its value.
4. Recover the sample and replace it into its tube.
5. Repeat No. 3 and 4 with each sample.
6. Use the DNA Concentration Equation to calculate the concentration of DNA in each sample. Multiply by any dilution factor, if the sample was diluted. Record the absorbance data, calculations, and your inferences on a data table.

Part II: Purity Determinations
Note: Calibrate the UV spectrophotometer at 280 nm using a TE buffer blank. Rinse the cuvette with deionized water as directed by the instructor. Then, add 1 mL of TE buffer.

7. Add 0.5 mL of a sample solution. Read the OD and record its value in the data table above.
8. Recover the sample and replace it into its tube.
9. Repeat No. 8 and 9 with each sample.
10. Calculate the ratio of ODs (A260/A280) for each sample, as in the example above. Multiply by any dilution factor, if the sample was diluted. Record these values in the data table.

Data Analysis/Conclusion

Evaluate the effectiveness of each extraction method you used in light of the spectrophotometer data concentration and purity determinations. Consult with others in the class. Which method appeared to be the most successful? Why? In what ways were other groups' best protocols similar to your best protocol?

Thinking Like a Biotechnician

1. What happens to the absorbance reading, concentration, and purity calculation if the DNA is too concentrated, for example, at 1 mg/mL? What must be done to solve this problem?
2. If an A260/A280 purity reading were calculated to be 2.8, what should the technician think?

Laboratory 11j   Transformation of *Arabidopsis thaliana*

Inspired by a lab activity found at www.woodrow.org/teachers/bi/1993/cell.html. This lab is under development with the help of Dr. Fred Hemple, Mendel Biotechnology Inc; Dr. Leonore Reiser, Carnegie Institute of Washington; and Joey Mailman, Biotechnology Student.

Recommended for use only if the instructor has the time, interest, and funds to secure samples from a local source and to work on process development.

Background

Arabidopsis thaliana (Arabidopsis) is a model organism in the plant genetics community. Its entire genome has been sequenced, and much of its growth and development are understood. It is also rather easy to transform Arabidopsis, using *Agrobacterium tumefaciens* (*A. tumefaciens*) and the Ti plasmid.

As the plant grows and flower buds appear, tiny ovules develop in the flowers. Scientists have had success dipping into, painting on, or spraying stems and young open flowers with *A. tumefaciens*/Ti plasmid broth culture. The *A. tumefaciens* infiltrates the plant tissue area and transfers Ti plasmid into some of the ovules. Transformed ovules are germinated on selection media into viable transformed plantlets and, when appropriate, transferred to potting soil (see Figure 11.12).

Purpose

Can Arabidopsis ovules by transformed with Ti plasmid carrying the neomycin phosphotransferase (NPT II) and beta-D-glucuronidase (GUS) genes?

Can the resulting genetically engineered seeds be tissue cultured to plantlets?

Figure 11.12.   Arabidopsis can be grown indoors under fluorescent lights. Its entire life cycle, from seed to flower and back to seed, takes about 2 months. This is one reason that Arabidopsis makes a good model organism. These plants are at various stages in their life cycle.
Photo by author.

Materials

Arabidopsis thaliana plants, wild type (Columbia), with flowers (see growing instructions)

Agar for *Agrobacterium,* LB agar (5 g sucrose, 1 g yeast extract-B, 0.5 g $MgSO_4 \cdot 7H_2O$, 50 μg kanamycin sulfate in 1 L)

Broth for *Agrobacterium,* LB broth (5 g sucrose, 1 g yeast extract-B, 0.5 g $MgSO_4 \cdot 7H_2O$, 50 μg kanamycin sulfate in 1 L)

Overnight broth suspension of *Agrobacterium* containing Ti plasmid or T-DNA with GUS and NPTII genes

Laminar flow hood	Lab gas lighter	Forceps, fine-tipped
Lysol® disinfectant	Sterilizer/autoclave	Plates of selection medium
Glasses, safety, plastic	Ethanol, 70%	(see below)
Bunsen burner	Sterile glass beakers	

Two sterile Petri dishes containing sterile selection medium:

Murashige and Skoogs Basal Salts (Sigma No. 5519)
3.0 mg/L of kinetin
0.3% mg/L of BAP
400 mg/L of carbenicillin (Sigma No. C3416)
20 mg/L of benomyl, 50% wetable
50 mg/L of kanamycin (Sigma No. K4378)
1% agar (10 g/L)
2% sucrose

5-bromo-4-chloro-3-indolyl glucuronide (X-Gluco) histochemical reagent
   10 mL of 50 mM phosphate buffer, pH 7.0 →
      combine 39 mL of 0.2 M NaH$_2$PO$_4$ (27.6 g/L) = monobasic
      + 61 mL of 0.2 M Na$_2$HPO$_4$ (53.6 g/L) = dibasic
   (This makes 100 mL of a 200-mM phosphate buffer.) Dilute the 200 mM phosphate buffer
   in a 1:4 ratio with distilled water.

X-GLUC stain: Dissolve 5 mg of X-Gluc in 100 mL of dimethyl formamide (optional)
Dissecting microscope
Transfer pipets
Sterile scalpel
Paper bags

Procedure

- Grow Arabidopsis plant until flower buds are just opening. (See growing instructions below.)
- Start the seeds several weeks to a month in advance of transformation. Depending on the temperature and moisture, their rate of growth is not completely predictable.
- Gather and prepare all reagents and media a few days ahead of time so that they will be ready when needed. Some of the reagents are light sensitive, so store them all in the dark. Be aware of which reagents are temperature-sensitive.

Part I: Growing Arabidopsis Seeds
From Vellanoweth Lab, CSULA (10/97) at www.calstatela.edu/faculty/vllnwth/grow.htm
Modified by Joey Mailman, San Mateo High School, 2004

Materials for Growing Seeds
   Arabidopsis seeds
   Six-cell planting trays (15×15 cm) with covers
   Petri dishes, 60×15 mm, sterile
   Water tubs for the planting trays
   dH$_2$O
   Plastic wrap
   3- to 4-L beaker
   Transfer pipets, 3 mL
   Plastic beakers, 1 mL
   Sterilizer/autoclave
   Aluminum foil
   Grow lights (optimally 25 to 30 cm above the soil)

A. Seed preparation
   1. Label a Petri dish and fill it with 15 mL of dH$_2$O.
   2. Add the seeds to be germinated and incubate at 4°C for 2 to 4 days, but no longer than a week.

B. Soil Preparation
   3. Into a large 4-L beaker, place approximately 2 L of potting soil, 1.5 L of vermiculite, and 1 L of perlite; mix the soil with the scoop. This recipe will fill about five planting trays.
   4. Add some water to the "soil" mixture until it is thoroughly damp, but not sopping wet. Wearing a dust mask is highly recommended.
   5. Transfer the soil mixture into three to four 1-L glass or plastic beakers. Cover them with aluminum foil and place them in the autoclave for 15 to 20 minutes at 15 to 20 psi. This soil must be used within a week or algae will form on the surface and it will need to be resterilized.

6. Obtain clean planting trays. Any algae, fungus, old seeds, or dead plants must be scrubbed off. Rinse in 5% bleach solution. Make sure the trays have drainage holes at the bottom.

7. Label the trays with the date that the seeds were sown, as well as the seeds' variety and your initials. Fill the trays to the top with the wet, sterilized soil. Spray the top of the soil surface with water to ensure it is thoroughly wetted.

C. Planting the Seeds

8. Using a transfer pipet, pull up a few seeds and some water from the tray (no need for accuracy here) and squirt them onto the surface of the soil. Ideally, there should be 6 to 10 seeds per cell, but do not put too many seeds in each tray because they will become overcrowded. Continue aliquoting until all the trays contain seeds, or until you run out of seeds.

D. Growing the Seeds

9. Place the trays in a tub reservoir (60 cm long, 30 cm wide, and 15 cm high) and fill it with enough water to cover the drainage holes of the plant trays. The soil must remain wet for the first two weeks of seed growth.

10. Cover the tub with plastic wrap. Place the tub reservoir under plant growth lights.

11. Once the first sprout appears, which should happen within a week, remove the plastic wrap, but continue to keep the water at the same level.

12. Record the number of seedlings per cell.

13. After about 3 weeks, it may be necessary to thin the seedlings to keep an optimum of two to three plants per cell.

14. Select six of the plants randomly for observation and, at the end of 4 weeks, record the stem height and the number of seed pods.

15. Determine the averages for the stalk height and number of seed pods per plant, and graph the data.

E. Harvesting of Seeds (If transforming plants, go to step 19.)

16. After about 1 to 2 months, the Arabidopsis will have tall stalks with pods of seeds. Once the pods begin to turn brown, cut the stalks near the bottom and place them in open plastic sandwich bags. This will break the pods and release the seeds (see Figure 11.13.)

17. Store the bags in a safe place and keep them open until the stalks turn brown. This will prevent condensation from forming inside the bag. Once the stalks are brown, the bags can be sealed.

18. Later, transfer only the seeds to a Petri dish and store them for later use.

Figure 11.13. Collecting Arabidopsis seeds.
Photo by author.

Part II: Arabidopsis Transformation

19. Gather plants that are ready to flower.

20. Transfer overnight *A. tumefaciens* culture to a sterile beaker.

21. Wipe the lab bench area with ethanol before placing the samples on it.

22. Turn plants over, and dip each opening flower into the *A. tumefaciens* culture.

23. Return plants to growing area. Allow time for seeds to develop. (See steps 16–18.)

24. Collect seeds in paper bags.

25. Gather and label plates of selection medium containing X-GLVC and Kana mycin.

26. Place seeds in ethanol solution for 5 minutes. Rinse in sterile distilled water.

27. Using the sterile forceps and a hand lens, spread about 40 seeds over the selection plate containing kanamycin and X-GLUC. Seeds that are not transformed will be killed by the kanamycin. Consequently, all germinated, healthy seedlings should be considered transformed (see Figure 11.14).

Figure 11.14. Performing an assay for the new traits coded on the inserted DNA. These seedlings are being screened for KanR (a trait acquired through genetic engineering) by growing them on Kan agar. Plantlets that do not contain the new gene will not grow on the Kan agar. Kanamycin kills wild-type (nontransformed) plant cells.

Photo by author.

28. Allow the seeds to stay on the media for 2 days. Examine 20 seeds' embryos for any blue color due to GUS activity. A dissecting microscope is required for this. Record the amount of blue you see and the number of embryos showing blue.
29. Transplant 20 seedlings, which appear to be alive and healthy, to soil following the hardening-off instructions in the African Violet Tissue Culture Lab (Lab 11d).
30. Optional: Remove chlorophyll from leaves and stain with X-GLVC stain.

Conclusion

Discuss your group's results, as well as your classmates' results, and determine whether there is evidence that you succeeded in inserting new genes (transform) into Arabidopsis plants. Suggest methods by which the transformation efficiency could be improved. What is the value if being able to transform a plant, such as Arabidopsis? List and explain at least two reasons for developing a protocol such as this one.

Laboratory 11k Confirmation of Plant Genetic Engineering through Polymerase Chain Reaction (PCR)

Developed with the help of Leonore Reiser and Nick Kaplinsky, Carnegie Institute of Washington; Dr. Frank Stephenson, Applied Biosystems, Inc; and Jeremy Quon, Tiffany Wong, Zoe Assaf, Nelson Chen, and Tim Toy, Biotechnology Students.

Recommended for use only if the instructor has a source of PCR reagents and the ability to have PCR primers made.

Background

In the previous activity, a Ti plasmid carrying both the NPT II and GUS genes was used to attempt to transform Arabidopsis plants. The NPT II gene confers kanamycin/gentamycin resistance to bacteria and plants that receive this gene. Kanamycin and gentamycin kill bacteria and plants that do not have the NPT II gene. By transforming Arabidopsis plants with the NPT II gene, Arabidopsis gains resistance to the antibiotics.

Another way to confirm successful transformation by the NPT II/GUS-containing Ti plasmid is to use PCR to recognize and amplify the foreign (GUS) gene in a suspected transformed plant. DNA isolation is made simple through kits like those created by Gentra Systems Inc. After isolating DNA and running a PCR reaction, a simple agarose gel can confirm the presence of the 700 bp GUS gene PCR product, and show that a transformation was, indeed, successful. Figure 11.15 shows flats of transformed Arabidopsis.

Figure 11.15. Flats of transformed Arabidopsis with flower stalks.
Photo by author.

Purpose

To determine whether Arabidopsis plants that are believed to be transformed with the Ti plasmid, show the presence of the GUS gene by PCR amplification.

Materials

Arabidopsis thaliana seeds, GUS-transformed using plasmid (pBIRG2) or equivalent
Reaction tubes, 1.7 mL and rack
Micropipets and tips
PureGene® Cell and Tissue Kit, No. D-5500A, Gentra Systems, Inc
Glass rods
Dry block heater/heat block, 65°C
Vortex mixer
Microcentrifuge, 16K × g
Isopropanol, 1 L
Ethanol, 70%
Distilled water, sterile

PCR tubes, 0.2 mL
Amplicycle® Kit (Applied Biosystems, Inc):
  10X PCR buffer
  25 m*M* MgCl$_2$
  AmpliTaq Gold® DNA Polymerase
  dNTPmix
Forward primer:
  3'ACTGAACTGGCAGAC-TATC5'
Reverse primer:
  5'TGACTGCCTCTTCGCT-GTAC3'
pCambria (0.005 ng/µL) containing B-glucuronidase gene (GUS) or alternative
Microcentrifuge

Thermal cycler, 96 well, 0.2 mL
Gel loading dye, DNA
Agarose gel, 2% in 1X TAE buffer
Electrophoresis buffer, 1X TAE
Plastic beaker, 1 L
Gel box, horizontal (for agarose gels)
DNA sizing standards, 100 bp ladder
Power supply
Weigh boat 5.5"×5.5"
Ethidium bromide, 0.5 µg/mL
Gloves and safety goggles
Gel photo imaging system
Gloves, large
Glasses, safety, plastic

Procedure

- Obtain several Arabidopsis leaves from a growing plant that is suspected to be transformed.
- Follow growing instructions from the previous lab (Lab 11j).

Part I: DNA Extraction and Isolation from PureGene® DNA Isolation Kit

A. Cell Lysis
1. Place one to three fresh leaves in a 1.7-mL tube.
2. Add 300 µL of cell lysis solution to the tissue, and grind it with a glass rod.
3. Incubate the cell lysate at 65°C for 60 minutes (samples can be stored at 4°C, if desired).

B. Protein Precipitation
4. Cool the sample to room temperature.
5. Add 100 µL of protein precipitation solution to the cell lysate.
6. Vortex the tube at high speed for 20 seconds.
7. Centrifuge at 13,000 to 16,000 × g for 3 minutes, until a green pellet is formed. Centrifuge longer if needed samples can be stored at 4°C, if desired).

C. DNA Precipitation
8. Pour the supernatant containing DNA into a clean 1.7-mL centrifuge tube containing 300 µL of 100% isopropanol.
9. Mix the sample by inverting gently 50 times.
10. Centrifuge at 13,000 to 16,000 × g for 1 minute. The DNA will be visible as a pellet ranging in color from off-white to light green.
11. Pour off the supernatant and drain the tube briefly on clean, absorbent paper. Add 300 µL of 70% ethanol and invert the tube several times to wash the DNA pellet.
12. Centrifuge at 13,000 to 16,000 × g for 1 minute. Carefully pour off the ethanol.
13. Invert and drain the tube on clean, absorbent paper and allow to air dry for 15 minutes (samples can be stored at 4°C, if desired).

D. DNA Hydration
14. Add 50 µL of DNA hydration solution.
15. Rehydrate the DNA by incubating the sample for 1 hour at 65°C, or overnight at room temperature. Tap the tube periodically to aid in dispersing the DNA (samples can be stored at 4°C, if desired).

Part II: Setting Up the PCR Reaction

16. Using the isolated DNA or water, set up a 0.2-mL PCR reaction tube and a negative control tube. See Table 11.2 for the volumes of DNA, polymerase, and other reagents to add to each 0.2-mL tube.
17. To pool the samples, spin the tubes in a centrifuge for 2 seconds. An adaptor may be necessary to spin these small-volume tubes.
18. Program the thermal cycler to run the thermal cycling program that follows. Place each tube in the thermal block. Record its location in your notebook and on the thermal cycling program chart.

Thermocycling Program
temperature / time
95°C/10 minutes
95°C/30 seconds
60°C/60 seconds
72°C/120 seconds
72°C/10 minutes
42°C/∞

Table 11.2.   **GUS/Arabidopsis PCR Reaction Matrix**

Reagent	Arabidopsis DNA (µL)	Negative Control (µL)
distilled water	26.0	31.0
10x PCR buffer	5.8	5.0
25 mM MgCl2	3.0	3.0
10 mM dNTP mix	4.0	4.0
AmpliTaq® Polymerase Gold	2.0	2.0
forward primer	2.5	2.5
reverse primer	2.5	2.5
amount of DNA used	4.2	0.0
total (µL)	50.0	50.0

Note: Prepare a diluted positive control (0.0005 ng/µL of pCAMBIA), if available.

Environmental Health and Safety Officer

Part III: Running the Gel to Check for the PCR Product

19. Add 5 µL of DNA loading dye to each PCR product sample tube.
20. Prepare a 2% agarose gel in 1X TAE buffer.
21. Load 25 µL of a sample into any lane except Lane 5.
22. Load 10 µL of 100 bp DNA standard to Lane 5.
23. Run the gel at 110 V for 30 to 40 minutes.
24. Stain with EtBr solution (20 minutes) and destain in deionized water (1 minute).
    Note: The supervisor will stain the gels with EtBr. Wear goggles and gloves.
25. Photograph the gel. Identify and label all the wells, standards, and bands. Identify any PCR product at 700 bp and any primer pieces.

Conclusion

Should all of the seeds that were collected and sampled be transformed? Explain. Which samples have a PCR product? What percentage of the samples amplified show the PCR product (yield)? Why might a sample that was transformed not have an amplification product? In terms of the original transformation of Arabidopsis with the GUS-containing Ti plasmid, what does this PCR prove?

If there is a PCR product, could any additional testing show that the DNA from the extraction actually contained the GUS gene? Explain.

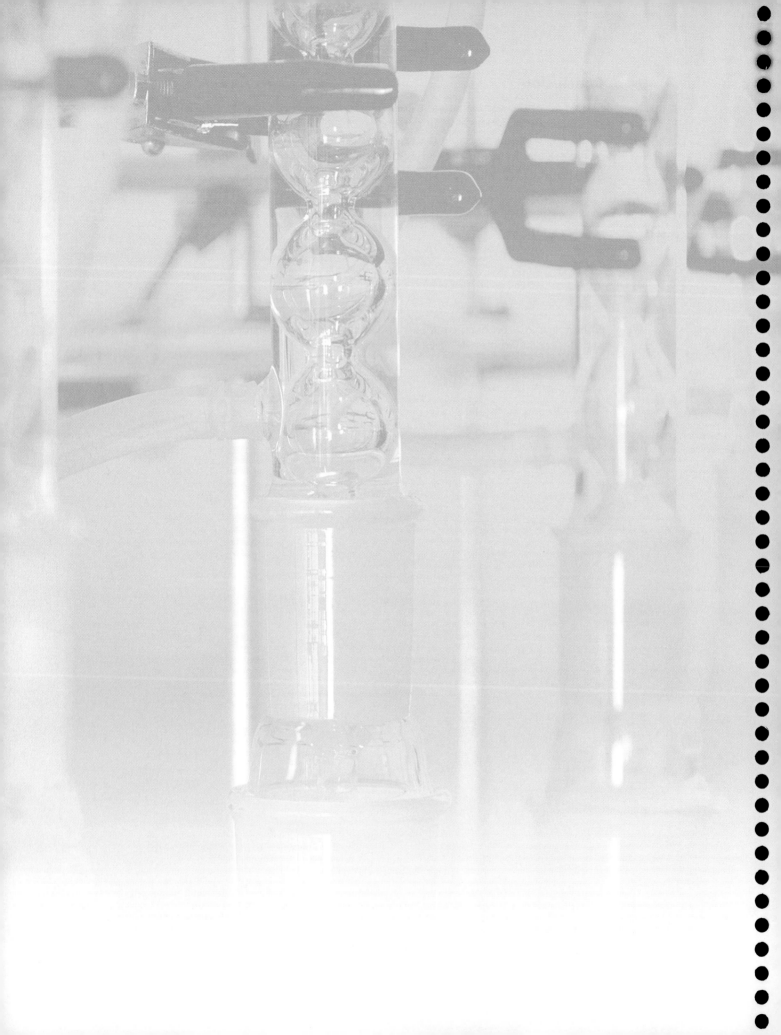

Chapter

12

Obtaining Molecules of Pharmaceutical Interest

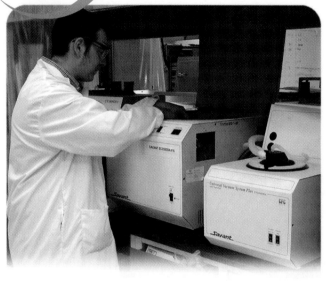

Dan Segal, a biotechnology laboratory intern in the Analytical Department of Discovery Partners International/ChemRx, uses a Savant SpeedVac® (Thermo Electron Corporation) to dry and concentrate newly created organic compounds prior to purity testing.
Photo by author.

The varied assortment of diseases and disease mechanisms require that scientists look for preventions and therapies from a variety of sources. Many pharmaceuticals and other therapies have come from native sources such as plants, animals, fungi, algae, and bacteria. Scientists have learned how to isolate and test specific naturally occurring organic compounds for their potential medicinal value,

Another source of drug candidates is compounds made by other organisms in a laboratory situation. Molecular biologists have learned how to trick certain organisms into producing compounds that other organisms normally create. Over the past three decades, many new compounds have been produced in commercial quantities using recombinant DNA and genetic engineering techniques.

Recently though, biochemists have applied long-standing organic chemistry practices to create many new small organic compounds that may be screened for pharmaceutical activity. These new drug candidates are synthesized by taking small molecules and attaching to them a few atoms or a new functional group. With the use of computers and robots, scientists can design and test thousands of new organic compounds created through combinatorial chemistry.

In the Chapter 12 lab activities you will learn some basic combinatorial chemistry techniques. Specifically, you will learn:

- how organic compounds may be extracted from plant tissue
- how to gather information about compounds using MSDS sheets
- how to synthesize new compounds through combinatorial chemistry
- how to screen new compounds using chemical tests
- how to screen samples for purity using melting point determinations and spectrophotometry

Many of the organic chemistry techniques that you will learn are used in companies whose strategies are to create, purify, and test new compounds for their medical applications.

Laboratory 12a   Using UV Spectrophotometry to Evaluate Caffeine Extraction

Background

Caffeine is an organic compound extracted from plants, such as coffee, tea, and cocoa. Although caffeine is not considered a medicine, it is an active ingredient in some over-the-counter drugs and prescription medications. Like all molecules, caffeine has a distinct interaction with light, which a spectrophotometer can measure.

Caffeine is a colorless molecule that produces a colorless solution (see Figure 12.1). Caffeine molecules do not absorb light in the visible spectrum, but, instead, they absorb certain wavelengths of ultraviolet (UV) light. Therefore, a UV spectrophotometer (UV spec) is used to study caffeine molecules in solution.

A UV spectrophotometer functions in the same fashion as a visible spectrophotometer. A deuterium lamp produces light of a certain range of UV wavelengths, and a grating splits the light into a spectrum of wavelengths. When UV light of a specific wavelength is shone on a sample, molecules in the sample either absorb the light or the light transmits through the sample. The detector determines the amount of light transmittance and displays the optical density (OD) value, or absorbance, in absorbance units (au.)

Caffeine molecules absorb certain wavelengths of light better than others. One characteristic of a molecule, such as caffeine, is its absorbance spectrum (the amount of absorbance at different wavelengths). Once a technician has determined the UV wavelength that gives the highest absorbance for caffeine (λ_{max}), that wavelength is used to detect caffeine molecules in other solutions. A high absorbance value, such as greater than 1.5 au, at caffeine's λ_{max} indicates a high molecular concentration.

Figure 12.1.   Coffee beans are the seeds from coffee plants. They are picked, cleaned, dried, and then roasted. Even though roasted coffee beans are brown, caffeine is colorless and requires a UV spectrophotometer for quantitation.
© Jeremy Horner/Corbis.

Purpose

What is the absorbance spectrum for caffeine in solution?
What is the concentration of caffeine in different clear solutions?

Materials

Environmental Health and Safety Officer

Caffeine	Tubes, 15 mL, sterile and racks	Pasteur pipet bulbs
Caution: Do not ingest caffeine or any other laboratory chemical.	Pipets and pumps	Suspected caffeinated solutions
	UV/Vis spectrophotometer	
	UV spectrophotometer cuvettes	
Balance, weigh boats, lab scoops	Pasteur pipets, 9"	

Procedure

Part I: Determining the Absorbance Spectrum for Caffeine
1. Prepare 10 mL of stock caffeine solution (0.1 mg/mL caffeine in deionized water) in a 15-mL tube.
2. Dilute the stock solution in a 1:10 ratio. Make 5 mL of this dilution. Label it 0.01 mg/mL.

3. Dilute the stock solution in a 1:20 ratio. Make 5 mL of this dilution. Label it 0.005 mg/mL.
4. Measure the absorbance of each solution at different wavelengths, beginning at 200 nm. Prepare an appropriate blank for this application. Continue to make absorbance readings every 10 nm until you reach 320 nm. Record the data in a data table.
5. Plot the data (the absorbance of each concentration of caffeine) as a three-line, line graph. Determine lambda$_{max}$ for the caffeine molecule. In the future, caffeine in solution will be studied at this wavelength.

Part II: Standard Curve for Caffeine Concentration of Unknown Solutions

6. Decide which dilution clearly showed lambda$_{max}$.
7. Make a serial dilution (such as five tubes in a 1:4 series) of caffeine in water using the dilution from step 6 (the new stock solution) as the starting solution. Record the concentrations of the new stock solution and the four dilutions in a data table.
8. Read the absorbance of the caffeine solutions from step 7 at lambda$_{max}$ (determined in step 5). Make a new data table to record the absorbance of these five standard, known caffeine solutions.
9. Plot the absorbance of the different concentrations of caffeine solutions on a line graph. Add a best-fit straight line to these data. (In Microsoft® Excel®, use "Add a trendline" and then select "Linear.")
10. From this graph, you will be able to estimate the concentration of caffeine in different beverages, either by drawing in each unknown's absorbance or by using the following equation:

$$y = mx + b$$

where y = the absorbance of the unknown sample
        m = the slope of the best-fit straight line
        x = the concentration of the unknown sample
        b = the y-intercept

Part III: Reading the Absorbance of Beverage Samples

11. Decide which solutions (unknowns) will be tested (Coke®, Diet Coke® [both by The Coca Cola, Co], Pepsi®, Mountain Dew® [both by PepsiCo, Inc], etc.). If a solution is carbonated, it must be left out overnight to "go flat."
12. Make absorbance readings for each unknown sample. Determine an appropriate blank for each application. For each unknown to be tested, make dilutions in water until the absorbance reading measures between 1.0 and 1.5 au. In a new data table, record the dilution and absorbance readings that meet the absorbance criteria for each unknown.

Data Analysis

Using the best-fit straight line that shows the relationship between the absorbance and concentration of known caffeine solutions, estimate the concentration of caffeine in the unknowns. Multiply the concentration determined on the standard curve by any dilution factor to attain the concentration of the original undiluted unknown. Add these data to the data table

Conclusion

In a short conclusion statement, report your estimation of each unknown's caffeine concentration. Compare your values with those of others in the class. Discuss the range and cause of variations in class results. Discuss the application of the UV spec in estimating the concentration of other molecules. How and when can this technique be used?

Thinking Like a Biotechnician

1. Why is it necessary for the carbonated drinks to "go flat" before taking readings?
2. Why do the pigments in the colas not interfere with the absorbance readings of caffeine?
3. Should the standard curve go through the "zero, zero" point? Why or why not?

Laboratory 12b   Using Material Safety Data Sheets (MSDS) to Recognize a Compound

Background

Procedures used in a biotechnology lab often require the use of reagents ranging from mildly irritating to very dangerous, and sometimes, mutagenic. To help prevent serious injury from chemical exposure, all chemical reagents are shipped from supply houses with an MSDS.

As you may recall from earlier lab activities, MSDS stands for "Materials Safety Data Sheet." The MSDS are created to provide a worker with the proper procedures for handling substances safely. MSDS are unique to a specific compound and manufacturer; each substance produced by each supply house has its own MSDS. When reagents are ordered, MSDS are sent with them. Some chemical supply houses, such as VWR International, publish exhaustive binders with MSDS for all the substances they produce. Often, the MSDS information is available on disks or on the Internet.

The MSDS are also available online at sites such as VWR Scientific Products. By going to the link, www.vwrsp.com, and searching for a product name, a page will come up describing the product. A link on that page to the MSDS for the compound will down load the MSDS.

A wealth of information about a chemical is found on its MSDS. Listed on the MSDS is information covering the following topics:

- chemical and company identification
- composition of ingredients
- hazards identification/emergency overview
- first aid measures
- fire fighting measures
- accidental release measures (spills/leaks protocol)
- handling and storage
- exposure controls/personal protection
- physical and chemical properties
- stability and reactivity
- toxicological information
- ecological information
- disposal considerations
- transport information
- regulatory information
- additional information

Purpose

To learn how to access and read an MSDS for chemicals used in a biotech laboratory.
To determine some of the physical characteristics of the compounds used and produced in aspirin production.

Materials

MSDS Web site or MSDS CD (Sargent-Welch # WLC9999-HYB)

Procedures

1. Find and review the MSDS for each of the compounds listed on the data table (see Table 12.1) or a comparable one from a different manufacturer.
2. Recreate the data table, and record the information requested for some important characteristics of the compounds and for safety procedures.

Table 12.1.   MSDS Information for Compounds in Aspirin Production

Substance	Manufacturer/ Catalog Number(s)	Molecular Weight (g/mol)	Melting Point (°C)	If Exposed to Skin?	If Ingested?
ethanol	EMD Chemicals/ VW0475-3				
salicylic acid	EMD Chemicals/EM-SX0060-I				
acetylsalicylic acid	ALFA AESAR/AAA12488-0E				
ferric nitrate	EMD Chemicals/EM-FX0225-I				
hydrochloric acid (HCl)	VWR/VW3200-2				
acetic anhydride	Mallinckrodt Baker/ MK242002				

Laboratory 12c   Synthesis of Aspirin, A Plant-Derived Pharmaceutical

This lab was developed with the assistance of Stephen Schram, San Mateo, California, 2003.

Background

In the late 1800s, salicylic acid, a compound that acted as a pain reliever, was extracted from willow plants. After initial use, however, the compound was found to irritate the stomach to such a degree that people could not take it.

A German scientist, Felix Hoffman, first synthesized acetylsalicylic acid, a compound that was less irritating to stomach cells, by transferring an acetyl group ($-CH_2$) to the salicylic acid molecule. Acetylsalicylic acid is the main ingredient in commercial aspirin (see Figure 12.2). This was one of the first examples of an organic synthesis.

The synthesis reaction is simple: salicylic acid from willow trees is combined with an organic compound, acetic anhydride (see Figure 12.3). To this day, aspirin is commercially produced in much the same way. Aspirin tablets contain acetylsalicylic acid, plus a few other ingredients to buffer the acidic aspirin.

Figure 12.2.   Aspirin was one of the first synthetically produced medicines.

Photo courtesy of Bayer Historical Department/Archives, Leverkusen, Germany.

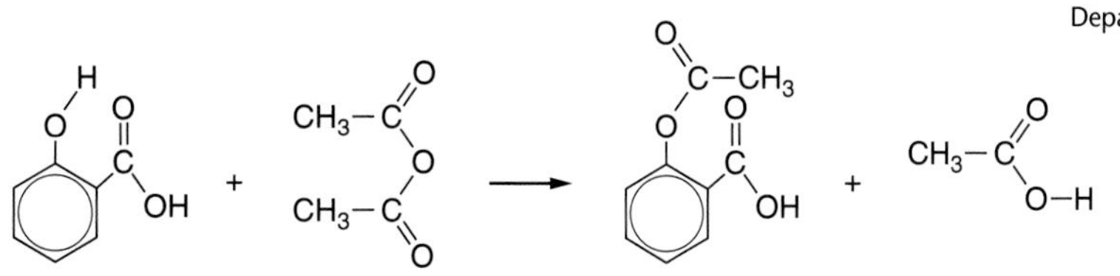

$C_7H_6O_3$	$C_4H_6O_3$	$C_9H_8O_4$	$C_2H_4O_2$
salicylic acid	acetic anhydride	acetylsalicylic acid **aspirin**	acetic acid

Figure 12.3.   Equation for Making Aspirin.   The transfer of an acetyl group to salicylic acid produces the compound acetyl salicylic acid, which is less harsh to stomach cells. Do you see where the acetyl group has been added?

Purpose

Can acetylsalicylic acid (aspirin) be synthesized from its precursor, salicylic acid, by combining it with acetic anhydride?

How pure is chemically synthesized aspirin compared with commercially produced aspirin?

Materials

Environmental Health and Safety Officer

Balance, weigh boats/paper, scoops
Salicylic acid
Test tube, Pyrex, 25×200 cm
Gloves, large
Glasses, safety, plastic
Hood, chemical fume
Acetic anhydride
Pipets, 5 mL, Pyrex
Pipet pump, for 5-10 mL pipets
Sulfuric acid, concentrated (*hazard)
Pasteur pipets, 9" and bulbs

Graduated cylinders, 100 mL
Beakers, 250 mL
Hot plate stirrer (or a Bunsen burner)
Bunsen burner and lab gas lighter
Ring stand and Biuret clamp
Glass rods
Test tube holder (Stoddard)
Filter paper, 12.5 cm
Funnels, Pyrex for 12.5 cm filter paper
Pipets, 10 mL

Ethanol, 95%
Rubber stopper, #5, (25×200 cm tubes)
Watch glass, Pyrex, 4" diameter
Tubes, 15 mL, sterile and racks
Tubes, glass, 13×100 mm and racks
Plug caps for 13×100 mm tubes
Pipets, 2 mL, and pumps
Ferric nitrate, nonahydrate, 1%
Micropipet, P-1000 and tips

Procedure

Part I (Day 1): Synthesis of Acetylsalicylic Acid

1. Weigh 1 g of salicylic acid on a piece of weighing paper.
2. Put the salicylic acid into a large test tube.
3. Put on safety glasses and gloves.
4. Under the chemical fume hood with the fan running, use a 5-mL glass pipet and pump to measure 3 mL of acetic anhydride.
5. Add the acetic anhydride to the test tube containing the salicylic acid.
6. Gently, swirl the test tube to mix.
7. Before beginning this step, note the following safety precautions:

Environmental Health and Safety Officer

   - **Do this procedure in a chemical fume hood. Do not inhale acid vapors.**
   - **Wear goggles and gloves.**
   - **Handle the sulfuric acid very carefully.**

   Under the chemical fume hood with the fan running, add five drops (approximately 100 µL) of concentrated sulfuric acid to the test tube. Swirl gently to mix.

8. Prepare a water bath by adding 60 mL of water to a 250-mL beaker. Using a Bunsen burner or, preferably, a hot plate, heat the water to boiling.
9. When the water bath is hot, clamp the reaction tube to the ring stand and place the tube in the boiling water. If you are doing this on a ring stand over a Bunsen burner, clamp the reaction tube to the ring stand.
10. Boil the mixture for about 5 minutes, until the solution is clear. Stir the reaction mixture to make sure that the salicylic acid has dissolved.
11. Cool the test tube under running water until it is cool enough to touch. Then, add 10 mL of ice water to the test tube. Hold the tube in a beaker of ice and water until a white solid forms (at least 20 minutes) in the tube. This is crude aspirin.
12. Fold a piece of filter paper into a cone. Put the filter paper in the glass funnel. Place a beaker under the funnel. Pour the aspirin mixture into the filter paper lined funnel. Rinse the test tube with 5 mL of water. Pour the rinse water through the aspirin in the funnel. Rinse the aspirin twice with 5 mL of water. The liquid that has come through the filter is known as filtrate, and it can be discarded. Leave the filter paper funnel with crude aspirin in it to dry overnight.

Part II (Day 2): Removing Impurities

1. Scrape the crude aspirin from the filter paper into a clean large test tube. Add 7 mL of ethanol.
2. Place the tube in a 250-mL beaker about half filled with water. Heat the water in the beaker until the aspirin dissolves. You may preheat the water in the beaker before putting in the tube of aspirin.

3. Add 15 mL of warm distilled water to the mixture in the test tube. If a solid forms, continue warming the beaker until it is completely dissolved.

4. Put a stopper in the test tube. Label the tube with your name. Let it stand at least 1 day in a cool place. Crystals of aspirin should begin to form in a few hours. If no crystals have formed after 24 hours, jar the test tube by flicking it with your finger.

5. Place the crystals in a filter or on filter paper, and wash them with 10 mL of cool water. Set the filter paper and crystals on a watch glass to dry overnight. It may take 2 days. Store dry crystals in a 15-mL tube or some other container.

6. Determine the mass of the aspirin recovered/synthesized in the class. Determine the yield recovery based on the mass of the starting reagents. Record these values in your notebook.

7. Draw a picture of the aspirin crystals. Compare the crystals of chemically synthesized aspirin with those of commercially produced aspirin. Use a magnifying hand lens, if available. Conduct a ferric nitrate test on each product.

   Test for salicylates by conducting a ferric nitrate test on the each of the prepared samples, following the procedure below. Compare these to positive controls (salicylic acid, acetylsalicylic acid) and negative controls (sodium chloride). Create a numerical system for ranking the color change compared with the positive and negative controls. Record all test results and descriptions in a data table.

Iron Testing for Salicylates

Mix 10 large crystals of the sample in 2 mL of dH_2O.
Add 250 μL of 1% ferric nitrate solution to the sample.
Observe the color, and compare to negative and positive controls.

8. Review an MSDS for salicylic acid from either a chemical supply house or an Internet site. Study the information provided on the MSDS. Find the melting point of pure salicylic acid.

9. Determine the melting point, compared with commercially produced aspirin (in the MSDS), following the procedures in Lab 12d. Record melting-point determinations on the previous data table.

   • Explain any discrepancies between the reported melting point and the observed melting point. Of what value are these data?
   • Compare other characteristics described on the MSDS, such as color and texture.

Conclusion

Discuss your success (yield and purity) at synthesizing aspirin (acetylsalicylic acid) from its precursor, salicylic acid. Give evidence for your statements. Discuss the results of the ferric nitrate test and what they might mean. Explain any discrepancies between the reported melting point and the observed melting point. Of what value are these data? Describe factors that could affect the success of the synthesis.

Thinking Like a Biotechnician

1. Give reasons for recrystallizing the aspirin. What is being removed with each wash? How does this affect the end product? How can you test your answer?

2. Propose other methods to determine the presence and purity of a synthesized acetylsalicylic acid product.

3. If it tested very pure, would it be safe to use your synthesized acetylsalicylic acid for medical purposes? Why or why not?

Laboratory 12d   Melting Point Determinations as a Quality Control Test of Purity

Background

The temperature at which a solid becomes a liquid is called the "melting-point temperature." Compounds have a particular, characteristic melting-point temperature that can be used to identify the compound and determine its purity. The closer a sample melts to the expected melting point, the more likely it is that the sample is pure.

Melting-point information can be obtained from several resources, including the Merck Index (Merck Publishing, Merck and Co., Inc) and the MSDS. In a quality control environment, there are instruments that will conduct a melting-point determination (see Figure 12.4). In our labs, it is easy to conduct a melting point determination using a capillary tube/melting-point apparatus (see Figure 12.5).

Purpose

How pure is chemically synthesized aspirin compared with commercially produced aspirin?

Materials

Environmental Health and Safety Officer

Hood, chemical fume	Ring stand and Biuret clamp	Thermometer, mercury,
Gloves, large	Capillary tubes, 100 mm,	−10°C to −260°C
Glasses, safety, plastic	open-ended	Rubber bands
Bunsen burner and lab	Pipets, 5 mL	Lab mitts or other
gas lighter	Pipet pump for 5-10 mL pipets	fire-resistant gloves
Test tube, Pyrex, 25×200 cm	Oil, mineral	Samples to be tested

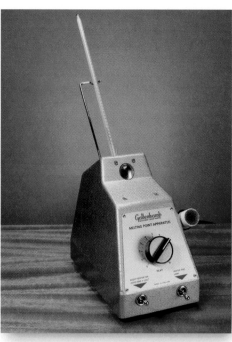

Figure 12.4.   **This instrument may be used to determine the melting point of a substance. A small amount of the sample to be tested is placed inside a tube. The tube is placed in the top of the apparatus and slowly heated while it is observed through the magnifying lens at the center right. When the solid-to-liquid transition is complete, the temperature is read from the mercury thermometer (yellow).**
© Andrew Lambert Photography/Science Photo Library.

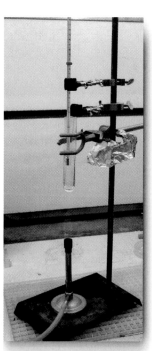

Figure 12.5.   **In this low-cost version of a melting point apparatus, a small number of crystals to be tested are added to a tiny capillary tube (closed at one end) suspended in oil. The oil is heated above 100°C. The technician, standing behind a fume hood shield, wearing safety goggles, can observe the temperature at which the crystals melt.**
Photo by author.

Environmental Health
and Safety Officer

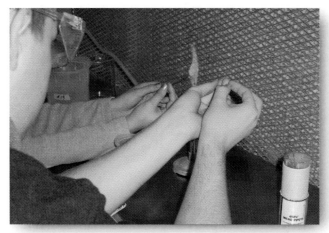

Figure 12.6.   **If you roll the end of a capillary tube in a flame, it will melt closed. It may take a few trials before a satisfactory closed end tube is made.**
Photo by author.

Procedure

Part I: Setting up the Melting-Point Measuring Apparatus

Safety Precautions:

Environmental Health
and Safety Officer

- **The following procedures should only be conducted in a chemical flow hood with the protective shield in the "down" position.**
- **Wear goggles and lab mitts when boiling oil.**
- **Tie hair back.**

1. Set up a Bunsen burner apparatus ring stand with a **large** test tube clamped into place, so that the bottom of the test tube is in the hottest part of the flame during heating).
2. Start the Bunsen burner flame. Heat a capillary tube in the hot part of the burner until it melts, closing one end. Turn off the flame.
3. Add a small amount of crystals of the substance to be tested to the open end of the capillary tube. Turn it over and tap the crystals down to the bottom of the closed end.
4. Using a rubber band to hold the capillary tube, secure the tube to the base of a mercury thermometer.
5. Using a pipet, carefully add 5 mL of mineral oil to the bottom of test tube.
6. Gently, place the capillary tube/thermometer in the test tube with the oil. Clamp the thermometer to the ring stand so that it will not fall over and break (see Figure 12.7).

Part II: Determining the Melting Point

Environmental Health
and Safety Officer

7. Heat the test tube in a hot flame, watching the temperature until it gets within 15°C of its expected melting temperature (based on the reported MSDS value). Make sure that the oil does not boil over or splatter. There should be no water in or around the hot oil. This could cause splattering and possibly a fire or burns.
8. Lower the flame substantially to slow the heating rate so that there is a better chance of seeing when the crystals melt.

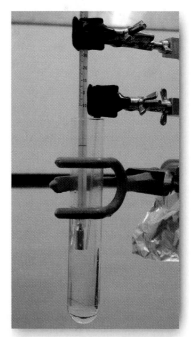

Figure 12.7.   **The capillary tube is adjacent to the mercury thermometer (narrow tube to the right of the thermometer) for easy reading.**
Photo by author.

9. Watch to see the temperature (range) at which the crystals melt.
10. Record all the melting temperatures of the sample(s) in a data table.
11. Repeat three times and average the results. Cool the oil back down to 20°C less than the expected melting temperature before doing another trial.

Conclusion

Analyze the results of the synthesis reactions. How close is the observed melting temperature to the expected temperature for each sample? Are the values close enough to conclude that the samples are the same? By what statistical method did you determine this? List some reasons why the values may be different than expected.

Thinking Like a Biotechnician

1. Why is the melting-point determination done in oil rather than water?
2. When the capillary tubes cool, what should be visible inside of them?
3. What will happen if one test has twice as many crystals in the melting-point determination as another test?

Laboratory 12e   Testing a Protocol: Extraction of Salicylic Acid from Willow

Background

The main, active ingredient in modern-day aspirin is the compound, acetylsalicylic acid. Acetylsalicylic acid is made through an organic synthesis process where an acetyl group from acetic anhydride is added to salicylic acid.

  Salicylic acid is produced by modifying salicin molecules (see Figure 12.2). Salicin molecules are found, in nature, in the leaves and bark of many species of willow (eg, *Salix alba*, *Salix tetresperma*, *Salix fragilis*) and a few species of poplar. Willow tissue may contain as much as 10% salicylin. It has been reported in several sources that salicin or salicylic acid is easily extracted from willow bark and leaves using 80% ethanol as a solvent, and conducting a series of extractions and separations (for example, see www.siu.edu/~ebl/leaflets/salicin.htm).

  In this activity, you will conduct a procedure for extracting salicylic acid from willow tissue to see if, and how well, it works. The procedure is in the midst of process development and has shown some promise. It is the technician's task to try the procedure and to evaluate the product and yield. If time allows, improvements in the process to increase yield may be attempted.

Purpose

Can pure salicylic acid be extracted from willow leaves or bark using the proposed protocol?

Materials

White willow bark, shreds	Erlenmeyer flasks, Pyrex,	Salicylic acid
Balance, weigh boats, scoops	250 mL	Sodium chloride
Mortar and pestle, 100 mL	Hood, chemical fume	Tubes, glass, 13×100 mm
Pipets and pumps	pH meter, electrode,	and racks
Ethanol, 95%	and buffers	Plug caps for 13×100 mm
Parafilm®	Hydrochloric acid, 1 *M*	tubes
Filter paper, 12.5 cm	Petroleum ether	Ferric nitrate, nonahydrate, 1%
Funnels, Pyrex for 12.5 cm	Petri dishes, 150×15 mm	Micropipet, P-1000 and tips
filter paper	O-acetylsalicylic acid	

Procedure

Use the method below or a method that you have found from a different source (if approved by your instructor).

1. Obtain a white willow leaf or bark sample.
2. Grind 3 g of plant tissue using a mortar and pestle with 15 mL of 80% ethanol solution (see Figure 12.8).
3. Allow the plant tissue-ethanol mixture to stand, covered with Parafilm®, for at least 24 hours.
4. Using a filter paper funnel, filter the solvent into a 250-mL flask and discard the solid.
5. Set the flask in a chemical fume hood with the fan running for approximately 1 week, or until all the ethanol has evaporated. Some crystals may be visible.
6. Add 10 mL of deionized water to resuspend any compound on the bottom of the flask. Calibrate a pH meter. Add enough 1 M HCl to the solution to bring it to pH 4.0. (This should produce salicylic acid, which is not charged and is hydrophobic (it does not "like" water).
7. Add 10 mL of petroleum ether. Swirl to mix.
8. Swirl again, and allow it to separate into two distinct layers.
9. Pipet off each layer and place into two large Petri dishes. Allow each layer to evaporate and crystals to grow. This may take several weeks. Placing the samples in a chemical fume hood with the fan running can speed the process.
10. For crystals in either sample, determine the percent (%) yield. To do this, divide the volume of crystals by 3 g of willow tissue (starting sample), then multiple by 100.
11. Using the MSDS for salicylic acid, from either a chemical supply house or an Internet connection, find the reported melting point of pure salicylic acid.
12. Test each sample for salicylates by conducting a ferric nitrate test on each of the prepared samples, following the procedure below. Compare these to positive (salicylic acid) and negative controls (sodium chloride).

Figure 12.8. Salicin is extracted from a willow tree sample by grinding the plant tissue and placing the material in an ethanol solution.
Photo by author.

Iron Testing for Salicylates

Mix 10 large crystals of the sample in 2 mL of dH$_2$O.
Add 250 uL of 1% ferric nitrate solution to the sample.
Observe the color and compare to negative and positive controls.

13. Determine the melting point of each sample, compared with a pure salicylic acid sample, following the protocol in Lab 12d.

Conclusion

Does it appear that salicylin (salicylic acid) was extracted from willow using the procedures outlined above? What proof do you have? If so, what yield of salicylic acid did the procedure give? If there was little or no yield, propose modifications in the procedures?

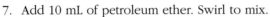

Thinking Like a Biotechnician

1. Considering your experience with alcohol precipitation of DNA, why is the petroleum ether added to the watery salicylic acid solution?
2. Why might willow leaves contain a large amounts salicylic acid?

Chapter 13

Making DNA Molecules

Mary Hansen is a Forensic Scientist and Biology Unit Supervisor for the Sacramento County District Attorney's Crime Laboratory. Her unit works on the identification and genetic marker typing of biological material derived from blood, semen, saliva, tissues, and hairs. The stability of DNA and the sensitivity of the typing methods have given law enforcement agencies the ability to solve current cases, cold cases, and cases involving "contact DNA," the DNA transferred when an individual's skin or mucosa makes contact with another person or object. The majority of the evidence examined is collected from victims of sexual assaults and homicides.

Photo courtesy of Mary Hansen.

The incorporation of new DNA and protein typing methods has had a major impact on several scientific disciplines. In forensic laboratories, for example, DNA sequencing and polymerase chain reaction (PCR) have helped reduce a large backlog of unsolved criminal cases. In other areas, including medicine, genetics, drug development, evolutionary studies, and environmental biotechnology, identifying difference between individuals and populations through DNA typing has become one of the foundations of research, development, and diagnostics.

In the Chapter 13 lab activities you will learn some basic DNA typing techniques, or in other words, how to identify DNA fragments. Specifically, you will learn how to

- synthesize DNA fragments, called oligonucleotides, that could be used as primers or probes in DNA sequencing, PCR, or other DNA studies
- transfer DNA fragments to a Southern blot membrane for analysis purposes
- visualize DNA fragments produced during DNA synthesis or PCR
- conduct a basic PCR reaction and use a thermal cycler
- use a database to gather information about data collected during a DNA investigation (bioinformatics)

Since DNA sequencing and PCR are modifications of DNA synthesis procedures, many of the methods used and the skills developed in these activities are similar to those used in sequencing and genomic studies. Using DNA or RNA fragments also are the foundation for searching for new genes and gene functions, as in microarray technology.

Laboratory 13a   DNA Synthesis in Vitro

Based on labs developed by Maureen Munn, PhD, University of Washington, Seattle, WA. Modified by Maria Abilock, BABEC, and Luhua Zhang, Biotechnology Student. Supported by Frank Stephenson, PhD, Applied Biosystems, Inc.

Note: This lab is recommended for use only if the instructor has the ability to have the required PCR primers and templates made.

Background

Oligonucleotides (short pieces of DNA) can be constructed in a test tube (*in vitro*) using a single-stranded DNA fragment as a template. A primer complementary to the 3' end of the template attaches and is used as the starting end of the oligonucleotide to be synthesized. With the appropriate concentrations of primer, dNTPs, polymerase, and other buffer reagents, the DNA polymerase (for example, Sequenase®, Amersham Biosciences, Inc.) can build an entire oligonucleotide fragment that is complementary to the template (see Figure 13.1). If any of the key ingredients are limited or missing, or the reaction is not conducted at the enzyme's optimum temperature of 37°C, the synthesis reaction will slow or stop.

Once a DNA synthesis reaction is complete, synthesis products may be run on a polyacrylamide gel to confirm the reaction. The synthesized fragments separate on the gel based on differences in length of only a few nucleotides. Gels can be visualized through ethidium bromide (EtBr) staining or the gel bands may be transferred to a membrane for Southern blotting (see following activities) and blot visualization.

In this activity, DNA strands of predictable lengths are built off a 60-base template DNA strand.

The template used has the sequence:

3'ACATGCTGCTGCCGGTCACAAGGCAATTCCTAAAAAGGGAAGGAACCCCGAAGGCCTTTT-5'

The primer used is 32 bases long and has the following sequence:

5'-biotin-TGTACGACGACGGCCAGTGTTCCGTTAAGGAT-3'

Notice the biotin molecule, "tagged" to the 5' end, for visualization purposes.

Purpose:

Can DNA fragments (oligonucleotides) of different lengths be synthesized *in vitro?*
How does varying the availability of DNA nucleotide triphosphates (dNTPs) affect DNA synthesis strand development?

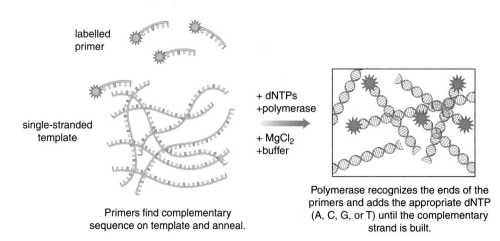

Figure 13.1.   **DNA Synthesis.**

Materials

Note: Table 13.1 includes some recipes and/or sources.

Tube rack for 1.7 mL tubes
Reaction tubes, 1.7 mL
Permanent lab marker pens
Micropipets and tips
DNA template at 1.5 pmol/μL
Biotin-tagged primer,
  1.5 pmol/μL
Reaction buffer
Distilled water, sterile

Lid locks, for 1.7 mL tubes
  (optional)
Water bath, 65°C
Floating rack (1.7 mL tubes)
Beaker, 400 mL, 12/PK,
  4 PK/CS
Thermometer, −20 to +150°C
No nucleotide mix
  (50 mM NaCl)
  - dATP mix (lacking dATP)

  - dCTP mix (lacking dCTP)
  - dGTP mix (lacking dGTP)
  - dTTP mix (lacking dTTP)
Microcentrifuge
DTT, 0.1 M
Sequenase (Polymerase),
  diluted 1:8
Dry block heater/heat block,
  37°C
Stop mix

Table 13.1.   Source of Reagents/Recipes for the DNA Synthesis Reactions

Reagent	Source/Recipe
Sequenase® Version 2.0	Amersham Biosciences Inc kit No. US70770
	(DNA polymerase) – diluted DNA polymerase = 8 μL DNA polymerase + 56 μL of cold polymerase buffer stored on ice
reaction buffer	in Amersham Biosciences kit
no nucleotide mix	50 mM of NaCl (100 mL = 0.25 g of NaCl, 100 mL of dH₂0)
0.1 M DTT	in Amersham Biosciences kit
-dATP, -dCTP, -dGTP, -dTTP mixes	in Amersham Biosciences kit; make from individual nucleotide mixes
complete nucleotide mix	in Amersham Biosciences kit; make from individual nucleotide mixes
stop mix	in Amersham Biosciences kit

The template and primers are prepared at 1.5 pmol/μL with the following sequence:

Template DNA
3'ACATGCTGCTGCCGGTCACAAGGCAATTCCTAAAAAGGGAAGGAACCCCGAAGGCCTTTT5'

Primer
5'-**biotin**-TGTACGACGACGGCCAGTGTTCCGTTAAGGAT-3'

The DNA sizing standard markers are prepared at 0.038 pmol/μL with the following sequence:

32 bp
5'-biotin-TGTACGACGACGGCCAGTGTTCCGTTAAGGAT-3'

45 bp
3'-ACATGCTGCTGCCGGTCACAAGGCAATTCCTAAAAAGGGAAGGAAC-5'-biotin

60 bp
3'ACATGCTGCTGCCGGTCACAAGGCAATTCCTAAAAAGGGAAGGAACCCCGAAGGCCTTTT-5'-
biotin

Hypothesis

- Read the procedures and, in your notebook, create a flowchart of the experimental steps. Then, draw a sketch to represent the length of the DNA fragments that should be synthesized in each of the six nucleotide tubes.
- Draw a sketch to represent the distance that the different DNA fragments should run on a PAGE gel compared with the standard DNA size markers listed in the materials list. Although you will not be able to check them until the gel run, when they are blotted and stained you should be able to predict how they would run on a gel.

Procedure

Part I: Attaching the Primer to the Template (Annealing)

1. Label a natural-colored 1.7-mL tube with your lab group's initials (or your own initials if you have not been assigned to a group), and the letters AM (annealing mix). Add the following ingredients **in the order listed** to this tube and close the lid **tightly** (see Table 13.2). Check off each ingredient as you add it. If a locking cap is available, place it on the top of the test tube after the last reagent is added.

Table 13.2. **Annealing-Mix Tube Reaction Matrix**

Ingredient	Volume (µL)
DNA template	2
biotin-tagged primer	2
reaction buffer	4
distilled water	12
total volume	**20**

65°C

2. To denature the primer and template molecules, place the AM tube, in a floating rack, in a 65°C hot water bath for 2 minutes. (This separates the DNA molecules and discourages random annealing.)
3. At the end of the 2-minute incubation, scoop up about 50 mL of the 65°C water into a 400-mL beaker. Place the AM tube, in its rack, into the beaker. Slowly, allow the AM tube to cool to 35°C or less for 15 minutes. Add a tiny bit of ice to the beaker to bring it to 35°C if it has not reached it after 15 minutes.

Part II: Preparing the Nucleotide Mixes

While the AM tube is cooling, prepare the nucleotide mixes in six different tubes, as follows (see Table 13.3):

4. Label six 1.7-mL tubes (colored, if available) with your lab initials, NM (nucleotide mix), and the numbers 1 through 6. If colored tubes are available, pick all of the same color to help keep track of your tubes in the rest of the experiment. Put 2.5 µL of the corresponding (premixed) nucleotide mix into each tube (see Table 13.3). Close each tube tightly.

Table 13.3. **Nucleotide-Mix Tube Ingredients**

Tube No.	Mix
1	no nucleotide control mix (this is lacking all the nucleotides)
2	complete nucleotide mix (with dATP, dGTP, dCTP, dTTP)
3	missing dATP (but contains all the other dNTPs)
4	missing dCTP (but contains all the other dNTPs)
5	missing dGTP (but contains all the other dNTPs)
6	missing dTTP (but contains all the other dNTPs)

5. Give the tubes a "wrist flick" or a quick spin in the centrifuge to pool the sample. Keep the tubes on ice until step 6.

Part III: Synthesis Reaction

37°C

6. Add 2 µL of 0.1 *M* DTT and 4 µL of diluted (1:8 ratio) DNA polymerase to the annealing mix in tube AM. Change tips after each dispensing to avoid cross contamination. Give the tubes a "wrist flick" or a quick spin in the centrifuge to pool the reagents. Keep the tube on ice until ready to use in the synthesis reactions.
7. A few minutes before starting the synthesis reactions, place the six nucleotide tubes into the 37°C water bath or a 37°C heat block for **at least 2 minutes.**
8. Add 3 µL of the AM mixture to each of the nucleotide tubes, No. 1 through 6. Pipet the mixture **directly** into the pooled NM solution in each reaction tube. **Change tips for each tube.** "Wrist flick" the tubes to pool the reactants.

Environmental Health and Safety Officer

9. **Immediately,** place the tubes back into the 37°C water bath or heat block. **These must stay warm.** Incubate the samples at 37°C for **at least** 4 minutes.

10. After incubation, add 4 µL of stop mix, which includes loading dye, to the tubes. Close the tubes tightly. Make sure the tubes are still labeled clearly. Spin to pool samples.

11. Put the tubes in a rack and freeze at −20°C until they are ready to use/run in the PAGE.

12. Confirm the presence of synthesis products by running the samples on a 10% TBE-urea gel (TBE stands for TRIS, boric acid, and EDTA) as described in the next activity. The sample fragments on the gel can be visualized through EtBr staining (15 minutes) or Southern blotting and visualization (following activities).

Thinking Like a Biotechnician

1. In this experiment, the type of dNTP in the reaction is varied so you can see the effect on strand synthesis. Make a prediction as to what negative consequences may result if the following key ingredients were varied.

   a) primer concentration
   b) DNA polymerase concentration

2. During the annealing reactions, the primer-template mixture is cooled very slowly from 65°C to 35°C. Describe what is happening in the AM tube during this period and what may happen if the AM tube is cooled too rapidly.

3. After all of the reagents are mixed together, what is the final concentration of template DNA in each of the synthesis-reaction tubes?

Laboratory 13b   Separating DNA Fragments on a PAGE Gel

Based on labs developed by Maureen Munn, PhD, University of Washington, Seattle, WA. Modified by Maria Abilock, BABEC, and Luhua Zhang, Biotechnology Student. Supported by Frank Stephenson, PhD, Applied Biosystems, Inc.

Note: This activity runs the DNA synthesis products, from the last activity, on a PAGE gel.

Background

The DNA synthesis fragments produced in the last laboratory activity are too small to be separated and analyzed on an agarose gel. DNA fragments that are smaller than 500 nucleotides in length are best separated and visualized on a polyacrylamide gel (PAGE), as shown in Figure 13.2. PAGE gels used for small DNA fragments are similar to those used in protein analysis, but they are prepared with different buffers. These gels are also run at a higher voltage.

It is common to use TBE buffer to prepare and run PAGE gels for DNA synthesis or sequencing fragments. TBE withstands the higher voltage better than does the TAE buffer commonly used for horizontal gel electrophoresis.

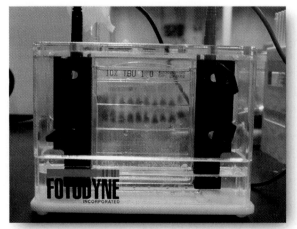

Figure 13.2. Bromophenol blue (dark blue) and xylene cyanol (light blue) track the movement of the DNA synthesis fragments. The colorless DNA fragments are transferred to blotting membrane and "stained."

Photo by author.

TBE buffer can be prepared in the lab or purchased in a concentrated form (10X or 5X) from a supply house. TBE gels may be purchased prepoured and ready to use. Once the gels are rinsed, labeled, and loaded with sample, they are run for 20 to 30 minutes at 200 V. The fragments travel through the gel based on their size. Once the gels are stained, their sizes are determined by comparing their positions with standard fragments.

In this activity, the DNA fragments, from the DNA synthesis procedure, will be run on a gel. In the next activity, the gel is blotted onto a membrane (Southern blotting) and run through a series of washes and stains. The fragments visualize on the membrane and can be further analyzed.

Purpose

To prepare and load a DNA PAGE gel.

To separate DNA synthesis samples (oligos) on a TBE-urea PAGE gel for future study.

Materials

Environmental Health and Safety Officer

TBE buffer concentrate, 5X	Permanent lab marker pens	Gel loading tips, PAGE
Beaker, plastic, 1 L	Gel Box, vertical, for	Power supply, 250 V
Gloves, large	10×10 cm PAGE	Lid locks, for 1.7 mL tubes
Glasses, safety, plastic	Pipets, transfer, 3 mL	Dry block heater/heat block,
TBE-urea gel, 1.0 mm,	Sizing standard markers, DNA	94°C
8% or 10%	synthesis, 0.038 pmol/μL	
	(Lab 13a)	

Procedure

Environmental Health and Safety Officer

Part I: Preparing Buffer

1. Prepare or purchase 1 L of 5X TBE buffer (recipe below)

5 X TBE Buffer: 1 L (concentrated buffer)

- 0.5 g of NaOH
- 54 g of TRIS base
- 3.7 g of EDTA, disodium salt (or 20 mL of 0.5 *M* EDTA solution)
- 27.5 g of boric acid

Measure dry ingredients. Add 800 mL of distilled water, and stir to dissolve. Add liquid EDTA, if appropriate. Adjust to a final volume of 1 L by adding distilled water. Store at room temperature.

2. Prepare 500 mL of 1X TBE buffer by diluting the 5X TBE. Show the calculation of the dilution in your notebook.

Part II: Preparing the Gel

Environmental Health and Safety Officer

3. Obtain a prepoured, TBE-urea (8% or 10%) polyacrylamide gel, and a vertical minigel box.
4. Wearing gloves and goggles, wash the outside of the gel by running tap water over it.
5. Gently, dry the gel cassette. Label the wells, and initial the gel cassette. If there is tape covering the bottom of the gel, pull it off.
6. Place the gel in the electrophoresis chamber **in the correct orientation,** labels facing the front of the gel box and the well side facing the internal buffer chamber.
7. Add enough 1X TBE electrophoresis buffer to the gel-box chambers to cover the wells and the bottom one-third of the gel.
8. Slowly, remove the comb from the top of the gel.
9. Using a transfer pipet or gel loading tips, rinse the gel wells with the 1X TBE buffer to remove the preservative. Rinse the equivalent of about 1 mL worth of buffer through each well. Be careful to not damage the fragile "fingers" that define the well. If any of them bend over, very gently take a gel-loading tip and straighten it out.
10. Place the top on the gel box and prerun the gel for at least 10 minutes at 200 V to heat the gels. Do not stop the prerunning until all your samples are in front of the gel, ready to load.

Part III: Preparing the Samples

Note: Do this while the gel is preheating.

95°C

9. DNA **must be single-stranded** to be interpreted for this activity. To separate (denature) the template strands from the newly synthesized DNA strands, place the six sample tubes from the DNA Synthesis Lab into the 95°C water bath or heat block for at least 3 minutes. If available, use lid locks to keep the lids of the tubes closed during heating.

Part IV: Loading and Running the Samples

10. If you are not an expert at loading a PAGE gel, practice with loading dye on Well No. 9 or 10. Turn the power back on, and run another few minutes to heat the gel again.

11. After the 3 minutes of sample heating and 10 minutes of gel heating, **quickly** load each sample onto the gel. Load 10 μL of each sample into the wells, starting at Well No. 2. Into Well No. 8, load 15 μL of the DNA standards. All samples, plus the standards, must be loaded within 2 minutes to keep the strands from reannealing. Change tips every time.

12. Run the gels for at least 20 minutes at 200 V, or longer if there is time. At most, run the gels until the bromophenol blue dye is 1 inch above the bottom of the gel.

13. At the end of the run, turn off the power, and remove the gel. The gel can be stained with EtBr or it may be blotted to a membrane (Southern blotting) for staining. Either method must be started within the hour since the DNA fragments on the gel will begin to diffuse.

Thinking Like a Biotechnician

1. At the end of the gel run, blue bands can be seen near the bottom of the gel. What are the blue bands? Where are the DNA synthesis fragments?
2. If the samples are loaded on the gel too slowly, the template and primer pieces will reanneal. What is the size of the template-primer complex compared with the template alone or any of the synthesized fragments? Why is it important to consider the template-primer complex?
3. Why does the TBE buffer have to be diluted from 5X to 1X? What consequences are expected if the buffer is not correctly diluted to 1X?

Laboratory 13c   Conducting a Southern Blot

Based on labs developed by Maureen Munn, PhD, University of Washington, Seattle, WA. Modified by Maria Abilock, BABEC, and Luhua Zhang, Biotechnology Student. Supported by Frank Stephenson, PhD, Applied Biosystems, Inc.

Note: This activity uses the PAGE gel from the last activity, upon which the DNA synthesis fragments were run.

Background

DNA on a gel is colorless and, therefore, not visible to the unaided eye. A DNA-PAGE gel can be stained with EtBr and photographed for analysis. More often, though, gels are transferred to nitrocellulose or a nylon membrane in a technique called blotting. When the sample being transferred is DNA, it is called a Southern blot. Blots are an easy way to handle (because they are less toxic), analyze, and preserve DNA fragments. In addition, the visualization methods for Southern blots are more sensitive to low concentrations of DNA.

In a blot, the gel is covered with a positively charged nylon membrane or nitrocellulose paper. Layers of absorbent filter paper are placed on top of the gel-membrane complex. Heavy weights or books are place on top of the paper. After 20 to 30 minutes, capillary action carries the DNA fragments from the gel up to the membrane. Drying binds (cross-links) the DNA to the membrane. Cross-linking is faster and more complete if the membrane is exposed to ultraviolet (UV) light in a cross-linker for 20 seconds. At this point, the DNA samples are fixed onto the membrane, but are not visible.

The DNA fragments can be visualized by using an appropriate staining procedure, such as the one in the next activity.

Purpose

To conduct a Southern blot transfer of DNA synthesis fragments from a gel to a nylon blotting membrane.

Materials

DNA synthesis PAGE gel in the cassette (from Lab 13b)	Pencil	Beakers, plastic, 1 L
	Forceps, fine-tipped, stainless steel	Filter paper, 12.5 cm
Spatula or dinner knife, metal		Plate, Plexiglass®, 10×10 cm
Pipets, transfer, 3 mL	Hybond N+ nylon membrane,	Textbooks, several, heavy
TBE buffer, 1X	Amersham No.RPN82B	UV crosslinker (optional)

Procedure

1. Gather the necessary supplies for the blotting procedure.
2. Place the gel on the lab bench, with the longer plate of the cassette on the bench top.
3. Using the metal spatula or knife, gently pry the short top plate off, lifting it slowly so that the gel does not rip. If the gel sticks to both plates, squirt some buffer between the gel and the short plate to help it come off. Don't worry if the gel sticks to the short plate instead of the long one. It just means that the lanes will be reversed on the membrane. You will be able to determine the loading order based on the location of the standards.
4. With a pencil, not a pen, label the upper right-hand corner of the nylon membrane with initials. The membrane is delicate. Do not touch it with your hands. Only use forceps.
5. Make a sandwich directly on top of the exposed gel by stacking the following layers in the following order (see Figure 13.3):

   a) the nylon membrane
   (Dip the membrane in TBE buffer, and lay it over the gel with the pencil mark facing down. Avoid trapping any air bubbles. Place it correctly the first time. If you try to reposition it, the DNA may smudge on it and you will lose sample.)
   b) five squares of dry Whatman paper or flat paper towel
   c) a Plexiglas® plate
   d) five heavy textbooks

   Leave the blot alone for at least 20 minutes.
6. Carefully remove the book, plate, and Whatman paper from the top of the membrane. Using forceps, lift the membrane by the edges, gently removing the membrane from the surface of the gel. If the gel sticks, squirt a little 1X TBE buffer between the membrane and the gel. Don't worry if a small amount of gel remains stuck to the membrane since this will be washed off later.
7. Lay the membrane **DNA side up** (pencil mark up) on a dry piece of paper. Cross-link the DNA fragments to the membrane by drying overnight or exposing it to a 20-second UV exposure in a cross-linker.

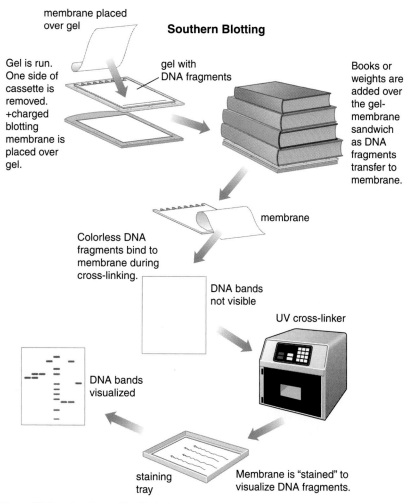

Southern Blotting

membrane placed over gel

Gel is run. One side of cassette is removed. +charged blotting membrane is placed over gel.

gel with DNA fragments

Books or weights are added over the gel-membrane sandwich as DNA fragments transfer to membrane.

membrane

Colorless DNA fragments bind to membrane during cross-linking.

DNA bands not visible

UV cross-linker

DNA bands visualized

staining tray

Membrane is "stained" to visualize DNA fragments.

Figure 13.3.   Southern Blot Technique

Cross-linking Instructions

- Dip a piece of Whatman filter paper in1X TBE buffer.
- Place the blotted membrane(s) on the wet Whatman filter paper, DNA side UP, in the UV cross-linker.
- Close the door.
- Irradiate the membranes with UV-254 light for 20 seconds. Depending on the model of cross-linker, this could be as easy as pressing the "start" button.

Conclusion

How does your blot look compared with others in the class? Is there evidence that the blot (transferring of molecules) was successful? Can you see DNA on the blot? If there is no visible DNA on the membrane, is there any evidence that the blotting (transfer of the DNA) was successful?

Thinking Like a Biotechnician

1. What may be the consequences of trapping a large air bubble between the gel and the nylon membrane during blotting?
2. Speculate as to why the cross-linker speeds cross-linking.

Laboratory 13d   Visualizing DNA on a Southern Blot

Based on labs developed by Maureen Munn, PhD, University of Washington, Seattle, WA. Modified by Maria Abilock, BABEC, and Luhua Zhang, Biotechnology Student. Supported by Frank Stephenson, PhD, Applied Biosystems, Inc.

Note: This activity "stains" the Southern blot membrane (from the last activity) that holds the DNA synthesis fragments.

Background

There are several methods of visualizing DNA on a Southern blot. In one technique, a complementary DNA probe, tagged with a radioactive label, finds its complement on the membrane and is visible as a spot on exposed x-ray film. Although this is a method commonly used in industry, there are disadvantages to using radioactive labels, not the least of which is the danger of exposure to radioactivity.

Another method of visualizing DNA bands on a membrane utilizes chromogenic agents. A chromogenic agent produces color. To use a chromogen, an enzyme complex is bound to the complementary DNA probe. The enzyme complex can cause a color change in a colored reagent when it is added to the membrane. The DNA that binds the enzyme complex turns color. In this activity, we will use an enzyme, alkaline phosphatase, which changes a yellow substrate, nitro blue tetrazolium (NBT), to a purple-blue color.

The alkaline phosphatase (AP) is attached to the DNA through a series of reactions that stack molecules on top of the DNA bands. After the AP is bound, a yellow NBT is added. The AP changes the color of the yellow NBT substrate to a bluish color. The colored molecules "stain" the DNA spot. On the blotted membranes, the DNA shows as faint blue bands where the AP has changed the color of the NBT.

In this experiment, visualization of DNA bands on the blot is possible because the primer used has a biotin molecule attached, or tagged, to it. During the visualization process, the biotin tag on the probe first binds a streptavidin molecule. Then, a second biotin molecule coupled to the AP enzyme is added to the streptavidin. The AP causes a colored reagent (NBT) to change from yellow to blue (see Figure 13.4). Any DNA band on the membrane, with a biotin-labeled primer attached, will turn a blue color from the staining procedure. Once colorized, the sizes of DNA synthesis products may be determined by comparing the distance their bands traveled on the gel/membrane to the distances the DNA standards of known length traveled.

DNA Fragment Visualization with AP

The biotin-tagged DNA fragment on the membrane is bound with streptavidin. Biotin-tagged alkaline phosphatase attaches to streptavidin. When NBT is present, AP converts it from yellow to blue. The blue NBT builds up on the DNA strand and makes it visible.

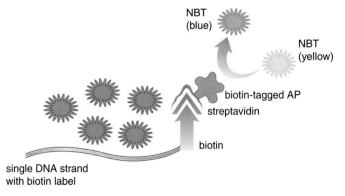

Figure 13.4. Visualization of a Southern blot with biotin-tagged alkaline phosphatase.

Purpose

To colorize the DNA synthesis fragments (oligonucleotides) on the Southern blot for the purpose of determining their size in bases.

Materials

Note: Recipes for solutions follow the Materials list. Class volumes of each solution are prepared a few days prior to staining the membranes. Teams should share the work of stock-solution preparation.

Glasses, safety, and gloves	Wash solution I	Biotin-tagged alkaline
Blotted membrane	Wash solution II	phosphatase, 0.38 mg/mL
(from Lab 13c)	Color substrate buffer	BCIP (X-PO4)/NBT color
Petri dishes, square, 100×15 mm	Stop solution	1.25/2.5 mL
Graduated cylinders, 25 mL	Forceps, fine-tipped,	Plastic wrap
Balance, weigh boats, scoops	stainless steel	Aluminum foil
Carboys, 5 L with spigot	Micropipets and tips	Beakers, 50 mL
Blocking solution	Streptavidin, 1 mg/mL	Filter paper, 12.5 cm

Reagents/Recipes (for staining 50 to 60 membranes)

Note: In your notebook, show all calculations for all solutions/reagents whether your group is preparing them or not.

Blocking Solution: 3 L needed
A 1-L recipe equals 125 mM NaCl, 25 mM sodium phosphate monobasic monohydrate, and pH 7.2, 5% sodium dodecyl sulfate (SDS).

Wash Solution I: 3 L needed
blocking solution diluted in a 1:10 ratio with deionized water

Wash Solution II: 4 L needed
A 1-L recipe equals 10 mM TRIS-HCl pH 9.5, 10 mM NaCl, and 1 mM MgCl$_2$.
Hint: Prepare 100 mL 1 M TRIS-HCl pH 9.5, and use it for the TRIS-HCl. Then add other solutes, and mix them together to equal a total volume of 1000 mL.

Color Substrate Buffer: 1 L needed
A 1-L recipe equals 100 mM TRIS-HCl, pH 9.5; 100 mM NaCl; 50 mM MgCl$_2$, 0.1 mM ZnCl$_2$.
Hint: Prepare 100 mL of 1 M TRIS-HCl, pH 9.5, and use it for the TRIS-HCl. Then add other solutes and mix them together to equal a total volume of 1000 mL.

Stop Solution (TE Buffer): 2 L needed
A 1-L recipe equals 10 mM TRIS-HCl, pH 8.0, 0.1 mM EDTA.

Safety Precautions

Environmental Health and Safety Officer

- **Wear goggles and gloves for the entire visualization procedure.**
- **Some of the solutions may be caustic.**
- **Use forceps to handle the membrane, and only touch it at the edges.**

Procedure

1. Place the nylon membrane, DNA side up (ie, pencil mark up), in a staining tray. Pour the first solution listed in the staining/visualization matrix (15 mL of blocking solution) into the tray (see Table 13.4).
2. Swirl the tray for the entire wash time listed in Table I, making sure that the solution completely covers the membrane.
3. At the end of the wash time, pour the solution into a sink or trash beaker, using the forceps to hold the membrane in the bottom of the tray, holding the membrane near the edge only.

4. Repeat steps 1 through 3 for each of the other washes outlined in the matrix, using the solutions and times given. Rinse the graduated cylinders between each use with distilled water. Check off each box as you complete each wash step.

   Caution:
   - Do not let the membrane dry out between washes.
   - Longer washes are better than shorter ones.

Table 13.4. **Staining/Visualization Matrix**

Solution	Composition	Wash Time
blocking solution	15 mL blocking solution	5 minutes with swirling
streptavidin solution	10 mL blocking solution + 10 μL streptavidin	5 minutes with swirling
wash solution I	20 mL wash solution I	5 minutes with swirling
wash solution I	20 mL wash solution I	5 minutes with swirling
biotin-tagged AP solution	10 mL blocking solution + 13.2 μL biotin-tagged AP	5 minutes with swirling
wash solution II	20 mL wash solution II	5 minutes with swirling
wash solution II	20 mL wash solution II	5 minutes with swirling
wash solution II	20 mL wash solution II	5 minutes with swirling
color solution **Do not rinse.**	15 mL color substrate buffer + 52.5 μL NBT + 52.5 μL X-phosphate	1 to 16 hours in the dark, covered, without swirling

5. After the color-substrate solution has been added, swirl one time only to mix, then cover the tray with plastic wrap. Next, cover the tray with foil to completely block out light. Make sure that it is easy to unwrap the top to check the color development. Put a label on the foil so it is distinguishable from other developing membranes.
6. Leave the tray in the dark spot to develop for 1 to 16 hours, checking the color development every few hours. Do not leave the membrane in this solution for more than 16 hours. When the DNA bands are visible, pour off the color-substrate solution, and pour in 25 mL of the stop solution. Swirl the tray for a few seconds, and then rinse twice with 50 mL of distilled water.
7. Place the membrane on a piece of filter paper to dry. When dry, glue the membrane, or a copy, into your notebook. Cover it with a small piece of plastic wrap and aluminum foil. Additional copies of the dry membrane can be made using a photocopier, photo-imaging system, or a digital camera.

Data Analysis

Label the top of the membrane to show the lanes and the contents of each lane. Write next to the membrane, not on it. Identify and label the DNA size standards. Determine which bands, in which of the lanes, represent synthesized oligonucleotides, primer-only strands, or primer-template complexes. Determine and record the length, in nucleotides, of the synthesized DNA fragment bands in each lane.

Conclusion

Review your hypothesis statements in Lab 13a. How well did your observed results match your expected results? Are there any extra bands present that were not expected? Explain. Are there any bands missing that should be present? Explain. Does the amount of color in each band support your hypothesis? Explain.

Thinking Like a Biotechnician

1. Each lab group is a replication of the DNA synthesis experiment. If one lab group had results different from the others, it was probably due to technician error. But, if all groups had the same unexpected results, a problem could exist in the shared materials, instruments, or procedures.

   Propose some reasons for the following:

   a. No groups had anything on their membranes except DNA loading-dye bands.
   b. All groups had sizing-standard bands visible on their membranes, but nothing else.
   c. All groups only had bands in one row higher than the 60-base standard and in one row at 32 bases.

2. If some of the six samples are shown to contain oligos, how might a technician determine the concentration of DNA remaining in the six sample tubes?

Laboratory 13e Using PCR to Amplify Regions of Lambda Phage DNA

This lab was developed by Frank Stephenson, PhD, Applied Biosystems, Inc and Maria Abilock, BABEC, for BABEC Member Teachers. It was modified for use in the San Mateo Biotechnology Career Pathway.

Note: Alternative kits and materials are listed under Materials for Non-BABEC users.

Background

Lambda bacteriophage is a virus that infects several species of bacteria, including *E. coli*. The genome of the lambda bacteriophage is approximately 48,500 base pairs (bp) in length, and the entire genome has been sequenced.

   If a technician wants to study or use a particular section of the lambda genome, the polymerase chain reaction (PCR) can be used to recognize the section and amplify it. Since the DNA of the lambda virus is easily isolated, it is available from several biological supply vendors. By understanding some PCR basics, a technician can order primers that will recognize the region of interest and make several billion copies in a few hours. The PCR product can be used in further studies or tests.

PCR Basics

- A DNA strand is separated (denatured) by high temperature.
- At a lower temperature, primers recognize and bind (anneal) to each side of the region of DNA to be amplified or copied.
- At a third optimum temperature, Taq® polymerase adds nucleotides [A, G, T, C (called dNTPS)] to the end of each primer and builds (extends) a strand complementary to each template.
- Two strands result, delineated by the primers on the ends.
- Each of the new strands is amplified again.
- An instrument called a thermal cycler manages the changes in temperature.

For a PCR reaction, two different primers must be designed to recognize the sequence just before and just after the region of interest. After primers bond to the template DNA, Taq polymerase builds the remaining region of interest from dNTPs in the reaction tube. For Taq polymerase activity, Mg^{2+} ions must be present, and the pH and temperature must be acceptable.

In this activity, genomic lambda DNA is probed to see how many amplification regions exist for the forward primer (P_F) and the reverse primer (P_R). After amplification in the thermal cycler, the PCR products are run on an agarose gel. The number of bands present in the PCR product tube represents the number of regions the primers recognized and amplified. A negative control will be prepared and run to ensure that there is no contaminant DNA present.

Purpose

How many regions of lambda DNA are amplified using the P_F primer and P_R primer? What are the sizes of the PCR product(s)?

Materials

Non-BABEC Users: Similar, although not identical, kits, materials, and activities are available from several vendors and some biotechnology educational support groups, including BioRad No. 166-0002EDU, Restriction Digestion and Analysis of Lambda DNA Kit; Carolina Biological No. 21-1222, Lambda Amplification Kit with 0.2-mL tubes

For BABEC Users

BABEC Lambda PCR kit:	Micropipets and tips	TBE gel, 1.0 mm, 10%, 10 well
Distilled water, sterile	Thermal cycler, 96 well, 0.2 mL	Gel loading tips, PAGE
PCR buffer, 10X	Gel loading dye, DNA	DNA sizing standards,
AmpliTaq® polymerase	Agarose, 2% in 1X TAE	100 bp ladder
dNTP MIX, 10 mM	buffer	Power supply
MgCl$_2$, 25 mM	Electrophoresis buffer, 1X TAE	Weigh boat 5.5"×5.5"
PC01 primer (forward primer)	Plastic beaker, 1L	Ethidium bromide, 0.5 µg/mL
PC02 primer (reverse primer)	Gel box, horizontal (for	Gloves and safety goggles
Lambda DNA	agarose gels) or Gel box,	Gel photo imaging system
PCR tubes, 0.2 mL	vertical, for 10×10 cm PAGE	

Procedures

- Be sure to pipet a mixture up and down gently after adding a new reagent to ensure proper mixing. Change tips each time you measure and dispense any reagent.
- Keep all reagents on ice.

Part I: Preparing PCR Reaction

1. Work in pairs. Obtain two 0.2-mL tubes. Using a fine-tipped permanent marker, label each tube with your lab initials and either "D" for DNA or "C" for the negative control.
2. Add the following reagents into each tube in the order listed (see Table 13.5). "Wrist flick" samples to the bottom after each addition.

Table 13.5. **Lambda DNA PCR Reaction Matrix**

Reagent	Lambda DNA (µL)	Negative Control (µL)
distilled water	26.0	31.0
10X PCR buffer	5.0	5.0
25 mM MgCl$_2$	3.0	3.0
10 mM dNTP mix	4.0	4.0
AmpliTaq® polymerase	2.0	2.0
PC01 primer (P_F)	2.5	2.5
PC02 primer (P_R)	2.5	2.5
lambda DNA	5.0	—
final volume	**50.0**	**50.0**

3. Place each labeled tube into the thermal cycler. Record the tube position on the thermal cycler chart and in your notebook.

4. Record/copy the thermal cycling program shown on the thermal cycler. Explain what happens in each stage of the thermal cycling.

5. Run the thermal cycling program: 95°C for 2 min; then 94°C for 15 sec, 37°C for 15 sec, and 72°C for 15 sec for 25 cycles; 72°C for 7 min; 4°C for an infinite time period. When completed, add 5 μL of DNA loading dye to each PCR product tube. Store at 4°C until you are ready to run a gel.

Part II: Running PCR Products on Agarose Gel

6. Prepare a six-well, 2% agarose gel in 1X TAE buffer (review the procedure in Lab 4i).

7. Load the following samples into the gel. Make sure there is loading dye in your sample (3 μL of loading dye for every 25 μL of sample).

> Well 1: 5 μL of 100-bp DNA standards
> Well 2: 25 μL of your Tube D (lambda PCR product)
> Well 3: 25 μL of your Tube D (lambda PCR product)
> Well 4: 25 μL of your Tube C (control-tube PCR product)
> Well 5: 25 μL of your Tube C (control-tube PCR product)
> Well 6: nothing

8. Draw a diagram of the gel in your notebook showing what was loaded into each well. Also, record the concentration of the gel and the type of buffer used.

9. Run the gel for 45 to 60 minutes at 110 V. Allow the loading dye to reach half way down the gel.

10. Stain the gel in EtBr solution for at least 20 minutes. Rinse in deionized water. Visualize on a UV-light box and photograph it.
    Note: Only the supervisor is to use EtBr. Wear goggles and gloves where EtBr is in use. Wipe up spills immediately.

11. Label the gel photo. Include labels for what was loaded in each well—the standard sizes, the primers, any primer bands (individual primer or primer-dimer), and the sizes of the unknown PCR products.

Environmental Health and Safety Officer

Data Analysis/Conclusion

Is there evidence of PCR product? If so, how many PCR products per lane and what are the sizes in base pairs? Compare your results with those of fellow technicians, and compare replications of the experiment. Do other replications support your data? Are there any bands in the negative control sample? Explain. Describe any unexpected bands and any possible explanations for their presence. If your gel confirms the presence of PCR product, what are possible applications for this product? How is this kind of information or product utilized in research and industry?

  *Thinking Like a Biotechnician*

1. A technician finds a long, white smear of DNA in a PCR product lane from about 500 bp down to 100 bp. What may be the cause of such a smear?

2. What might cause many bands at random positions in all lanes, including the control?

Laboratory 13f   Extracting DNA from Human Cells for PCR and Sequencing

This lab is adapted with permission from Genetic Origins (www.geneticorigins.org), © Dolan DNA Learning Center, under the direction of David A. Micklos. This version is based on a modification developed for use by BABEC-member teachers and students by Frank Stephenson, PhD, Applied Biosystems, Inc, and Maria Abilock, BABEC. Alternative kits and materials are listed under "Materials for Non-BABEC Users" in Laboratory 13g.

Background

With a few precautions, DNA can be extracted from cells for PCR or DNA sequencing in much the same way as DNA is extracted from bacteria cells. Cells may be burst open and proteins precipitated out of solution (see Figure 13.5).

Ions that are released from the cell can interfere with Taq polymerase activity and inhibit the PCR reaction. To remove the ions out of the DNA sample, a step is added using the chelating agent, Chelex® (Bio-Rad Laboratories) chelating beads. Chelating agents bind ions and remove them from solution. Although some ions are needed in PCR, the technician adds the desired ions at the correct concentration when they are needed.

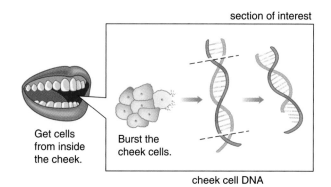

Figure 13.5.   **Cheek Cell DNA Isolation.**

Purpose

To isolate human DNA from cheek cells for PCR and DNA-sequencing analysis.

Materials

Balance, weigh boats, scoops	Paper cup	Chelex® resin beads
Sodium chloride	Micropipets and tips	Vortex mixer
Tubes, 50 mL, sterile and rack	Reaction tubes, 1.7 mL	Lid locks, for 1.7 mL tubes
Filtering flasks, 250 mL	and rack	Dry block heater/heat block,
Vacuum pump and "trap" jar	Permanent lab marker pens	99°C
Pipets, 10 mL and pump	Microcentrifuge	

Procedure

Part I: Reagent Preparation

1. For a team of four, prepare 50 mL of 0.9% NaCl solution. In your notebook, record the calculation for this preparation and include a drawing of how it is prepared.
2. Filter sterilize the 50 mL of 0.9% NaCl solution using a filter flask and vacuum apparatus. Label the filter flask and store the solution at room temperature.

Part II: DNA Extraction and Preparation

- Do not eat or drink anything for at least 30 minutes before collecting a cheek-cell sample.
- To prevent possible disease transmission, discard all used cups and extra saliva after use.

1. Using a sterile pipet, transfer 10 mL of 0.9% NaCl (saline) solution into a paper cup. Place the 10 mL of saline in your mouth and vigorously swish for 30 seconds.
2. Expel the saline solution into a cup. Cells lining the inside of the mouth are in the saline solution.
3. Swirl to mix the cells in the cup, and transfer 1000 μL of the liquid into a 1.7-mL tube.
4. In a balanced centrifuge, spin your sample tube for 1 minute.
5. Carefully, pour off and discard the supernatant. **Careful! Do not disturb the pellet of cells.**

Environmental Health
and Safety Officer

6. Add 30 µL of fresh 0.9% saline solution, and pipet in and out to resuspend the cell pellet. It is critical that all the cells in the pellet are resuspended.

7. Withdraw 30 µL of the cell suspension and add it to a previously prepared 1.7-mL tube containing 200 µL of 5% Chelex® resin beads. Shake well or vortex briefly to mix. **Note: It is critical that the correct amount of Chelex® beads is used. When getting the 200 µL of Chelex®, invert the tube containing the Chelex® beads just before measuring to suspend them.**

8. Secure the tube containing the cell suspension and Chelex® with a locking cap, and place the tube in a 99°C heat block for 10 minutes. During this time, the sample will boil and the cells will burst open, releasing their contents, including DNA. Transfer to ice for 1 minute.

9. Shake your tube well, or vortex briefly, and place the tube in a balanced centrifuge for 1 minute. The purpose of this step is to move all of the Chelex® resin beads to the bottom of the tube.

10. Using a new tip, extract 60 µL of the cheek-cell DNA sample and place it into a new, *labeled* tube. **Do not transfer any Chelex® beads with the DNA sample.**

11. Store your cheek-cell DNA sample at 4°C for up to 1 week for later use in PCR or DNA sequencing. Long-term storage should be at –20°C.

Thinking Like a Biotechnician

1. How could the purity and concentration of the check-cell DNA sample be determined?
2. Do these cheek-cell DNA sample tubes contain genomic DNA? Yes or no? Explain.

Laboratory 13g   DNA Typing by PCR-Genotype Determination of an Alu Insert

This lab is adapted with permission from Genetic Origins (www.geneticorigins.org), © Dolan DNA Learning Center, under the direction of David A. Micklos. This version is a modification developed for use by BABEC-member teachers and students by Frank Stephenson, PhD, Applied Biosystems, Inc, and Maria Abilock, BABEC. Alternative kits and materials are listed under "Materials for Non-BABEC Users."

Background

In this experiment, PCR is used to amplify a region (locus) of human DNA. The region of interest is called an "Alu insert." The Alu insert is a sequence of DNA of approximately 300 bp long. The sequence is called an Alu insert because it contains an Alu restriction-enzyme site.

Over millions of years, the Alu sequence has been copied and reinserted rather randomly throughout the primate genome. There are approximately 1.2 million copies of Alu in the human genome. These sections appear to have originated from DNA coding for ribosomal RNA.

The Alu sequence (300 bp in length) we are looking for, PV92, is one that has inserted itself into a particular region of approximately 415 bp in length (noncoding regions) on chromosome No. 16. Each person possesses two alleles for this particular Alu insert, one from each parent. This mutation (change in the genome at PV92) arose in some geographic region and people have carried it to other parts of the world. By genotyping the human population, scientists can propose theories for the origin of the PV92 mutation.

There are three possible genotypes an individual may have for the Alu locus. A person can have two Alu inserts (A+A+), one from each parent, so there are two chromosomes with the same alleles at the same locus (see Figure 13.6).

Individuals may have one chromosome with the Alu insert and one without it (A+A-), so there are two chromosomes with the different alleles at the same locus (see Figure 13.7).

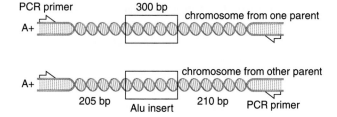

A+ A+ =
each parent gave
a chromosome
containing the
Alu insert

Figure 13.6. **A+A+ Alu Genotype**

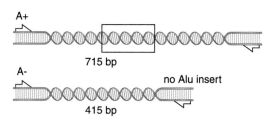

Figure 13.7. **A+A- Alu Genotype**

Individuals may have two chromosomes with no Alu insert (A-A-), so there are two chromosomes with the same alleles at the same locus (see Figure 13.8).

A+A+ individuals (homozygotes) will have a band only at approximately 715 bp (300 + 415). A+A- individuals (heterozygotes) will have bands at approximately 415 bp and 715 bp. A-A- individuals (homozygotes) will have bands only at approximately 415 bp.

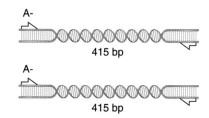

Figure 13.8. **A-A- Alu Genotype**

To find the Alu loci, primers are added that recognize the DNA on each end of the Alu locus to be amplified. The PCR duplicates the sections into billions of pieces in a few hours (see Figure 13.9). The fragments are run on a gel to be visualized and analyzed.

Purpose

What are your genotypes for this Alu (PV92) insert on chromosome No. 16?
What are the frequencies for each genotype within the class population?

Materials

For Non-BABEC Users:

Biorad Laboratories No. 166-2100EDU, PV92 PCR Informatics Kit
Edvotek, Inc, No. 333 25 Individual Reactions and 6 Gels with InstaStain® Ethidium Bromide
   Carolina Biological Supply Company No. 21-1230A Alu DNA Extraction and Amplification Kit
   with 0.2 mL tubes

For BABEC Users:

PCR tubes, 0.2 mL	Gel loading dye, DNA	Gel loading tips, PAGE
Micropipets and tips	Agarose, 2% in 1X TBE buffer	DNA sizing standards, 100 bp
Permanent lab marker pens	Electrophoresis buffer, 1X TBE	ladder
BABEC Alu PCR kit:	Plastic beaker, 1 L	Power supply
Primer mix and master mix	Gel box, horizontal (for	Weigh boat 5.5"×5.5"
Prepared cheek cell DNA	agarose gels)	Ethidium bromide, 0.5 μg/mL
samples	Gel box, vertical, for 10×10 cm	Gloves and safety goggles
Distilled water, sterile	PAGE	
Thermal cycler, 96 well, 0.2 mL	TBE gel, 1.0 mm, 10%, 10 well	

Procedure

- Use new pipet tips for each transfer. Measure carefully.
- Do not touch the inside of the tube.

Part I: Setting Up the PCR Tubes

1. Obtain a sterile 0.2-mL PCR tube.
2. Using a fine-tip permanent marker, label the PCR tube on the top with your ID number.

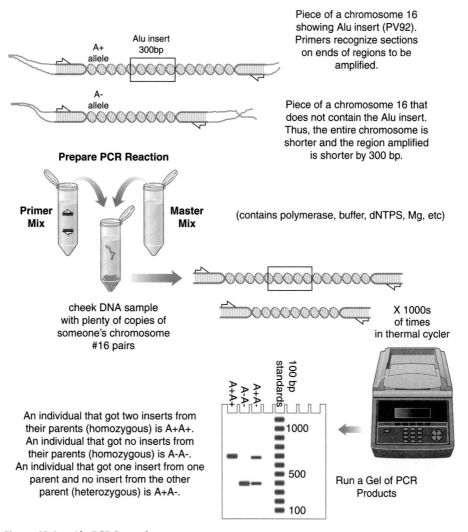

Piece of a chromosome 16 showing Alu insert (PV92). Primers recognize sections on ends of regions to be amplified.

A+ allele

Alu insert 300bp

A- allele

Piece of a chromosome 16 that does not contain the Alu insert. Thus, the entire chromosome is shorter and the region amplified is shorter by 300 bp.

Prepare PCR Reaction

Primer Mix

Master Mix

(contains polymerase, buffer, dNTPS, Mg, etc)

cheek DNA sample with plenty of copies of someone's chromosome #16 pairs

X 1000s of times in thermal cycler

An individual that got two inserts from their parents (homozygous) is A+A+. An individual that got no inserts from their parents (homozygous) is A-A-. An individual that got one insert from one parent and no insert from the other parent (heterozygous) is A+A-.

100 bp standards

A+A+
A-A-
A+A-

1000

500

100

Run a Gel of PCR Products

Figure 13.9. Alu PCR Procedures

3. Add 20 μL of master mix to the tube. What is in the master mix? What is the advantage of using a "master mix"?
4. Add 20 μL of the primer mix **directly into** the master mix in the bottom of the PCR tube.
5. Pipet up and down several times to mix the contents of the tube.
6. Give the PCR tube a quick "wrist flick" to pool the mixture into the bottom of the tube.
7. Add 10 μL of your prepared cheek-cell DNA sample to your master-mix/primer-mix tube. **Take the DNA only from the top of the tube contents. Make sure there are no Chelex® resin beads contaminating your sample.**
8. Give the PCR tube a quick "wrist flick" to pool the mixture into the bottom of the tube. Pipet up and down several times to mix the contents of the tube.
9. Again, give the PCR tube a quick "wrist flick" to pool the mixture into the bottom of the tube.
10. If necessary, relabel the tube.

Part II: Running the PCR Reaction
11. Make sure the thermal cycler has been programmed for this Alu PCR reaction (see Table 13.6)
12. Positive and negative controls should be made and run as space allows.
    The +control contains 20 μL master mix, 20 μL primer mix, 10 μL control DNA.
    The -control contains 10 μL sterile water, 20 μL master mix, 20 μL primer mix.
13. Put your PCR tube(s) in the thermal cycler. In your notebook, record the position of your tube(s) in the thermal cycler. Also, mark the position of your tube(s) on the thermal cycler diagram provided.

Table 13.6. **Alu PCR Thermal Cycle Program** (30 cycles)

Temperature (°C)	Time	Purpose of Step
95	10 min	AmpliTaq® Gold activation
94	30 sec/cycle	denaturation
60	30 sec/cycle	annealing
72	120 sec (2 min)/cycle	extension of strands
72	10 min	final extension
4	∞	storage

14. When all samples are in the thermal cycler, start the program. After the program is completed, the samples remain in the thermal cycler at 4°C until the next day.

15. Prepare either a 10% TBE vertical gel or a 2% agarose gel for loading. Draw a diagram of the gel in your notebook showing what was loaded into each well. Mark the position of your sample(s) on the gel diagram. Also, record the concentration of the gel and the type of buffer used.

16. Add 5 µL of loading dye to your PCR tube(s). Cap the tube(s), and wrist-flick the dye to the bottom.

17. Mix the contents of the PCR tube by gently flicking the bottom of the tube with your fingers (a finger flick). Give the PCR tube a quick "wrist flick" to pool the mixture into the bottom of the tube.

18. Load 5 µL of DNA standards (100 bp markers) into Wells 5 and 10 of the gel.

19. Load 20 µL of each sample for a PAGE gel or 25 µL of each sample for an agarose gel.

Part III: Running the Gels
For PAGE Gels:

20. Plug the gel box into the power supply. Turn on the power supply and run the gel at 35 mA.

21. Run the gel for about 30 to 45 minutes, until the loading dye is approximately 1 inch from the bottom of the gel.

22. Turn off the power supply and remove the gel from the gel box.

23. Crack open the gel cassette. The gel will stick to one side of the cassette.

For Agarose Gels: Run the gel at 110 V for 45 to 50 minutes.

Part IV: Staining the Gels

24. Transfer the gel from the cassette tray to a weigh boat containing distilled water.

25. Carefully, pour off the water, and add 10 mL of EtBr. Stain for 10 minutes (PAGE) or 20 minutes (agarose gel).
    Caution: Only the supervisor is to use EtBr. Wear goggles and gloves where EtBr is in use. Wipe spills immediately.

26. Pour off the EtBr and save for future staining. Rinse the gel in distilled water.

27. Place the gel on a UV-light box. Observe the bands and determine their size in base pairs by comparing them with the DNA size standards.

28. Take a photograph of the gel using a photoimaging system.

29. Glue your photograph into your notebook. Label the gel photo with the type of gel and running conditions. Label the gel wells with what was loaded into each.

30. Identify your genotype for the Alu locus. Record this in the data section.

31. Make a data table to record the frequency of each genotype in the sample population. Does it appear that the Alu insert mutation is found more frequently in one ethnicity than another?

Environmental Health and Safety Officer

32. Compare these population frequency data with those reported at the Allele Server Internet site of the Dolan DNA Learning Center of Cold Spring Harbor Laboratory.

   - Go to www.bioservers.org.
   - Click "Enter" under "Allele Server."
   - Click the question mark (?) at the upper right corner for directions on accessing data sets or entering your own group data. (Check with your instructor if you are unsure about the steps.)

Thinking Like a Biotechnician

1. Why is the band for 415 bp so much darker than the band for 715 bp?
2. Considering the class's data and the data reported at the Allele Server, why are there so few of one genotype compared with the others?

Chapter 14
Advanced Protein Studies

A technician in a protein characterization lab prepares a gel for a Western blot. A Western blot transfers peptide bands from a gel onto a membrane or nitrocellulose paper. Using an antibody specific to a particular peptide sequence, the technician can recognize a protein of interest on the blot. The antibody has a reporter molecule attached to it, which makes the antibody-antigen binding visible.
Photo by author.

Throughout this lab manual, methods of recognizing and characterizing molecules or reactions have been presented. DNA extractions and preparations, DNA gel analysis, DNA synthesis, and PCR are essential for DNA identification, fingerprinting, sequencing, and genomics.

The goal of a protein scientist is to be able to recognize specific proteins and quantify their presence, activity (if any), and concentration. Toward that end, you have worked with basic protein characterizations utilizing protein indicators, antibody-antigen interactions, spectrophotometry, polyacrylamide gel electrophoresis (PAGE), and protein chromatography.

In the following activities you will learn some additional advanced protein characterization techniques that are used in research and development, assay services, quality control, and diagnostic testing. Specifically, you will learn how to

- use antibodies to recognize antigens during product development, manufacturing, and diagnostic testing
- set up and run a qualitative enzyme-linked immunosorbent assay (ELISA) for the purpose of confirming the presence of a specific protein
- recognize the difference between a qualitative and quantitative ELISA and how the latter might be performed
- prepare and conduct a Western blot for the purpose of recognizing a specific protein
- visualize ELISA and Western blot products using antibodies conjugated with enzymes that produce chromogenic (colored) products

Since protein molecules are complicated and very diverse, many of the diagnostic tests and characterization methods require sophisticated equipment and methods. HPLC, protein crystallography, protein sequencing, and NMR are just a few of the techniques that are too sophisticated for the classroom but are easily learned with experience in PAGE, chromatography, ELISAs, and Western blots.

Laboratory 14a   Using an ELISA to Identify Meat Samples

Inspired by a lab activity originally developed by Nancy Lightbody and David Nordstrom, University of Southern Maine, under National Science Foundation Grants #HRD 9628307 and #HRD 9800241. Modified by Dan Segal, Biotechnology Student, 2003.

Background

An ELISA can be used to recognize and quantify a specific protein in a protein mixture. This is very useful in protein production and purification, since technicians must be able to determine the presence and concentration of a protein of interest. In the meat industry, ELISAs are used to determine if samples are contaminated with other meat products.

In the ELISA below, a protein from pig blood serum, pig immunoglobulin G (IgG), can be recognized by a pig anti-IgG antibody. Since both IgG (an antigen) and anti-IgG (an antibody) are colorless, an enzyme that causes a color change (horseradish peroxidase [HRP]) is bound to the anti-IgG. When the anti-IgG/HRP binds to IgG in a sample and tetramethylbenzidine (TMB) is added, a blue color change occurs, indicating the antibody-antigen recognition. The more antibody-antigen recognition, the more the color changes. This color change can be measured using a spectrophotometer in an ELISA plate reader.

In the ELISA procedure, a sample thought to contain a protein of interest (pig IgG) is coated onto the bottom of wells in a 96-well ELISA microtiter plate. Protein in the sample that does not stick is washed off with phosphate-buffered saline (PBS) buffer. A blocking solution containing milk proteins is added to cover any remaining exposed plastic in the wells. Excess blocking solution is washed off with PBS. Anti-pig IgG antibody/HRP is added. It should only bind to pig IgG molecules. In this way, a sample contaminated with pig meat (blue) can be distinguished from the sample free of pig molecules (clear). Adding acid in a final step changes the blue colors to yellow. The more yellow, the higher the concentration of target protein in the sample.

Figure 14.1.   How can one be certain that ground beef does not contain some less-expensive filler meats?

Photo by author.

Purpose

Do samples of ground beef show evidence of pork contamination?

Materials

Gloves and safety goggles	pH meter, electrode, and	TMB solution (diluted 1:2)
Balance, weigh boats, scoops	buffers	Reaction tubes, 1.7 mL
1X PBS:	Hydrochloric acid, 1 *M*	and rack
Na phosphate, monobasic,	Sodium hydroxide, 10%	Cow serum
1-hydrate	Tubes, 15 mL sterile and racks	Pig serum
Na phosphate, dibasic,	Permanent lab marker pens	Sheep serum
anhydrous	Pipets and pumps	Suspected serum samples
Sodium chloride	Vials, 5 mL	Micro-titer plate, 96-well
Nonfat milk powder	Micropipets and tips	Hydrochloric acid, 0.5 *M*
Beakers, 250 mL	Anti-pig IgG/HRP	
	(diluted 1:80,000)	

Procedure

Part I: Prelab Preparation of Reagents

1. Prepare 100 mL of 1X PBS wash solution; store at room temperature:

> 1X PBS Buffer =
> 1.9 mM NaH$_2$PO$_4$ (monohydrate), 8.1 mM Na$_2$HPO$_4$ (anhydrous), 150 mM NaCl, pH 7.3

   In your notebook, show the calculations and make a diagram to explain how to make this three-chemical buffer.

2. Prepare 10 mL of blocking solution (10 mL of 5% nonfat milk in 1X PBS solution. Store at 4°C). In your notebook, show the calculations and make a diagram to explain how to make this solution.

3. Place 2.5 mL of diluted (1:80,000 dilution) anti-pig IgG antibody conjugated with HRP enzyme in a 3.5-mL sterile tube. **The supervisor will prepare the stock diluted anti-pig IgG solution for all groups (1.25 μL of anti-IgG + 100 mL of 1X PBS).**

4. Place 2.5 mL of 1:2 diluted TMB solution into a 3.5-mL sterile tube.

5. Place 500 μL of 0.5 M HCl into a 1.7-mL microtube.

6. Place 400 μL of each of the extracts of cow, pig, and sheep serum (known samples) into separate 1.7-mL microtubes.

7. Place 400 μL of each unknown sample (extract of beef sample suspected to be contaminated with pork) into a separate 1.7-mL microtube.

Part II: Experimental Protocol

8. Obtain a 96-well microtiter plate.

9. Label six columns of three rows with "C," "P," "S," "-C," "Unk1," and "Unk2." These labels mark where three replications of the cow, pig, sheep, negative control, and unknown samples will be placed.

10. Add 125 μL of the appropriate sample to each well. Gently tilt to swirl. Let stand for 5 minutes.

11. Remove **all** of the contents of each well with a micropipet.

12. Add 125 μL of 1X PBS wash solution to each well. Gently swirl to rinse, and remove with a micropipet.

13. Add 250 μL of blocking solution to each well. Gently tilt to swirl. Let stand for 10 minutes.

14. During the blocking waiting period, draw a diagram to show the rows of wells being filled. Label the diagram to show which serum is being added to each well.

15. Remove **all** of the blocking solution from each well.

16. **Rinse 5 times** with 250 μL of 1X PBS. Let each rinse sit for 1 minute before removing.

17. Add 125 μL of the diluted HRP-linked pig anti-IgG antibody to each well. Gently tilt to swirl. Let stand for 15 minutes.

18. Remove **all** of the antibody solution. **Rinse 5 times** with 250 μL of 1X PBS. Let each rinse sit for 1 minute before removing.

19. Quickly add 125 μL of diluted TMB solution to each well. Gently tilt to swirl. Look for a color change. Check after 5 minutes for evidence of a change. The HRP oxidizes the TMB molecules (the HRP transfers electrons from hydrogen peroxide to TMB), which causes them to turn blue.

20. After 10 minutes, record the degree of blueness in each well (0 = no blue/clear; 5 = medium blue) on a data table.

21. After 15 minutes, add 30 μL of 0.5 M HCl to each well. The acid turns the blue TMB to a yellow color and denatures the HRP so that no further reaction occurs. The amount of yellow color, compared with the negative control, is an indication of the amount of protein that the ELISA antibody recognizes. In a data table, record the amount of yellow in each well (0 = no yellow/clear; 5 = "lemon yellow").

22. In your notebook, record the color results of all the replications of each test in a data table. Present the data in numerical form.

Data Analysis and Conclusion

Study the colors of the known solutions, both positive controls and negative controls. Are they the colors you expected them to be? Why or why not? Compare the results of the known solutions to the unknown(s). Is there evidence of pork contamination in either of the unknowns? Explain and give evidence. Discuss the possible errors in this type of experiment that may result in false positives or false negatives. Propose some other applications of this technology to both the meat industry and the biotechnology industry.

Thinking Like a Biotechnician

1. What is the most likely reason for all of the wells showing color (false positive results)?
2. Propose a method to decrease the number of false positive results.
3. How can the data be made more quantitative? Is there an instrument that can quantify the amount of color in each well? Describe how these readings could be taken.
4. In your notebook, draw and label a schematic to show what is attaching to what in the ELISA plate wells during the ELISA and color development.

Laboratory 14b   Using a Western Blot to Identify Actin

Developed by Lior Tamir, San Mateo High School, 2002, with the assistance of Betsy Turner, PhD, Angiogenix Inc., Burlingame, CA. Modified by Dan Segal, Biotechnology Student, 2003.

Background

When studying proteins on a denaturing SDS/polyacrylamide gel, the approximate molecular weight and number of polypeptides in a protein may be estimated. Once the banding pattern for a protein is known, it can be used to identify the protein in samples.

However, since there are so many proteins with similar molecular weights, a method to identify a specific protein is valuable. The Western blot technique allows for the recognition and visualization of a particular protein. In a sample of hundreds of proteins, as in cell extracts, a Western blot helps find one protein among hundreds.

Western blots use a rather specific method of recognizing molecules in an antibody-antigen reaction. Antibodies can be purchased that recognize the unique shape of a molecule and bind to it. Using antibodies that have attached colored markers, enzymes, or other reporter molecules attached to the antibodies, a technician can visualize a molecule of interest.

In the Western-blot procedure below, the protein "actin" is identified. Actin is found in all cells. Its function is to maintain the structure of the cell. Actin is also found in high concentration in muscle cells where it is involved in muscle-cell contraction.

For this blot, a TRIS/BIS-acrylamide (TRIS/BIS) gel in a PAGE is run with samples of actin. The gel is blotted onto a membrane using a Western-blot transfer unit. The membrane is treated with an anti-actin antibody that binds only to actin. Another secondary (2°) antibody recognizes the constant region of antibodies and binds to the anti-actin antibody. The 2° antibody has an enzyme (alkaline phosphatase [AP]) attached to it. When Nitro Blue Tetrazolium (NBT) is washed over the blot, alkaline phosphatase changes the NBT from yellow to blue, and you can see it deposited on the actin band.

Purpose

Is a suspected 43-kD band on a PAGE gel really the protein, actin?

Materials

Note: Several of the buffers used in this procedure will be good for only 2 to 3 days. Prepare fresh buffers for each run of the experiment. Recipes follow the procedures.

Gloves and safety goggles
Actin, bovine
Phosphate buffered saline
   (PBS), 10X
Tubes, 15 mL sterile and racks
Permanent lab marker pens
Reaction tubes, 1.7 mL
   and rack
Micropipets and tips
Suspected actin samples
   (from Lab 5g)
Microcentrifuge filter tubes,
   10 kD
Microcentrifuge, 16K × g
Distilled water, sterile
Gel loading dye, PAGE/SDS
   (Lab 5g)

Dithiothreitol (DTT), 0.1%
Dry block heater/heat block,
   70°C
Gel box, vertical, for PAGE
Bis-TRIS Ge, 10%, 1.5 mm,
   10-well
Running buffer
Transfer pipets, 3 mL
PAGE gel loading tips
Protein sizing markers,
   15-150 KD
Power supply
Western Blot Transfer kit:
   sponge blotting pads
Transfer buffer
Filter paper
Nitrocellulose paper

Wash buffer
Block buffer
Diluent buffer
1° antibody, anti-actin
2° antibody, goat anti-rabbit
   IgG/AP
Stop solution
Color substrate buffer
BCIP (X-PO4)/NBT color
   1.25/2.5 mL
Plastic wrap
Aluminum foil
Beakers, 50 mL
Filter paper, 12.5 cm
Graduated cylinder, 25 mL,
   12/CS

Procedure

Part I: Actin Positive-Control Sample Preparation

1. One lab group should prepare 5 mL of 1 mg/mL actin in 10X PBS for the class to use as a positive control. In your notebook, show the calculations and make a diagram to explain how to make this solution.
2. Divide the stock positive control into 10- to 500-μL aliquots. One aliquot goes to each group. Others are stored at −20°C.
3. Conduct a 1:10 serial dilution of one of the 1-mg/mL aliquots to a final concentration of 100 μg/mL. In your notebook, draw a diagram to explain how to make a serial dilution.

Part II: Suspected Actin Sample Preparation

1. Add 500 μL of a suspected actin/seafood sample to a 10-kD centrifuge filter tube. Add 500 μL of 10X PBS.
2. Spin the tube in a balanced microcentrifuge at 12,000 × g for about 2 minutes. Most of the buffer should have filtered through to the bottom chamber.
3. Repeat step 5 until no blue dye remains in the sample. This accomplishes a buffer exchange without significantly diluting the sample.
4. Add enough 10X PBS to bring the sample volume back to 500 μL.

Part III: PAGE Sample Preparation

1. Prepare sample tubes for electrophoresis following the matrix below:

Sample	H$_2$O (μL)	100-μg/mL Sample (μL)	Sample (μL)	Loading Dye (μL)	0.1% DTT (μL)
actin 100 μg/15 μL	29.1	3.3		12.6	5.0
actin 200 μg/15 μL	25.8	6.6		12.6	5.0
actin 400 μg/15 μL	19.2	13.2		12.6	5.0
unknown sample 1			34.4	12.6	5.0
unknown sample 2			34.3	12.6	5.0
unknown sample 3			34.4	12.6	5.0

Note: Add water first and DTT last.

2. Heat the mixed samples at 70°C for 10 minutes. Give the tubes a 2-second spin in a micro-centrifuge to pool the samples.

Part IV: Electrophoresis

1. Set up a 10-well, 10%-TRIS-BIS gel in a vertical gel box. Prepare for loading.
2. Load the samples according to the reaction matrix below:

Lane	Sample	µL to Load
1	leave empty	-
2	protein molecular weight standards	5.0
3	actin 100 µg/15 µL	15.0
4	actin 200 µg/15 µL	15.0
5	actin 400 µg/15 µL	15.0
6	protein standards	5.0
7	unknown sample 1	15.0
8	unknown sample 2	15.0
9	unknown sample 3	15.0
10	leave empty	

3. Run at 200 V for approximately 45 minutes, or until blue dye reaches the bottom of the gel.
4. Meanwhile, prepare five sponge-blotting pads by soaking them in transfer buffer. Five minutes before the gel is finished, soak the nitrocellulose membrane and the filter paper in the transfer buffer.

Part V: Western Transfer

1. Remove the gel from the cassette using a gel knife, and cut off the foot and wells.
2. Rinse the gel box with distilled water (dH$_2$O).
3. Assemble the gel membrane sandwich according to the diagram (see Figure 14.2). Be careful not to touch the membrane or the gel with your hands.
4. Transfer at a constant 30 V for 1 hour.
5. Meanwhile, prepare the wash, blocking, and diluent buffers and solutions, plus the primary antibody solution.

Part VI: Western Blot Staining

1. After 1 hour, remove the transfer membrane from the gel box, and place it in blocking buffer. Rotate it at room temperature for 1 hour.
2. Add 150 µL of 1° anti-actin antibody to 100 mL of diluent buffer.
3. Place the transfer membrane in 1° antibody solution. Store at 4°C overnight.
4. Pour off the 1° antibody solution, and cover the membrane with a wash buffer. Rotate the membrane in three volumes of wash buffer for 5 minutes each time, and then pour off the wash buffer.

Western Blot Gel/Transfer Membrane Sandwich

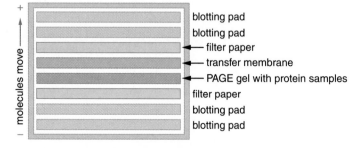

Figure 14.2. **A Western Gel/Membrane Setup.**

5. Add 50 μL of the 2° goat anti-rabbit antibody to 100 mL of diluent buffer. Transfer the membrane to the 2° antibody solution, and rotate it at room temperature for 1 hour.

6. Pour off the 2° antibody solution, and cover the membrane with a wash buffer. Rotate the membrane in three volumes of wash buffer for 5 minutes each time, and then pour off the wash buffer.

7. Add 52.5 μL of X-phosphate and 52.5 μL of NBT to 15 mL of color substrate buffer.

8. Add the NBT mixture to the membrane, and cover it with foil. Let the membrane soak in the NBT solution, without moving it, for 1 to 3 hours.

9. Use 10 mL of stop solution to stop the membrane staining.

10. Allow the membrane to dry in the dark for 24 hours. When you return to the lab, glue the membrane into your notebook and label it (wells, standards, and actin) without writing on the membrane. Membranes can be photographed or photocopied for copies.

Recipes for Buffers and Solutions

Running Buffer

First, make the morpholineethanesulfonic acid (MES)/SDS running buffer (20X) by mixing the following chemicals with dH_2O to a final volume of 35 mL:

Chemical	Amount (g)	Concentration
MES	6.832	1.00 M
TRIS-BIS	4.242	1.00 M
SDS	0.7	69.3 mM
EDTA	0.21	20.5 mM

Dilute the 35 mL of MES/SDS running buffer (20X) to 700 mL using dH_2O.
Set aside 200 mL of running buffer.
Add 1 mL of 0.1% DTT as a reducing agent to the remaining 500 mL (use this as the 1X running buffer).

Transfer Buffer

First, make the transfer buffer by mixing the following chemicals with dH_2O to a final volume of 50 mL.

Chemical	Amount (g)	Resultant Concentration (mM)
bicine	4.08	500.0
TRIS-BIS	5.232	500.0
EDTA	0.3	20.5
chlorobutanol		1.0

Mix the 50 mL of transfer buffer (20X), 100 mL of methanol, and 1 mL of 0.1% DTT, and dilute the mixture to 1000 mL using dH_2O.

Wash Buffer

PBS/0.01% Tween

Mix 100 mL of 10X PBS and 100 μL Tween. Dilute to 1000 mL with dH_2O. (When you add the Tween, cut the tip off a P-1000 micropipet tip, and use the cut pipet tip on a P-1000 micropipet. While stirring, add the Tween to 10X PBS/dH_2O solution. This is necessary due to Tween's adhesive qualities.)

Block Buffer

2% nonfat dry milk/PBS/0.01% Tween

Mix 100 mL of wash buffer with 2.0 g nonfat dry milk.

Diluent Buffer

1% BSA/PBS/0.01% Tween

Mix 200 mL of wash buffer with 2.0 g BSA.

1° Actin Antibody

anti-actin developed in rabbit
Sigma brand, A-2066

2° Rabbit-Alkaline Phosphate (AP) Antibody

goat anti-rabbit IgG-AP
Sigma brand, A-3687

Actin Stock Standard

bovine actin, 1 mg/mL in sterile PBS, pH 7.5
Sigma brand, A-3653
Store at -20°C in 100 μL of aliquots.

Stop Solution (Dilute with dH$_2$O)

10 mM TRIS-HCl, pH 8.0
0.1 mM EDTA

Color Substrate Buffer (Dilute with dH$_2$O)

100 mM TRIS-HCl, pH 9.5
100 mM NaCl
50 mM MgCl$_2$
0.1 mM ZnCl$_2$

Data Analysis/Conclusion

Did any bands develop on the Western-blot membrane? If so, is there evidence of standard bands, known actin bands, and unknown bands containing actin? Give evidence and explanations for your statements and results. If some of the bands are missing, give several reasons for how that may have happened. Recommend several ways to produce a blot that has darker protein bands and a lighter blue background. Explain how and why this type of blot is used in industry.

Thinking Like a Biotechnician

1. What is the most likely reason for no bands appearing anywhere on a membrane?
2. What may be a reason for the unknown samples not showing actin bands, while the known samples show actin bands?
3. In your notebook, draw a schematic diagram to show what is attaching to what on the membrane during color development.